From Your Friends At The MAILBOX® Magazine

SCIENCE Made Simple

Units From *The* Intermediate *Mailbox*® Magazine

Editor In Chief
Margaret Michel

Manager Of Product Development
Charlotte Perkins

Editor
Irving P. Crump

Copy Editors
Debbie Blaylock, Lynn B. Coble, Gina Sutphin

Artists
Jennifer Bennett, Cathy S. Bruce, Pam Crane, Teresa Davidson, Susan Hodnett, Becky Saunders, Barry Slate, Donna Teal

Cover Artist
Pam Crane

Typographer
Lynette Maxwell

About This Book

Explore the wonder and beauty of science with *Science Made Simple: Units From* The *Intermediate* Mailbox® *Magazine*. This compilation of teaching units—selected from 1987 to 1993 issues of *The* Intermediate *Mailbox*® magazine—will prove to be an invaluable classroom resource.

Table Of Contents

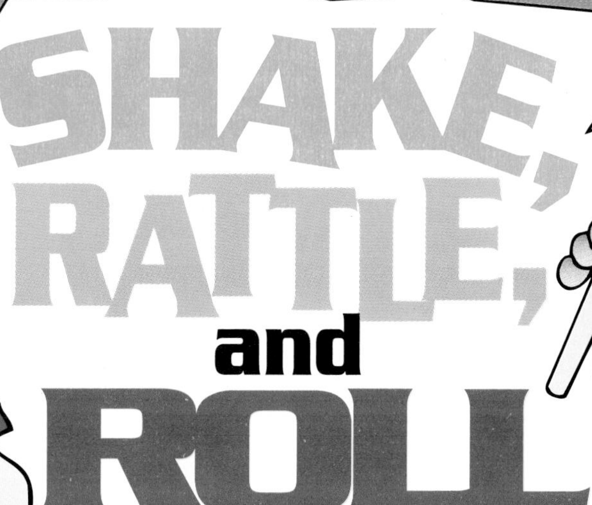

SHAKE, RATTLE, and ROLL

A Hands-On Exploration Of Earthquakes

Why does Mother Nature shudder, shake, quiver, and quake? Help students understand the mysteries of earthquakes with the following hands-on activities and reproducibles.

by Bill O'Connor

Background For The Teacher

In the past, major earthquakes have resulted in tragic losses of life and property. Today seismologists better understand the causes of earthquakes and can sometimes even predict them! Engineers use special building techniques to minimize damage, especially in areas where soft soils amplify earthquake motion. Populations can also be warned of huge tidal waves, or *tsunamis*, caused by earthquakes. Prepared (and informed) people are better able to avoid the harm resulting from nature's most devastating phenomenon. And as students learn more about earthquakes, they'll also gain a better knowledge of the structure of our planet.

Pam Crane

Anatomy Of An Earthquake

How And Why Does An Earthquake Occur?

Earthquakes occur when stresses cause large rock formations under the earth's surface to move suddenly, usually at a crack *(fault)* in the rock. These stresses within the crust are often created by *tectonic forces*, believed to come from the movement of hot rock within the upper mantle of the earth. Tectonic forces cause sections of the crust called *plates* to move, or "drift," around the surface of the earth.

Where Do Earthquakes Occur?

If plates are moving at places where they meet, earthquakes and volcanoes may be common. The "ring of fire" around the Pacific Ocean is an example. The earthquakes that occurred in Alaska (1964) and in San Francisco (1906) were tectonic in origin. However, major earthquakes can occur far from plate boundaries, as they did in New Madrid, Missouri (1811–12), and in Charleston, South Carolina (1888).

What Kinds Of "Waves" Does An Earthquake Make?

Earthquakes send vibrations through the earth in the form of *primary waves* and *secondary waves.* Primary waves travel faster, can be transmitted by both solid and liquid materials, and cause vibrations in a manner similar to sound waves. Secondary waves travel only through earth's solid materials.

What Is The Epicenter?

The exact location of an earthquake is determined by the accurate timing of waves at different locations, where they are recorded with *seismographs.* The point on the surface of the land directly above the actual quake movement is known as the *epicenter.*

What Is A Seismograph?

Seismographs help determine the energy, or *magnitude,* of an earthquake, as measured on the Richter scale. Each number 1–10 on the scale represents ten times the energy of the preceding number. The San Francisco earthquake (1906) has been estimated at 8.25 on the Richter scale; California's second-most-severe earthquake (1989) was rated 7.1.

Earthquakes: Simple Hands-On Activities

How Do Stresses Build Up In The Earth's Crust?

Bring a dry stick to class. Explain to students that rocks, like the dry stick, can bend somewhat under pressure. Demonstrate how the stick can bend. Ask students what will happen if the bending stress becomes too great. Then bend the stick until it snaps. Explain that this is what happens in an earthquake.

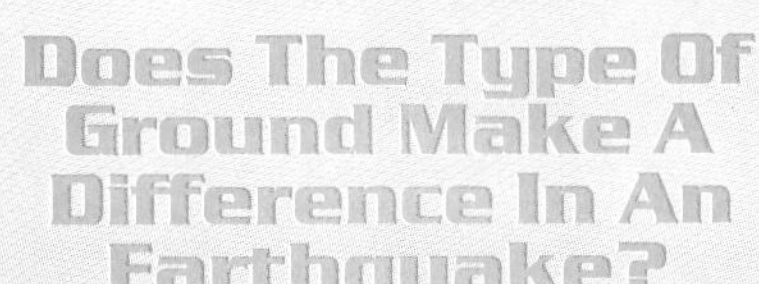

What Causes Earthquakes?

Provide students with modeling clay in several colors. Have the students make flat strips of the different colors of clay, then stack the strips to form layers. The edges of the layers should be visible. Trim with a table knife if necessary. Next have each student push the opposite ends of the clay together. He should observe that the layers bend, fold, and, perhaps, break. This is what happens to layers of rock, causing earthquakes.

Does The Type Of Ground Make A Difference In An Earthquake?

Try the following teacher-directed experiment to demonstrate the effects of an earthquake on different types of soil.

Materials:

two large pans, at least three inches deep; water; unflavored gelatin, one packet per two cups needed (see Step 1); iodine (optional, to prevent spoilage); firm soil, enough to fill one pan; large cooking pot; hot plate; spoon; other assorted materials to represent miniature structures: matchboxes, small cereal boxes, small lightweight blocks, checkers, dominoes, math pattern blocks, toothpicks, tape, straws, cardboard

Preparation:

1. Make enough gelatin, according to package directions, to fill one of the pans. (To find the volume of your pan, multiply its length, width, and depth in inches. Then divide the product by 14.5 to determine the number of cups of gelatin you'll need to fill the pan.)
2. While it is still liquid, add two drops of iodine per cup of gelatin to prevent spoilage.
3. Allow the gelatin to set in one pan. This pan represents unconsolidated soils.
4. Fill the second pan with firm soil or clay. This pan represents bedrock.
5. Stack dominoes, matchboxes, and other small items in each pan to represent structures.

Procedure:

1. Place both pans on a table. Simulate an earthquake by lifting one end of the gelatin pan a few centimeters off the table and dropping it. Observe the waves which travel through the gelatin. They are like *seismic waves* in the earth. Observe the effect of the waves on the items you placed on the gelatin.
2. Repeat the procedure with the pan of soil.

Observations:

You'll probably observe that the buildings on the gelatin suffer more "damage" than those built on the more solid material. The gelatin continues to vibrate for seconds after the shock. This type of vibration accounts for the damage done to structures in an earthquake. Of course, the buildings on the solid material may topple too!

Pam Crane

What Are Primary And Secondary Waves?

Waves travel through the earth just as they do through air and water. Earthquakes create two types of waves: *P* (primary) waves and *S* (secondary) waves. *P* waves travel faster. They are caused by the compression and release of rocks, and resemble sound waves.

- Demonstrate *P* waves by stretching a Slinky™ toy along the length of a table. Have a student hold each end. Have the student at one end compress the first 30 or so centimeters of coils at his end, and then release them. Observe the motions of the remaining coils of the toy. You'll observe that they moved in the same direction as the compressed coils moved.
- To demonstrate *S* waves, have one student move his end of the Slinky™ sharply back and forth one time. Again observe the movement of the coils. You'll observe that they move in a sideways direction, perpendicular to the Slinky™. In an earthquake, these waves could also move vertically. They are like waves of water in the ocean.

How Do Earthquakes Affect The Surface Of The Earth?

Students should now have a better understanding of the causes of an earthquake. But what happens at the surface of the earth during an earthquake? Students will find out with the following cooperative activity.

Materials needed for each group:

two boards, modeling clay, twigs, assorted materials to make miniature structures

Preparation:

1. Lay the boards side by side.
2. Cover the boards with a thin layer of clay.
3. Make trees, roads, houses, fences, and other structures and add them to the surface.
4. Make sure that some of the items extend from one board to the other.

Procedure:

Hold one board firmly; have another student slide the other board in a parallel fashion (see illustration).

Observations:

Students should observe the effects of the board's movements on the surface features, especially the area where the two boards abut. Have the students rebuild their models and experiment with other directions of movement: a separation, forcing together, and an up-and-down movement.

Name ______________________________

A Tour Of "Down Under"

What does the inside of the earth look like? The drawing below shows what many scientists think. Read the description of each part of the earth. Then label the parts and color them according to the code.

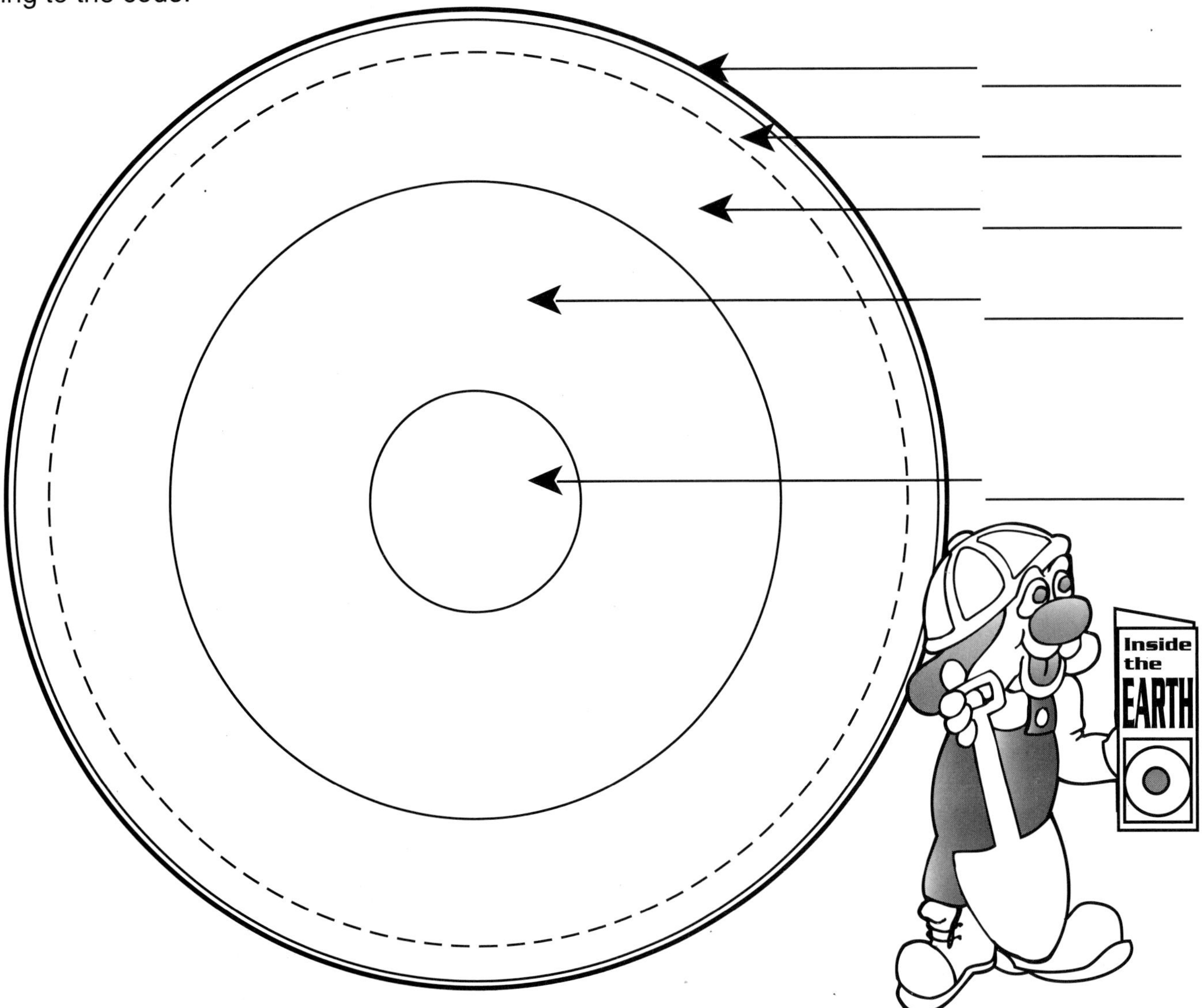

[yellow] Scientists believe that the **outer core** is made of melted iron and nickel. It is much denser than the rock layers above it. The temperature of the outer core can range from about 4000° to 9000° F.

[light brown] The **mantle** lies below the asthenosphere. It is a thick layer of solid rock. Many scientists believe that the mantle transfers heat from the core to the surface.

[blue] The **crust** is made of many plates which "float" above the asthenosphere. The crust is thicker and lighter at the continents and thinner and denser at the ocean floor.

[black] Scientists think that the **inner core** is made of solid iron and nickel. These materials sank to the center of the earth while it was still in a molten form.

[orange] The **asthenosphere** lies just underneath the crust. Because of great heat and pressure, it flows very slowly. It is this motion in the asthenosphere that causes the continents to drift.

Bonus Box: Since no one can go there, how do we learn about the inside of the earth? Research to find out the methods and tools used by scientists.

Puzzling Plates

The puzzle pieces below show the *tectonic plates*. Geologists think that the crust and upper layer of the mantle are not one sheet of solid rock. Instead it is divided into about 12 enormous plates and many smaller ones. These plates "float" like icebergs on the top of the asthenosphere.

Directions: Cut out the nine pieces and place them on a sheet of construction paper, making a rectangular map of the earth. Hint: Begin by placing the Pacific Plate in the center of your paper. When you have fit the pieces together correctly, glue them to the paper. Color each plate a different color.

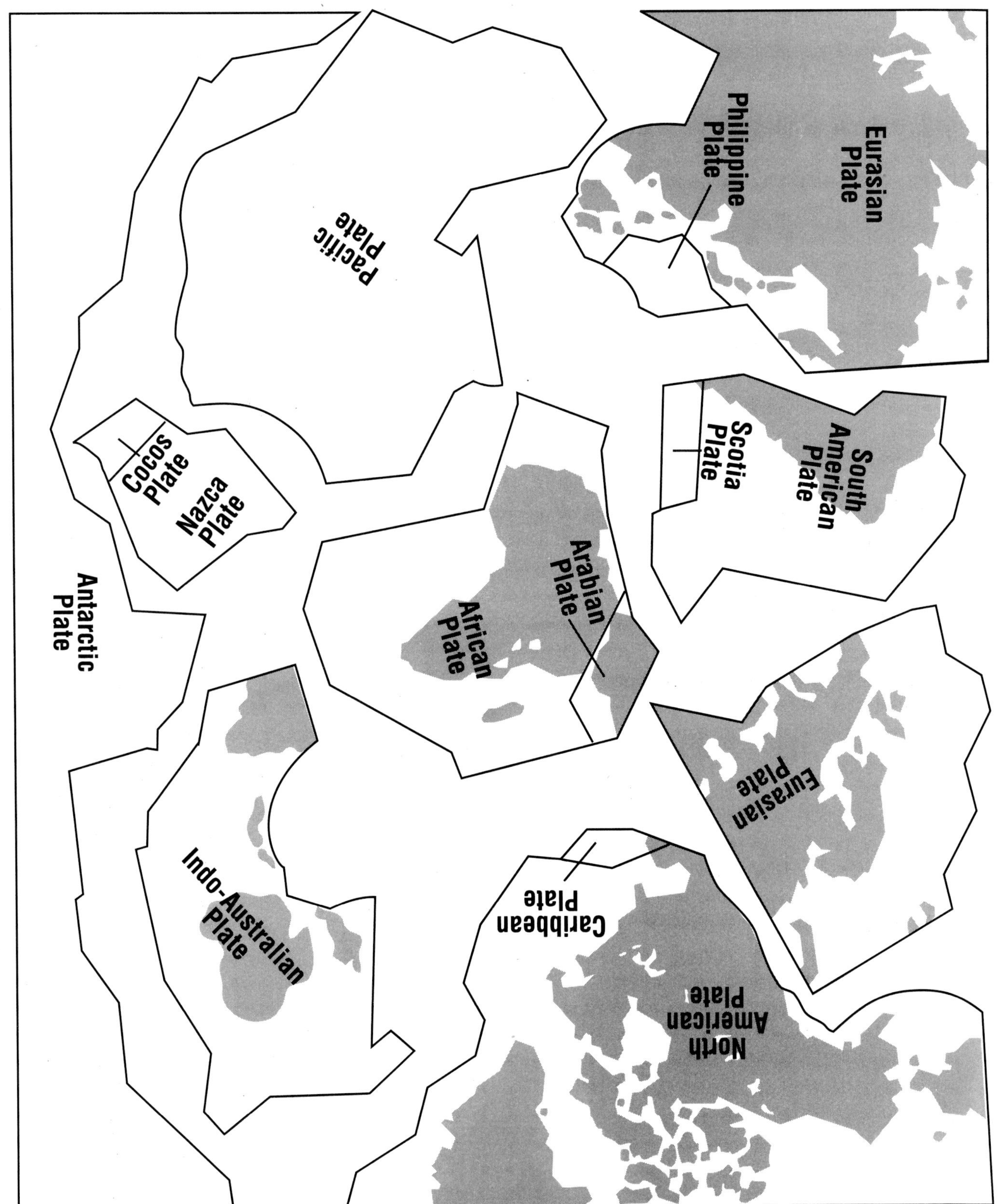

Name ____________________

A Whole Lot Of Shakin' Going On!

Scientists locate the epicenter of an earthquake by timing the seismic waves that arrive at recording stations. The closer the recording station is to the epicenter, the sooner the waves arrive. Earthquakes occurred in San Pedro County on March 8, October 2, and November 22. The chart lists the distance of each earthquake from each recording station.

Directions:

1. Cut out the map and glue it to the middle of a large sheet of white construction paper.
2. Use a compass to draw a circle around each recording station for the March 8 earthquake: at Santa Ana, the radius of the circle is 12 cm; at Mudville, the radius is 9 cm; and at San Juan, the radius is 5 cm.
3. Go over the three circles with red crayon.
4. The point where the three circles intersect is the epicenter of the March 8 earthquake.
5. What city on the map was closest to the epicenter? Write it in the chart.
6. Follow the same steps for the October 2 and November 22 earthquakes.

Recording Station	**March 8 (red circles)**	**October 2 (blue circles)**	**November 22 (green circles)**
Santa Ana	12 mi.	4.5 mi.	11 mi.
Mudville	9 mi.	11.5 mi.	5.5 mi.
San Juan	5 mi.	12.5 mi.	9.5 mi.
City nearest to epicenter			

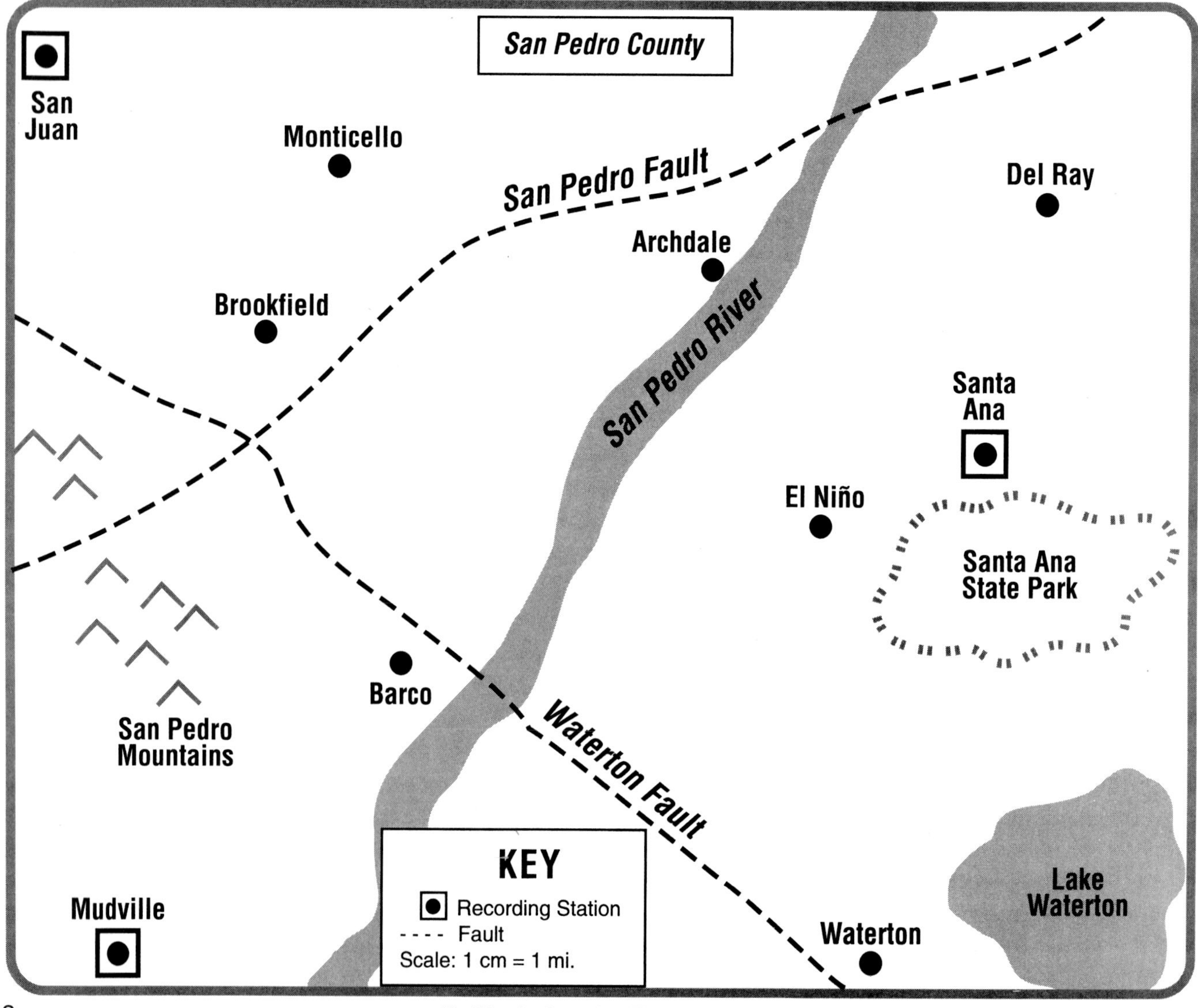

Name ______________________________

Earthshaking Words

Have you added lots of new words to your science vocabulary? The puzzle below contains many words about earthquakes that you're probably more familiar with now. Use the earthquake words in the word banks to help you complete the puzzle. Some of the letters are already included to help you get started!

Clues

Across

2. molten rock
4. the earth's center
7. a strong emotion
9. a break between rock formations
10. big quake in New _____, MO (1812)
11. movement of the continents
13. upper mantle layer
16. hazard after a quake
18. weighing instrument
19. _____ager; adolescent
20. spring string flyers
21. measure of a quake's power
25. a type of precipitation
26. _____graph: records vibrations
28. site of 1964 Alaska earthquake
29. surface location of a quake

Down

1. city of famous 1906 earthquake
2. earth layer beneath the crust
3. ____ = length x width
4. site of South Carolina earthquake (1888)
5. ____ the clues carefully!
6. outer earth layer
8. rubber boat
12. inventor of magnitude scale
14. sections of earth's crust
15. tidal wave
17. part of earth's crust above water
19. forces that move continents
22. the largest continent
23. abbreviation for large U.S. automaker
24. opposite of yes
27. a set of two

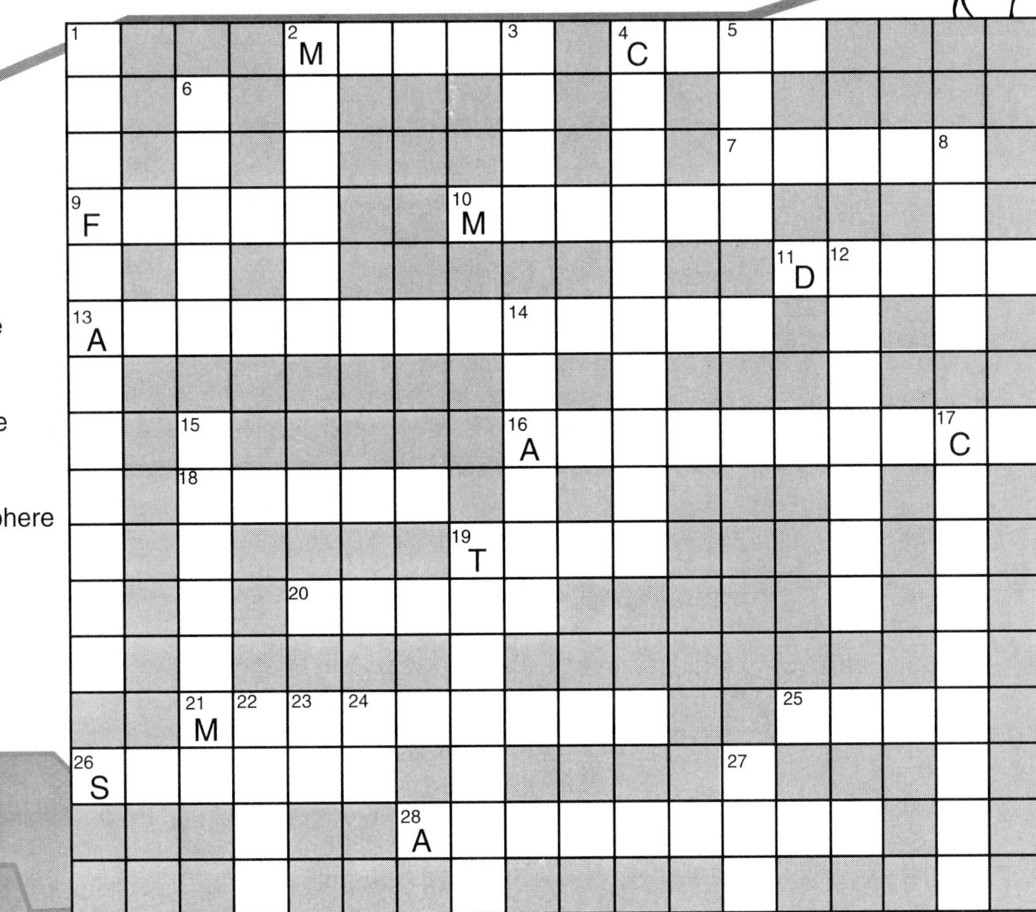

Word Bank

continent
epicenter
magnitude
Richter
Anchorage
plates
asthenosphere
tectonic
fault
seismo

Word Bank

aftershock
crust
magma
San Francisco
mantle
core
Charleston
tsunami
Madrid
drift

Adventures In The

From the smallest insect to the largest mammal, the Animal Kingdom is a fascinating world for scientists of all ages. Take your students on a science safari with the following activities and reproducibles.

by Mary Anne Haffner and Sue Ireland

DOLPHIN

You're In A Class By Yourself!

Start a science bulletin board; then step back and let your students finish it! Use yarn and construction-paper cards to create a chart showing the five classes of vertebrates. Divide students into five groups, one for each class. Have the groups add characteristic cards to the board as shown. Groups finish the board by adding magazine pictures or original drawings of animals from their classes. Repeat this activity to introduce your students to the six classes of invertebrates.

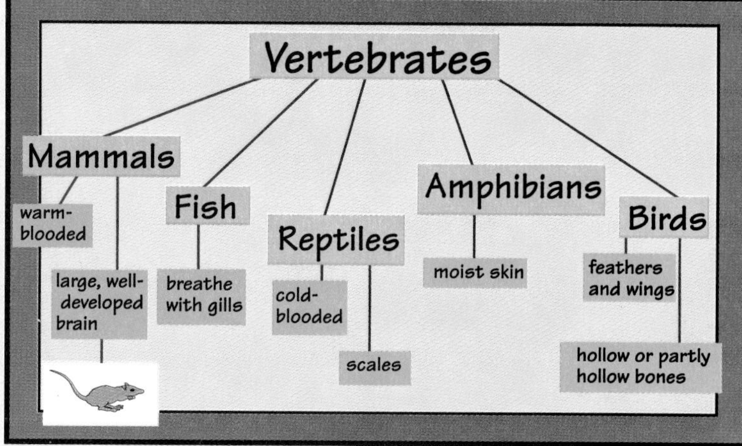

Why Classify?

With over a million kinds of animals to study, how can scientists know each one's special characteristics? One way is to classify animals according to similarities. Scientists divide the Animal Kingdom into six subdivisions: *phyla, classes, orders, families, genera,* and *species.*

As a class, brainstorm a list of common household items to classify. Have students discuss and vote on two "phyla" in which to divide the items: metal/nonmetal, electrical/nonelectrical, useful/decorative, etc. (Explain that when scientists separate animals into different groups, they start with the *most noticeable* thing that sets certain animals apart from others.) Then divide your students into small groups. Have each group divide the list further and share their subdivisions with the class.

Classification Station

"IT'S ALIVE!" Then it's either a member of the Plant, Animal, or Protist Kingdom. Give your class an opportunity to observe members of these kingdoms. Duplicate copies of the lab sheet on page 12. Provide the following items for students to observe: a houseplant or flowering plant; a small animal such as a fish, guinea pig, frog, or insect; a slide prepared with a sample of pond water.

Have each student observe the samples and record his observations on the lab sheet. Use the information students gather to discuss the similarities and differences among the three kingdoms.

(One member of the Protist Kingdom, the paramecium, is found in ponds and streams containing decaying plants. To prepare slides for this observation, boil one liter of water containing a handful of hay or dried grass. Place the mixture in a jar with a few grains of boiled rice. Let the mixture stand for two days. Then add some pond water. Let the mixture stand for several more days. Prepare a slide with one drop of the mixture.)

Animal Kingdom

WALRUS

Skeleton Scrutiny

Want your students to "bone up" on vertebrates? Call on a local veterinarian to provide you with visual aids such as X rays to place on an overhead projector, charts of animal skeletons, and actual sample skeletons. Use these materials to help students observe the characteristics of vertebrates, and the similarities and differences among the five vertebrate groups.

Characteristics of vertebrates:

1. A vertebrate has a backbone and *cranium* (braincase).
2. Vertebrates have either a bony or cartilaginous backbone called a *spinal column.*
3. A vertebrate's skeleton supports the body and protects the internal organs.
4. All vertebrates are *bilaterally symmetrical.* (The left and right sides are alike.)
5. Vertebrates never have more than two pairs of limbs.

Biology Relay

Play a quick review game to reinforce identification of vertebrates and invertebrates. Divide the class into two teams. Line up each team's members behind each other. Give the first person on each team a clipboard holding a piece of paper labeled with an animal group. At your signal, the student writes the name of an animal belonging to that group. He then passes the clipboard to the student behind him. The game continues until one team has passed its clipboard to the end of its line. As a class, check both teams' responses. Award one point for each correct answer. The team with the most points wins.

LLAMA

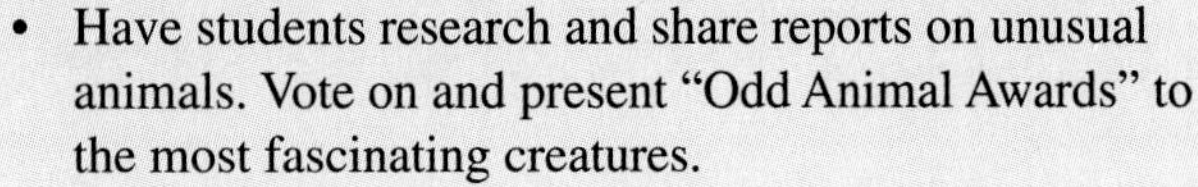

In Search Of Spineless Specimens

Did you know that there are more than 20 times as many invertebrates as there are vertebrates? Give students the task of teaching each other about this fascinating (and less familiar) group of animals. Divide your class into six research teams, one for each invertebrate group: sponges, coelenterates, echinoderms, worms, mollusks, arthropods. Each group is responsible for creating a display about its invertebrate group. Encourage groups to use a variety of media, such as taped or written reports, models, actual samples or skeletons, overhead transparencies, scrapbooks, mobiles, trivia collections, posters of animals in their environments, magazines, videos, and resource books.

Animally Awesome Activities

- Have students research and share reports on unusual animals. Vote on and present "Odd Animal Awards" to the most fascinating creatures.
- For a fun art activity, challenge each student to create a new animal. The new beast must have at least one characteristic from each of the five groups of vertebrates.
- Got an extra five minutes? Have each student list 20 letters of the alphabet down one side of his paper. Challenge the student to list an animal beginning with each letter. For a real challenge, have students list only mammals and birds, or fish and insects.
- Head to your local drugstore when it's time to study insects. Many pharmacies will donate pillboxes for displaying insect specimens.
- Who hasn't heard of being "as busy as a beaver" or "as wise as an owl"? As students learn more about animal behavior, have them suggest new similes using animals. How about "as fragile as a jellyfish" or "as cautious as a prairie dog"?

Name ____________________

Classification Station Lab Sheet

Observe carefully and complete the chart.

Animal Kingdom	Plant Kingdom	Protist Kingdom
Name of organism:	Name of organism:	Name of organism:
Method of locomotion:	Method of locomotion:	Method of locomotion:
Description of habitat:	Description of habitat:	Description of habitat:
Reaction to stimulus: bell: light:	Reaction to stimulus: bell: light:	Reaction to stimulus: bell: light:
Physical appearance:	Physical appearance:	Physical appearance:
Other observations:	Other observations:	Other observations:

Bonus Box: On the back of this sheet, list three ways in which the organisms are alike and three ways in which they differ.

Note To Teacher: Provide each small group of students with a microscope or hand lens, a small bell, and a flashlight. See "Classification Station" on page 10 for instructions.

Name ____________________

Simply Spine-Tingling!

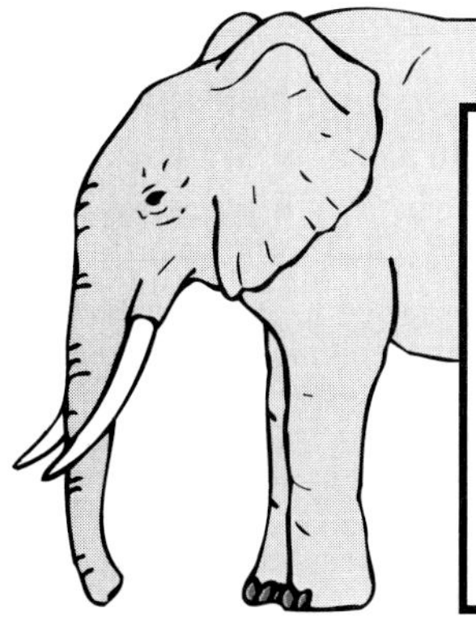

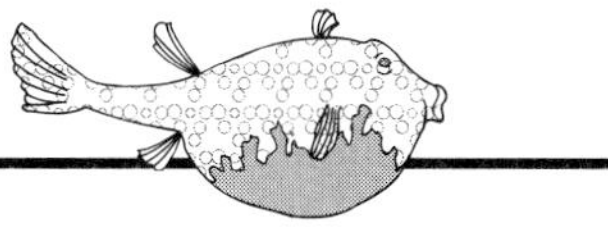

Directions:
Put a **1** before every phrase that describes mammals.
Put a **2** before every phrase that describes birds.
Put a **3** before every phrase that describes reptiles.
Put a **4** before every phrase that describes amphibians.
Put a **5** before every phrase that describes fish.
Hint: Some phrases describe more than one group of vertebrates.

____ dry, scaly skin

____ warm-blooded

____ most live on land and in water

____ breathe mainly through gills

____ breathe with lungs, skin, or gills

____ breathe with lungs only

____ eyes usually on sides of head

____ have hair or fur at some time in their lives

____ hollow or partly hollow bones

____ most give birth to live young

____ cold-blooded

____ young feed on mother's milk

____ moist, scaleless skin

____ wings and feathers

____ most use fins to swim

____ large, well-developed brains

____ lay hard-shelled eggs

____ dinosaurs were members of this group

____ most lay leathery eggs

____ eggs enclosed in jellylike substance

Write each of these animals under the correct vertebrate group: **tern, anaconda, tilapia, auk, newt, tuatara, goby, potto, caecilian, marmoset.** Use a dictionary or encyclopedias to help you.

Mammals
1. ____________________
2. ____________________

Birds
1. ____________________
2. ____________________

Reptiles
1. ____________________
2. ____________________

Amphibians
1. ____________________
2. ____________________

Fish
1. ____________________
2. ____________________

Bonus Box: Use an encyclopedia to find out more about one of the animals listed above. On a piece of art paper, draw a picture of the animal. Below the picture write an interesting fact about the animal.

Name ____________________

Science Alliance

As you complete an activity, color the slide.

I will complete ____________________

activities by ____________________.
(date)

____
(student's signature)

1. Create a new way of classifying mammals, insects, and reptiles. Explain your method in a chart, poster, or written report.

2. Make a diorama showing an animal in its habitat. Use a burger box, take-out salad container, or shoebox.

3. Prepare a slide of a freshwater organism.

4. Visit a pet store. Make a list of animals there. Classify each animal as a vertebrate or invertebrate.

5. Explore the grocery store and find three examples of each: invertebrate, vertebrate, plant, and protist.

6. Investigate an animal that is considered endangered. Find out one way that the state or federal government is trying to preserve this animal. Explain a solution of your own.

7. Illustrate the meaning of *food chain.*

8. Graph the life expectancies of ten vertebrates. Include at least one example from each of the five classes of vertebrates.

9. Make a word search puzzle of 20 to 25 vertebrates. Provide a word bank.

10. Design and make a gameboard and question cards on animals which are native to your area.

11. Make a chart which lists ten animals and how they defend themselves from their enemies.

12. On an index card, write information about a vertebrate or an invertebrate. Include an illustration of the animal on the back. Complete three cards.

Staple this contract inside a file folder. Use the folder to store your work.

Note To Teacher: Have each student fill in the box with the required number of activities, due date, and signature.

Name ____________________

Puzzling Protists

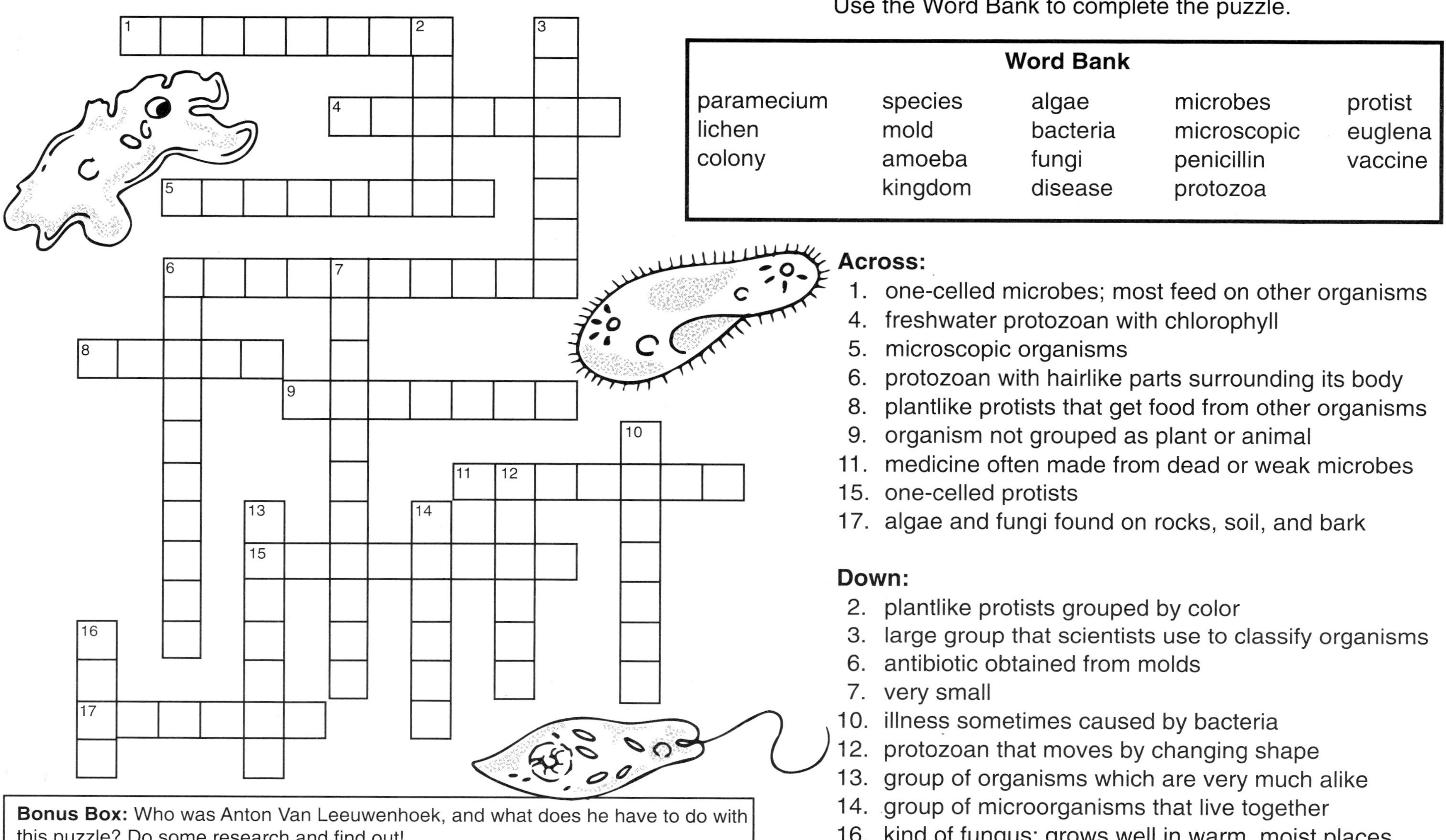

Use the Word Bank to complete the puzzle.

Word Bank

paramecium	species	algae	microbes	protist
lichen	mold	bacteria	microscopic	euglena
colony	amoeba	fungi	penicillin	vaccine
	kingdom	disease	protozoa	

Across:

1. one-celled microbes; most feed on other organisms
4. freshwater protozoan with chlorophyll
5. microscopic organisms
6. protozoan with hairlike parts surrounding its body
8. plantlike protists that get food from other organisms
9. organism not grouped as plant or animal
11. medicine often made from dead or weak microbes
15. one-celled protists
17. algae and fungi found on rocks, soil, and bark

Down:

2. plantlike protists grouped by color
3. large group that scientists use to classify organisms
6. antibiotic obtained from molds
7. very small
10. illness sometimes caused by bacteria
12. protozoan that moves by changing shape
13. group of organisms which are very much alike
14. group of microorganisms that live together
16. kind of fungus; grows well in warm, moist places

Bonus Box: Who was Anton Van Leeuwenhoek, and what does he have to do with this puzzle? Do some research and find out!

BEGINNING CHEMISTRY

A CLOSE-UP LOOK AT THE METHOD AND MYSTERY OF CHEMISTRY

Chemical changes happen all around us: a fire burns, iron rusts, milk sours, and plants make food. Chemical changes even take place *inside* our bodies as we digest food and use oxygen. Use the following teacher demonstrations and hands-on activities to stir the interests of students with the wonders and fun of chemistry.

by Bill O'Connor

BACKGROUND FOR THE TEACHER

Chemistry is the study of substances: what they are made of, how they act, and how they change. A chemist wants to know why a chemical change takes place and how it can be controlled. This knowledge has led to the development of many inventions, including synthetic fibers, drugs, and other useful substances. Chemical changes take place when a substance breaks down or combines with another to produce one or more new substances that have different properties.

Chemistry involves all of the senses: hearing, sight, smell, taste, and touch. It helps us understand and explain many of the events that we observe in daily life.

SAFETY FIRST!

Safety is important in every classroom. And safety-mindedness is even more important when students are involved in science activities. The following tips will help you and your students become more aware of safety during experiments and activities that involve chemicals:

- Store equipment and materials properly.
- Always supervise students when they work with chemicals. Give clear, complete directions before students begin.
- Remind students not to taste or touch substances without your permission.
- Students should not touch their eyes, mouth, face, or body when working with chemicals.
- Students should wash their hands thoroughly after completing an activity.
- To avoid waste, dispense chemicals in small containers.
- Insist that students measure amounts carefully. No dumping!
- Be especially careful with candle flames. Tie back long hair and roll up loose sleeves.
- Make sure students are aware of fire drill and other emergency procedures.

MATERIALS LIST

Most of the materials needed to complete the teacher demonstrations and student experiments in this unit are simple household items. Ask students and parents to help you gather the following supplies.

- ***apples***
- ***baking soda (sodium bicarbonate)***
- ***candles***
- ***cooking oil***
- ***diluted household clear ammonia (Mix 1 cup ammonia to 3 cups water.)***
- ***drinking glass***
- ***Epsom salt***
- ***hot plate***
- ***hydrogen peroxide***
- ***jars (covered and uncovered)***
- ***knife***
- ***lemon juice***
- ***matches***
- ***measuring cup***
- ***measuring spoons***
- ***milk***
- ***nails (uncoated steel)***
- ***paint (latex)***
- ***paintbrushes***
- ***pan***
- ***pennies***
- ***pie plates (aluminum)***
- ***pitcher***
- ***plastic bottle with cork or rubber stopper***
- ***red cabbage (1 head)***
- ***salt***
- ***saucepan***
- ***sponges***
- ***spoons***
- ***steel wool (plain)***
- ***strainer***
- ***sugar***
- ***tea bag***
- ***tissue***
- ***vinegar***
- ***water***
- ***wire***

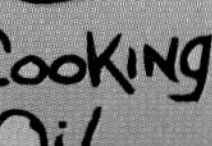

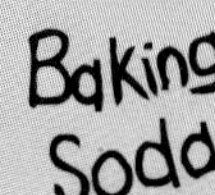

Barry Slate

Where Did The Sugar Go?

(Teacher Demonstration)

1. Measure one teaspoon of sugar into an aluminum pie plate.
2. Heat the sugar on a hot plate set at medium.
3. Ask students to describe what they observe.

The sugar melts, turns brown, then black. Sugar is a carbohydrate, *a chemical compound made of carbon, hydrogen, and oxygen. Heat causes the sugar to decompose. The hydrogen and oxygen form water (steam). The carbon is the black solid which remains.*

Rust, Rust, Everywhere!

(Student Experiment)

1. Soak a steel wool pad in vinegar for a few hours.
2. Stuff the pad into the bottom of a narrow glass or jar.
3. Stand the glass upside down in a pan of water. Place the pan where it won't be disturbed.
4. Refill the pan with water if it gets low, but don't move the jar!
5. Observe the jar for three days. Record your observations.

Over a few days, the water will rise into the glass. This happens because the iron in the steel wool has combined with the oxygen in the glass to form iron oxide. The pressure inside the jar is reduced as the oxygen is consumed. The outside air pressure forces more water inside the glass.

Turn Water Into "Milk"

(Teacher Demonstration)

1. Mix four teaspoons of Epsom salt in half a glass of water.
2. Stir until the salt is completely dissolved.
3. Add about one-fourth cup of diluted household clear ammonia (see materials list) and stir.
4. Ask students to record their observations.

A chemical change occurs. The dissolved substances (ammonia, Epsom salt) combine and form a new substance that does not dissolve in water. The result is a suspension *of tiny solid particles.*

5. Leave the above mixture undisturbed for several hours.
6. Ask students to record their observations.

The mixture becomes cloudy and milky as the tiny solid particles break down and dissolve.

Simple Oxidation

(Student Experiment)

1. Place some steel wool (the kind without soap) in vinegar. Leave overnight.
2. Remove the steel wool and rinse it with water.
3. Place the steel wool in a covered jar with a few drops of water.
4. Record your observations.

Rusting is a very common chemical change. Iron combines with oxygen in the air to form a new substance, iron oxide, *which we know as* rust.

Rust Prevention

(Student Experiment)

1. Cover three new, uncoated steel nails with cooking oil.
2. Use a clean brush to paint three other nails with latex paint. Allow themto dry.
3. Leave three nails as they are.
4. Place all of the nails in a jar with a damp sponge.
5. Observe the nails each day for five days. Make a chart and record your observations of the three groups of nails.

The untreated nails will begin to rust. The nails coated with oil and paint don't rust because the steel is not in contact with oxygen. Rusting is a chemical reaction between a metal and oxygen in the air. Metal objects are often painted or oiled to prevent rusting.

Rapid Oxidation—Something's Burning!

(Teacher Demonstration)

To introduce this demonstration, ask students, "What happens to the wax when a candle burns?"

1. Hold a metal spoon in a candle flame for a few seconds; then remove it.
2. Ask students to observe the bottom of the spoon.

A black substance forms on the bottom of the spoon. This substance is carbon. *Candle wax is a chemical compound made of carbon and hydrogen. When a spoon is placed over a candle flame, some of the carbon from the wax sticks to the spoon before it completely burns.*

Continue the demonstration by asking students, "What happens to the hydrogen?"

1. Hold an inverted glass jar over the candle flame, but not too close.
2. Hold the jar over the flame for about 30 seconds.
3. Ask students to observe what happens.

Moisture forms on the inside of the jar. The hydrogen in the candle wax has chemically combined with oxygen in the air to form H_2O—water!

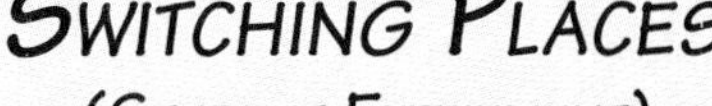

Homemade Ink

(Teacher Demonstration)

1. Place a tea bag in a jar of very hot water for ten minutes; then remove it.
2. Boil some rusty steel wool for several minutes in enough vinegar to cover.
3. Pour off the vinegar.
4. Add to the vinegar a small amount of hydrogen peroxide.
5. Ask students to describe what happens.

There will be a color change.

6. Add the vinegar to the tea in the jar.
7. Ask students to describe what happens.

The color will change to black. A chemical change has occurred because there was no black substance before! Have students use paint-brushes to write with the "ink" that you have made.

Switching Places

(Student Experiment)

1. Use the same vinegar/salt solution from "Homemade Cleanser" (see below left).
2. Rub two steel nails with steel wool until they are very shiny.
3. Place one nail in the vinegar/salt solution. Leave the other nail as is.
4. After about 50–60 minutes, remove the nail from the solution.
5. Compare the two nails. Describe what you think happened.

You should notice a thin coating of copper on the nail that was in the vinegar/salt solution. That's because the solution contained copper from the pennies. The copper in the solution changed places with the iron in the nail—another chemical reaction!

Homemade Cleanser

(Student Experiment)

1. Place several pennies in a small jar with some vinegar and salt.
2. Wait for a few minutes; then remove the pennies. Save the vinegar/salt solution.
3. Describe the pennies' appearance. Were there any changes?

The vinegar and salt combine to produce hydrochloric acid, *which reacts with the oxidized copper on the pennies and dissolves it. Some people clean brass or copper objects with catsup, which contains vinegar and salt.*

Acidic Milk

(Teacher Demonstration)

1. Add vinegar to milk.
2. Heat in a saucepan on a hot plate.
3. Ask students to describe what happens.

A chemical reaction occurs, changing the milk protein into a solid form. The same reaction causes sour milk to curdle when bacteria in the milk produce lactic acid.

4. Save the solid protein *(casein)* obtained from the milk for the "Homemade Glue" activity on page 19.

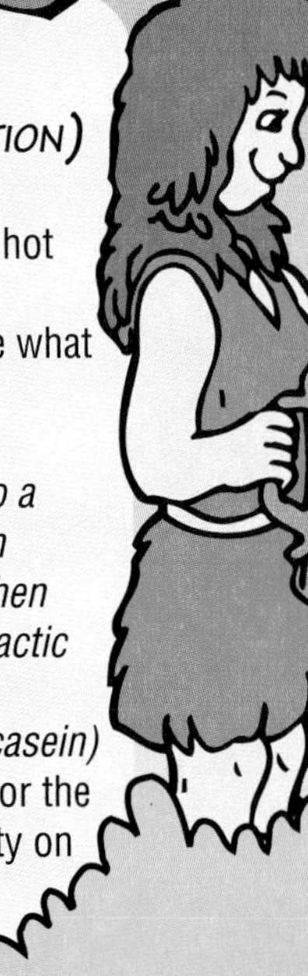

Testing For Acids And Bases

(Reproducible Lab Activity: Page 20)

Many common substances are *acidic* or *basic*. Students can learn more about this property by using easy-to-make indicators that change color when substances are added. One such indicator is red cabbage juice. To make:

1. Cut up one head of red cabbage.
2. Boil the cabbage in four quarts of water.
3. Refrigerate the liquid in a sealed container.
4. Use the liquid within 72 hours.

Ask students to help provide the substances listed in the data table on page 20. To complete the lab activity, provide each small group of students with two to three cups of red cabbage juice, several small jars or paper cups, plastic spoons, and a copy of page 20.

Homemade Glue

(Student Experiment)

1. Place the casein (curds) obtained from the milk in the "Acidic Milk" demonstration on page 18 in a strainer to separate it from the liquid (whey).
2. Mix a teaspoon of baking soda with the curds, stirring until smooth.
3. Allow the mixture to "age" overnight.
4. Try out your "glue." How does it compare with school glue?

Oxidation Prevention

(Student Experiment)

1. Carefully cut up an apple into slices.
2. Divide the pieces between two aluminum pie plates.
3. Soak the pieces in one plate in lemon juice. Leave the other pieces as the control group.
4. After a few hours, what difference do you observe between the apples in the two plates?

The untreated slices will gradually turn brown as the chemicals in the apple react with oxygen. The vitamin C (ascorbic acid) in lemon juice prevents this oxidation.

Make A Fire Extinguisher

(Teacher Demonstration)

1. Light a warming candle and lower it inside a large glass. Use a piece of wire as a handle.
2. Mix together one cup of vinegar and four teaspoons of baking soda in a pitcher.
3. After the fizzing subsides, "pour" the invisible carbon dioxide slowly—as if it were a thick liquid like honey—from the pitcher into the jar. Do not pour out any liquid.
4. Ask students to describe what happens and why.

The candle flame goes out as the CO_2 (carbon dioxide) takes the place of the air in the jar.

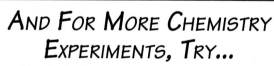

The Pressure's On!

(Teacher Demonstration)

Gather the materials needed for this activity and complete the demonstration outdoors.

1. Pour a half cup of vinegar into a plastic bottle that has a cork or rubber stopper.
2. Wrap two teaspoons of baking soda in a tissue.
3. Drop the tissue into the bottle and quickly insert the cork.
4. Aim the top of the bottle away from everyone.
5. Ask students to describe what happens and why.

The pressure inside the bottle builds up and pops out the cork with great force. This demonstrates that a new substance (a gas) has been produced by a chemical reaction.

And For More Chemistry Experiments, Try...

- *Chemically Active! Experiments You Can Do At Home* by Vicki Cobb
- *Chemistry For Every Kid: 101 Easy Experiments That Really Work* by Janice P. Vancleave
- *Chemistry Magic* by Edward Palder
- *Chemistry Experiments For Children* by Virginia L. Mullin
- *Chemistry Experiments* by May Johnson
- *Kitchen Chemistry: Science Experiments To Do At Home* by Robert Gardner
- *Science For Kids: 39 Easy Chemistry Experiments* by Robert W. Wood

Name(s)______________________________ Group chemistry experiment

Acid Or Base?

Acid or base? Work with your group to test the substances listed in the table.

Purpose: To determine if a substance is an acid or a base.

Hypothesis: Which substances do you think are acids? ______________________

Bases? ______________________

Neither? ______________________

Materials needed for each group:

2–3 cups of red cabbage juice (provided by your teacher)
substances listed in table (as many as possible)
small paper cups
plastic spoons

Procedure:

1. Pour a small amount of cabbage juice into a cup.
2. Add some of the substance that you want to test.
3. Stir with a clean spoon.
4. Observe. Record in the table any color change. Write *none* if there is no noticeable color change.
5. Acids will turn the liquid red. Bases will turn the liquid blue or green. Write your conclusion in the table. Write *neutral* if there is no color change.

Data Table		
Substance	**Observation:** What color do you observe?	**Conclusion:** Is the substance an acid, a base, or neutral?
1. orange juice		
2. baking soda		
3. vinegar		
4. a cleaning product		
5. cream of tartar		
6. a soft drink		
7. salt water		
8. aspirin		
9. apple juice		
10.		
11.		
12.		

Bonus Box: Test three other substances. Show your results in rows 10–12 of the table.

 Note To Teacher: See "Testing For Acids And Bases" on page 19 for information on how to make red cabbage juice indicator.

Name(s)____ Group chemistry experiment

Powder Puzzle (A "Chemystery")

Use your chemistry sense to determine the identity of the mystery powder. Is it sugar? Baking soda? Cornstarch? A combination of these? Or possibly *none* of the above?

Purpose: Find out the identity of the mystery powder.

Hypothesis: What do you think the mystery powder is? (Remember: Do **not** taste any substance!) ______

____

Materials for each group:

sugar
sodium bicarbonate (baking soda)
cornstarch
mystery powder
drinking glass
water
vinegar
iodine
red cabbage juice indicator
candle
spoons
small paper cups
dropper
potholder
teaspoon

Procedure: Complete each test on each powder. Write your observations in the corresponding boxes in the table. After completing a test, wash spoons and other containers before beginning the next test.

Water Test: Add one spoonful of powder to half a glass of water. Stir.

Vinegar Test: Drop a small pinch of powder into a spoonful of vinegar.

Iodine Test: Place three or four drops of iodine on a small amount of powder in a spoon. (Remember: Iodine is a poison. Be especially careful! Wash your hands thoroughly if you get any iodine on them.)

Acid/Base Test: Place a small amount of powder in red cabbage juice. Acids will cause a red color; bases will result in green or blue. No change means the substance is neutral.

Heat Test: Place a half teaspoon of powder into a spoon. With your teacher's assistance, heat the powder over a candle. Use a potholder to hold the spoon.

	Water Test	Vinegar Test	Iodine Test	Acid/Base Test	Heat Test
Powder #1 Sugar					
Powder #2 Cornstarch					
Powder #3 Sodium Bicarbonate					
Powder #4 Mystery Powder					

Note To Teacher: Provide each group of students with labeled containers of the three powders and the "mystery powder." The mystery powder can be one of the three listed, a combination of them, or salt. See "Testing For Acids And Bases" on page 19 for information on how to make red cabbage juice indicator.

Fizz Biz
(Create Your Own Experiment!)

Here's your chance to show off your chemistry know-how! Work with a group to create and complete an experiment.

Directions:

1. Read the information under "Fizzing Chemistry."
2. Choose a question to answer.
3. Write an experiment that will answer the question. Use the experiment report form shown on the right as your guide.
4. Gather the materials that you need to complete the experiment.
5. Complete the experiment. Write your observations and conclusions on your experiment report form.

Fizzing Chemistry

The fizzing that occurs when you drop a headache tablet into a glass of water is a chemical reaction. The chemicals in the tablet cannot react until they dissolve in water. Answer one of the following questions by completing an experiment.

1. How long does it take for the tablet to completely dissolve? Can this be changed?
2. Is a gas produced? Which one?
3. Does the tablet contain starch?
4. Is the tablet an acid or a base?
5. Is the liquid (that contains the dissolved tablet) an acid or a base?
6. After all of the fizz is gone, is the remaining liquid an acid or a base?
7. Will the liquid have a chemical reaction with:
   - copper pennies?
   - Epsom salt?
   - vinegar?
   - baking soda?
   - iodine?
8. Will crystals form if the liquid is allowed to evaporate?
9. Will steel nails rust faster in this liquid than in water?
10. Can you prevent the tablet from reacting when it is placed in water?
11. How does the tablet behave in other liquids? Try a non-water liquid such as cooking oil.
12. What is the effect of heating the tablet in a candle flame (with an adult's assistance)?
13. Make up your own question to answer: ____________________

Monkeying Around With The Five Senses

Seeing is believing—or is it? Everything we know about the world comes to us through our five senses. But can we always trust our sense organs? Invite students to monkey around with that question using the following "sense-sational" hands-on activities and reproducibles.

by Bill O'Connor

Background For The Teacher

Our five senses—sight, hearing, touch, smell, and taste—connect us with the world that we inhabit. Yet sometimes that connection seems to get crossed!

Our sense organs receive information from the environment, but they do not interpret that information. The eyes, ears, skin, nose, and tongue send nerve impulses to the brain. The brain then organizes the impulses into perceptions like images, sounds, tastes, odors, and touch sensations. We may perceive things differently depending on how our brain interprets them. The activities that follow will help your students to learn about how the brain interprets sensations.

As your students complete the activities, explain to them that scientists must rely on their senses to understand the world too. Because our senses can be misleading, scientists must be careful to measure or observe carefully. Scientific instruments like the microscope, telescope, and spectrometer were invented to help us use our senses more accurately. Some of these activities will show students how to give their senses a helping hand.

Monkeying Around With The Sense Of Smell

The fragrance of fun will permeate your room when students test their sense of smell with the following activities. To prepare, wet a piece of cloth or cotton with a drop of household ammonia; then place the material in a plastic sandwich bag. Prepare several other aroma bags using familiar scents such as garlic, peppermint or lemon extract, perfume, vinegar, etc.

Activity 1: Ask a student to smell each aroma bag and describe the odor. Require the student to use descriptive words rather than evaluative ones like "yucky." After that student identifies each aroma, blindfold another student and have her try to identify each odor when a bag is held up to her nose. Keep a record of the correct aromas and the guesses on the chalkboard. What happens to the accuracy of the guesses after a while? *(**Explanation:** There will be more incorrect guesses than correct ones after about ten trials, as the subject's sense of smell becomes fatigued.)*

Activity 2: Have a student inhale from one of the aroma bags for three minutes. (Make sure that the student takes breaths of fresh air frequently.) After three minutes, blindfold the student. Ask him to identify three objects that are held under his nose: the aroma he has been smelling, an object with a different odor, and an object that is odorless. Test him several different times with each object. Can the student identify each object correctly each time? Is it possible to identify the aroma that was inhaled as well as the other aromas? What does this tell us about our sense of smell? *(**Explanation:** The student who smelled one of the aromas for several minutes will have more difficulty identifying that aroma. Our receptors for smell become "fatigued" after a while. A person may become used to a familiar odor, while someone entering the room will notice it immediately.)*

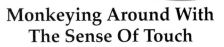

Monkeying Around With The Sense Of Touch

Reach out and touch your students' curiosity with these explorations about the sense of touch.

Activity 1: Fill one bucket with hot tap water, another bucket with cold water, and a third bucket with lukewarm water. Have a student put his left hand in the hot water and his right hand in the cold water. After one minute, have him put his left hand in the lukewarm water. How does it feel? Now have the student put his right hand into the lukewarm water. How does this hand feel? What does this experiment tell us about the reliability of our skin's sense of temperature? What would be a more accurate method of finding the temperature of water? *(**Explanation:** The lukewarm water feels different to both hands because the messages sent from the hands' sensory receptors to the brain are confused. The right hand adapted to the cold water, so it senses the lukewarm water as hot. The left hand, which adapted to the hot water, senses the lukewarm water as cold.)*

Activity 2: Give each pair of students a copy of the reproducible lab sheet on page 28, three sharpened pencils, and tape. Have students tape two of the pencils together so that their points are even. After everyone has completed the activity, ask students which areas of the body have the most accurate sense of touch. Why do students think this is so? *(**Explanation:** Students will probably find that their guesses are more accurate when the palm, fingertip, and lips are being tested. These areas have more touch receptors than other parts of the body. There is an increase in the pain experienced in areas that have more nerve endings. In order to feel two pencil points, the point must touch two different receptors.)*

Monkeying Around With The Sense Of Hearing

Are two ears really better than one? Do both ears hear the same sounds? Investigate the sense of hearing with this activity:

Activity: Provide a blindfold, a flashlight, and a small pillow or folded cloth. Have students sit in chairs in a circle. Place a stool in the center of the circle. Choose one student to sit on the stool, blindfolded and holding the flashlight. Select two other children to be the "recorder" and the "chooser." Draw a chart as shown on the chalkboard.

To begin, have the chooser silently point to one of the students sitting in the circle. That child claps once. The student sitting in the center turns and aims the flashlight in the direction from which the sound came. If the flashlight beam hits the child who clapped, the recorder records it as a "hit." If it completely misses the child, the recorder records it as a "miss." If the beam strikes a child on either side of the student who made the sound, the recorder records it as a "close miss." Repeat this procedure ten times, choosing students from different parts of the circle to be the sound markers.

Next have the student firmly place the pillow over one ear, holding the flashlight in the other hand. Repeat the experiment, filling out a second chart. How do the scores compare? Try the experiment a third time with the other ear. Does the change make any difference? Allow several students to sit in the center and test their ears. Are some students more proficient than others at locating sounds? *(**Explanation:** Our two ears hear sounds differently because of their location. The brain uses these differences, such as the timing, phase, and loudness of sounds, to locate the source of the sound.)*

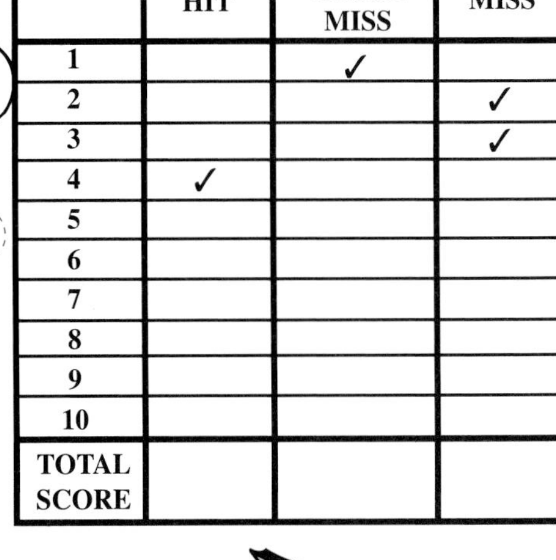

	HIT	CLOSE MISS	MISS
1		✓	
2			✓
3			✓
4	✓		
5			
6			
7			
8			
9			
10			
TOTAL SCORE			

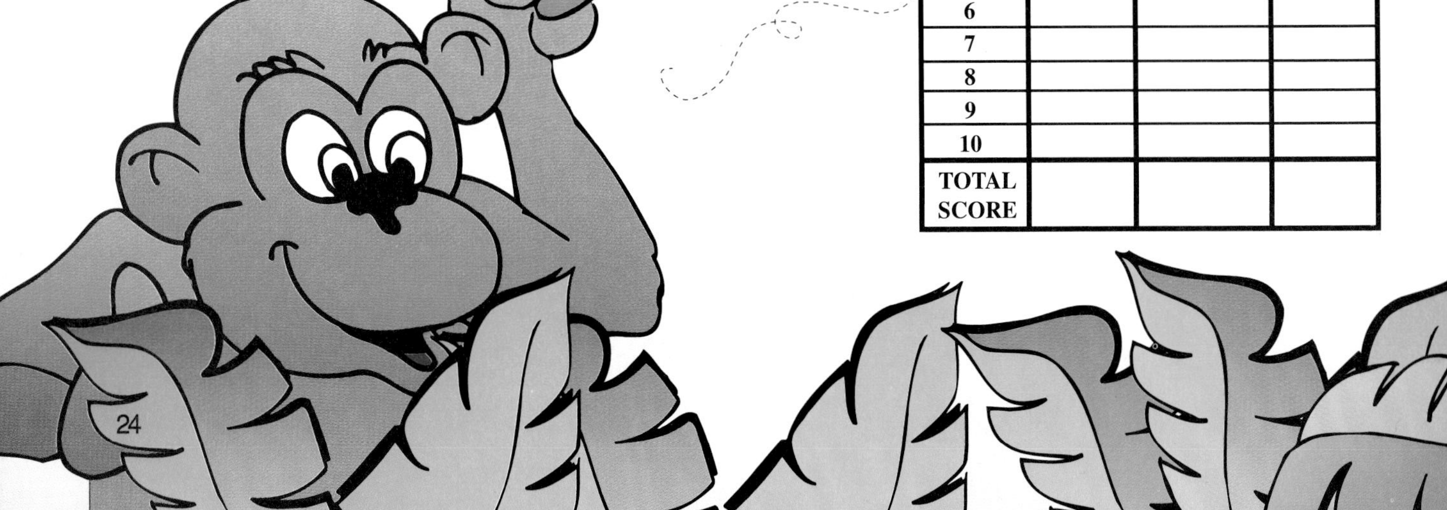

Monkeying Around With The Sense Of Sight

When was the last time you thought your eyes were playing tricks on you? Give students a chance to fool their brains with the following simple experiments.

Activity 1: Hold a pencil about eight inches (20 centimeters) in front of your eyes. Close your left eye. Line up the pencil with an object in the distance, like a door frame. Without moving your head or the pencil, open your left eye and close your right eye. Now where is the pencil against the background?

Now focus both eyes on the background. How many pencils do you see? Focus your eyes on the pencil. How many background objects do you see? What does this tell you about your eyes? *(**Explanation:** Our two eyes see things from slightly different angles. The brain merges the two images into one. The differences between the two images give us the perception of distance.)*

Activity 2: Touch the tips of your two index fingers together horizontally, about three inches in front of your nose. Focus your eyes on the background, not on your fingers. What do you see? Move your fingers slightly apart. How do you explain this strange illusion? *(**Explanation:** The fingers will appear as one. When you move them apart, a "floating finger" will appear! The brain attempts to make sense of the images from the two eyes in this way.)*

Activity 3: Roll a piece of notebook paper into a tube about one inch in diameter. Hold the tube in your right hand; then look through the tube with your right eye. Hold your left hand up, palm facing you, next to the left side of the tube. Look straight ahead through the tube. What is your brain doing now? *(**Explanation:** The student will see a "hole" in his left hand as his brain attempts to make one image out of two.)*

Monkeying Around With The Sense Of Taste

Is our sense of taste always reliable? To find out, pair each child with a partner. Provide each pair with two copies of the reproducible on page 27 and the following materials: small cubes of apple, potato, and pear; toothpicks; a blindfold; two paper cups filled with water; a pencil.

After completing the experiment and discussing its results, have each pair of students repeat the steps with different foods. Which foods could students recognize even with their noses closed? Why?

Reading About Your Senses

It makes sense to bring excellent trade books into your study of the five senses. Try these titles:

How To Really Fool Yourself: Illusions For All Your Senses by Vicki Cobb, HarperCollins Children's Books, 1981

Experimenting With Illusions by Robert Gardner, Franklin Watts, Inc.; 1990

The Science Book Of Sound by Neil Ardley; Harcourt Brace Jovanovich, Inc.; 1991

Sounds Interesting: The Science Of Acoustics by David Darling, Macmillan Children's Book Group, 1991

The Magic Of Sound by Larry Kettlekamp, Morrow Junior Books, 1982

Topsy-Turvies: Pictures To Stretch The Imagination by Mitsumasa Anno; Weatherhill, Inc.; 1970

Upside-Downers: More Pictures To Stretch The Imagination by Mitsumasa Anno; Weatherhill, Inc.; 1971

Opt: An Illusionary Tale by Arline and Joseph Baum, Viking Children's Books, 1987

Jeepers Peepers!

There's more to these puzzles than meets the eye! Look at the optical illusions on this page; then answer the questions in each box.

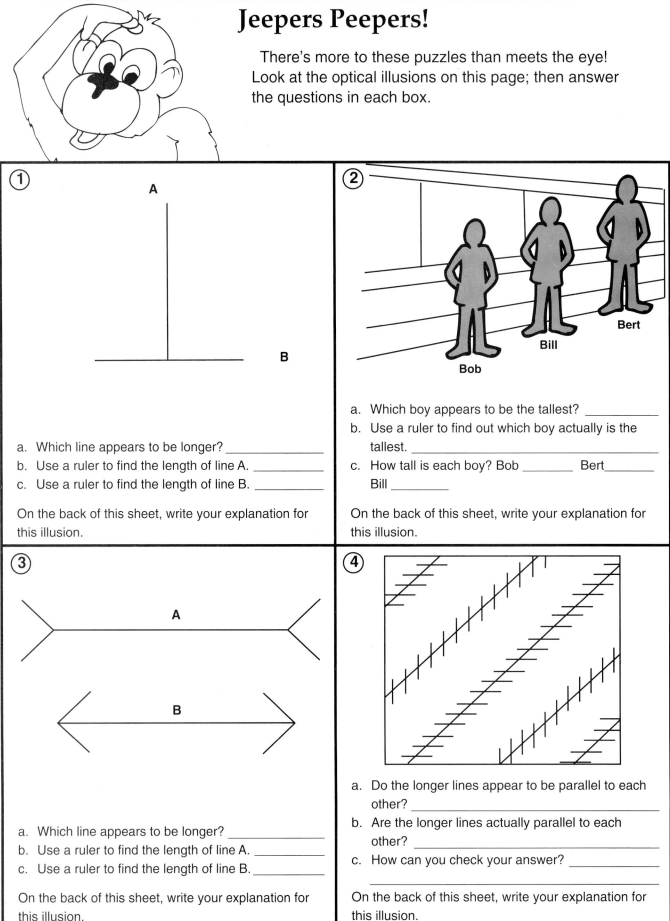

1

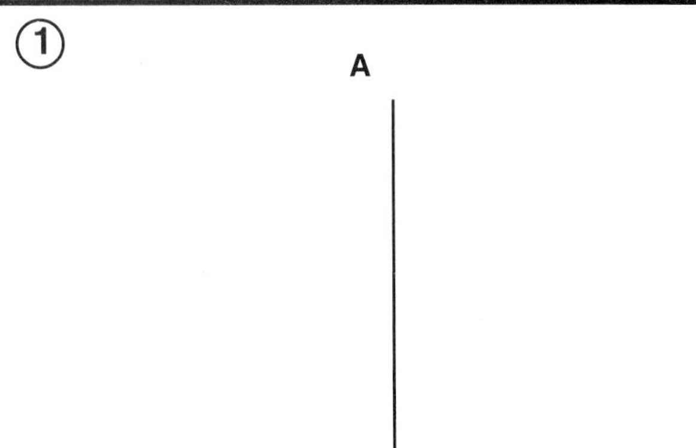

a. Which line appears to be longer? ____________
b. Use a ruler to find the length of line A. ____________
c. Use a ruler to find the length of line B. ____________

On the back of this sheet, write your explanation for this illusion.

2

a. Which boy appears to be the tallest? ____________
b. Use a ruler to find out which boy actually is the tallest. ____________
c. How tall is each boy? Bob ________ Bert________ Bill ________

On the back of this sheet, write your explanation for this illusion.

3

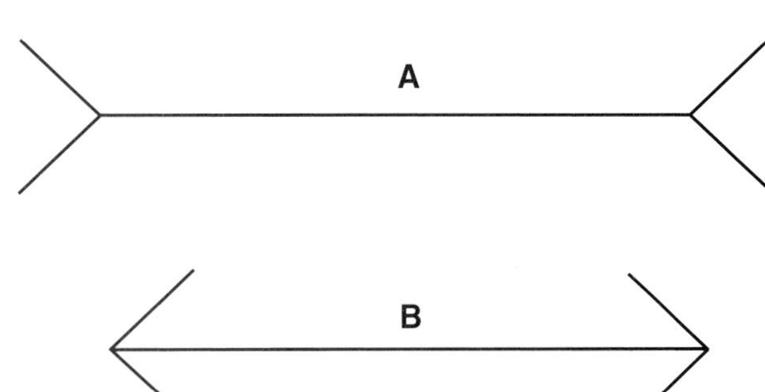

a. Which line appears to be longer? ____________
b. Use a ruler to find the length of line A. ____________
c. Use a ruler to find the length of line B. ____________

On the back of this sheet, write your explanation for this illusion.

4

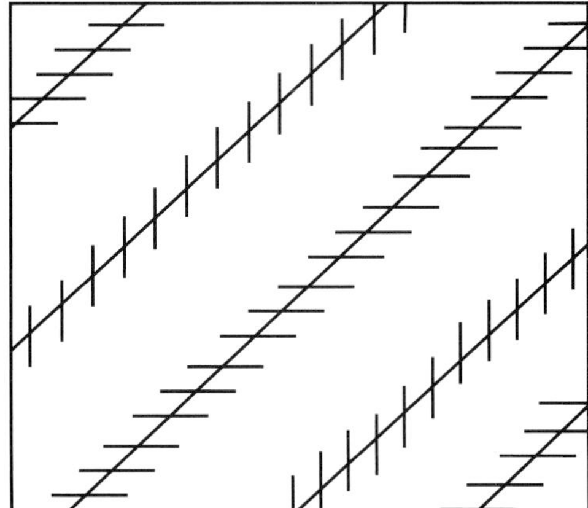

a. Do the longer lines appear to be parallel to each other? ____________
b. Are the longer lines actually parallel to each other? ____________
c. How can you check your answer? ____________

____

On the back of this sheet, write your explanation for this illusion.

Name ______________________________ Completing an experiment

Do You Have Good Taste?

Try this "tasty" experiment with a partner; then switch places and let your partner test you.

Materials:

cubes of apple, potato, pear
two paper cups filled with water
toothpicks
pencil
blindfold

Steps:

1. Blindfold your partner.
2. Ask your partner to stick out his or her tongue; then use a toothpick to place a cube of apple, potato, or pear on the tongue.
3. Ask your partner to guess the food on his or her tongue. Write the food tried and your partner's guess in the chart.
4. After each taste, have your partner rinse his or her mouth with water.
5. Repeat the steps until you have tested ten times. Add to find the total correct guesses.
6. Now ask your partner to hold his or her nose. Repeat steps 1–5.
7. Switch places with your partner and complete his copy of the chart. Be sure to use fresh pieces of food and a new toothpick.

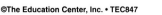

NOSE OPEN			NOSE CLOSED		
Food Tried	**Partner's Guess**	**Correct?**	**Food Tried**	**Partner's Guess**	**Correct?**
1.			1.		
2.			2.		
3.			3.		
4.			4.		
5.			5.		
6.			6.		
7.			7.		
8.			8.		
9.			9.		
10.			10.		
Total correct: ______			**Total correct:** ______		

Note To Teacher: See "Monkeying Around With The Sense Of Taste" on page 25.

Names ______________________________

____

Reach Out And Touch Someone

Are some areas of your skin more "touchy" than others? To find out, complete this experiment with a partner.

Materials:
three sharpened pencils
tape
a pencil (for writing)

Steps:
1. Tape two of the pencils together so that their points are even (see illustration).
2. While your partner's eyes are closed, gently touch the palm of his or her hand with either the single pencil point or the two taped together. DO NOT PRESS HARD. Ask your partner whether he or she feels one or two points. Record his or her guess on the chart by putting a check mark (✔) in the proper column.
3. Repeat step 2 until you have tested your partner's palm ten times.
4. Repeat steps 2 and 3 for the other body parts on the chart.
5. Now switch places. Have your partner give you the test.
6. On the back of this sheet, list the areas of the body that have the most accurate sense of touch. Explain why you think this is so.

Partner 1: ______				Partner 2: ______			
Body Part	Correct Guess	Incorrect Guess	Times Tested	Body Part	Correct Guess	Incorrect Guess	Times Tested
palm			10	palm			10
back of hand			10	back of hand			10
fingertip			10	fingertip			10
back of arm			10	back of arm			10
ankle			10	ankle			10
lips			10	lips			10

Note To Teacher: See "Monkeying Around With The Sense Of Touch" on page 24.

Name ______________________________ Completing an experiment

Do You Hear What I Hear?

Have you ever watched an old cowboy movie on television? If you have, you may have seen a scout trying to figure out how close a buffalo herd was. The scout knelt down and put an ear to the ground. The hoofbeats of the thundering buffalo herd traveled through the ground and reached the scout's ear.

Would you have made a good buffalo scout? To find out, try this experiment with a partner.

Materials: ticking watch or nonelectric clock; long, clean table; yardstick or meterstick

Steps:

1. Put one ear on one end of the tabletop; then close your eyes.
2. Have your partner place the watch or clock at the opposite end of the table.
3. Ask your partner to begin moving the watch or clock toward you.
4. As soon as you hear the watch or clock ticking, raise your hand.
5. Measure the distance from your ear to the spot at which you could first hear the watch or clock.
6. Repeat the experiment with your other ear.
7. Now switch places and let your partner take the test.

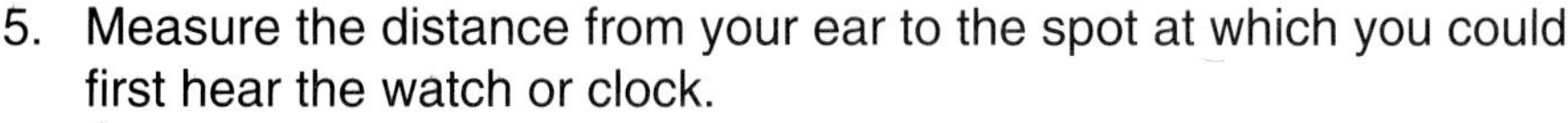

I reckon those buffalo are about five miles from here.

Name ______________________________ Writing topics

Writing Is Simply "Sense-sational"!

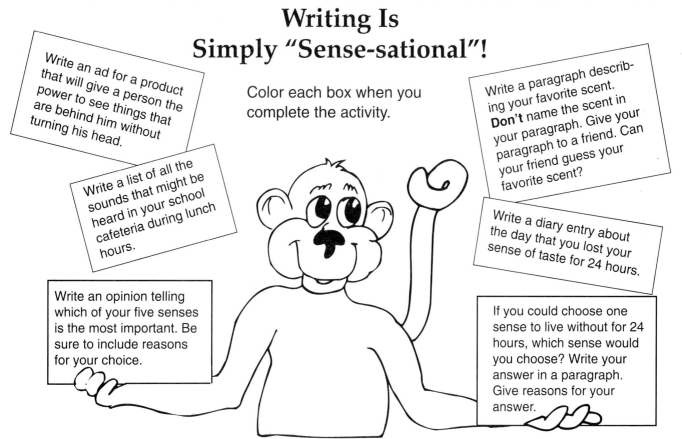

Color each box when you complete the activity.

Write an ad for a product that will give a person the power to see things that are behind him without turning his head.

Write a list of all the sounds that might be heard in your school cafeteria during lunch hours.

Write an opinion telling which of your five senses is the most important. Be sure to include reasons for your choice.

Write a paragraph describing your favorite scent. **Don't** name the scent in your paragraph. Give your paragraph to a friend. Can your friend guess your favorite scent?

Write a diary entry about the day that you lost your sense of taste for 24 hours.

If you could choose one sense to live without for 24 hours, which sense would you choose? Write your answer in a paragraph. Give reasons for your answer.

Understanding, Appreciating, OUR WORLD'S

Why teach about the world's forests? Because forests are the lungs of the earth! They are homes to jaguars, tigers, gorillas, and millions of other species of plants and animals. We depend on forests for our shelter, air, water—and our very lives. Take your students on an excursion into this green world with the following creative activities and reproducibles.

by Bill O'Connor

Background—The Earth's Forests

Forests occur around the earth in places where it's not too cold or dry for trees to grow. There are several major types of forests. At high latitudes are the *northern coniferous,* or *boreal,* forests. These forests consist of needle-leaved, evergreen trees that can survive harsh winters. These trees also provide much of our paper pulp and building lumber. Farther south are the *temperate deciduous* and *temperate mixed* forests, which include the more familiar tree species. These trees also provide pulp and lumber, as well as various hardwoods used for furniture. They are especially important because they grow in areas with dense human populations. *Tropical deciduous* and *tropical rain* forests are found in the earth's tropics. Because they receive ample sunlight and grow year-round, they are an important factor in global ecology.

Five thousand years ago, 50 percent of the earth's land surface was forested. Today that figure is only 20 percent! Forest destruction is now occurring faster than ever. Most deforestation happens in the tropics, where people cut and burn trees to clear land for farming and grazing. Tropical forests are also threatened because of the world demand for such woods as mahogany, teak, rosewood, and lauan. Half the world's people consume 60 percent of the world's wood harvest to cook their food. Air pollution is another threat to forests. And, of course, forests are losing ground to development and timbering, especially in the United States.

Gifts From Our Forests

Brainstorm with students the benefits we reap from our world's forests; then share with them the following information:

- In developed countries, forests provide lumber, paper, and cardboard.
- In less-developed areas, people depend on the forest primarily for fuel.
- Trees provide us with fruits, nuts, cacao, coffee, tea, maple sugar, and spices.
- Tropical forests may provide us with many new food-producing species in the future.
- Useful drugs, such as *quinine* and *curare,* are obtained from trees.
- Seventy percent of the 3,000 plants having known cancer-fighting substances come from rain forests.
- Trees prevent erosion by anchoring soil with their roots and breaking the fall of rain.
- Forests absorb rainfall and release it gradually, thus reducing flooding.
- Trees may even promote rainfall by returning water to the atmosphere through their leaves *(transpiration).*
- The major producer of atmospheric oxygen is forests.

And Conserving

FORESTS

Grow A Tree

Where do trees come from, anyway? To help youngsters understand one answer to this question, try the experiment on page 36. First take a nature walk around your school grounds to collect acorns, if any are available. If not, ask students to bring some from home. Students will also need water, soil, planting containers, black paper, and copies of the experiment. As a follow-up to the activity, make plans to plant the class's seedlings in the spring.

Plant A Tree

Plant a tree on your school grounds to emphasize the importance of forests. Obtain a tree root ball from a local nursery. Then consult your groundskeeper for an appropriate planting site, avoiding areas with poor drainage. Prepare a hole deeper than the root ball and three times its width. Chop up the removed soil, mix with a little compost or peat moss, and replace it in the hole around the root ball. Make sure that the root ball is not too high or too low in the hole. Fill in around the root ball with the remaining soil. Tamp the soil down firmly with your feet. Water thoroughly, creating a big puddle around the tree when you're finished. Water frequently during the first few months, especially during cold, dry weather. If exposed to wind, stake the tree. Drive stakes into the ground just outside the dug area. Use wires or cords (covered with cloth or rubber hose where they contact the tree) to secure the tree to the stakes. Mulching is also very helpful. Use bark, pine needles, grass clippings, paper, or plastic to cover the ground above the roots. This will keep the soil moist. Trees are best planted in the fall, but can also be planted in winter or spring. Imagine the excitement when your students see the buds swell and the first leaves appear in the spring!

Adopt A Tree

How observant are your students? Have each choose a tree near his or her home to "adopt." Instruct students to observe and study their trees over a period of time that you predetermine. Ideally, observing a tree for an entire school year would provide students ample opportunities to see firsthand the changes that nature brings. Provide each student with a copy of the reproducible tree project on page 37 and a folder in which to store his work.

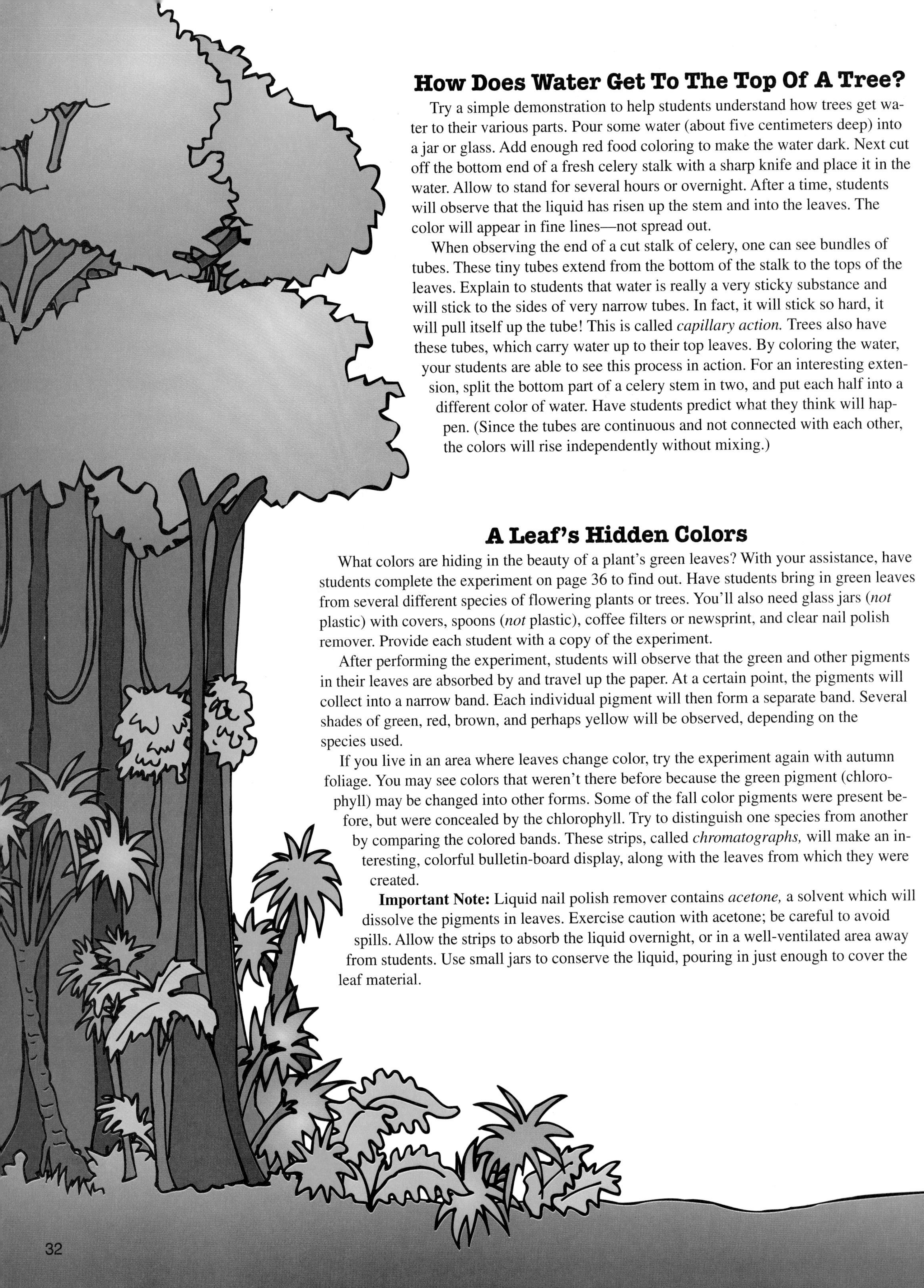

How Does Water Get To The Top Of A Tree?

Try a simple demonstration to help students understand how trees get water to their various parts. Pour some water (about five centimeters deep) into a jar or glass. Add enough red food coloring to make the water dark. Next cut off the bottom end of a fresh celery stalk with a sharp knife and place it in the water. Allow to stand for several hours or overnight. After a time, students will observe that the liquid has risen up the stem and into the leaves. The color will appear in fine lines—not spread out.

When observing the end of a cut stalk of celery, one can see bundles of tubes. These tiny tubes extend from the bottom of the stalk to the tops of the leaves. Explain to students that water is really a very sticky substance and will stick to the sides of very narrow tubes. In fact, it will stick so hard, it will pull itself up the tube! This is called *capillary action.* Trees also have these tubes, which carry water up to their top leaves. By coloring the water, your students are able to see this process in action. For an interesting extension, split the bottom part of a celery stem in two, and put each half into a different color of water. Have students predict what they think will happen. (Since the tubes are continuous and not connected with each other, the colors will rise independently without mixing.)

A Leaf's Hidden Colors

What colors are hiding in the beauty of a plant's green leaves? With your assistance, have students complete the experiment on page 36 to find out. Have students bring in green leaves from several different species of flowering plants or trees. You'll also need glass jars (*not* plastic) with covers, spoons (*not* plastic), coffee filters or newsprint, and clear nail polish remover. Provide each student with a copy of the experiment.

After performing the experiment, students will observe that the green and other pigments in their leaves are absorbed by and travel up the paper. At a certain point, the pigments will collect into a narrow band. Each individual pigment will then form a separate band. Several shades of green, red, brown, and perhaps yellow will be observed, depending on the species used.

If you live in an area where leaves change color, try the experiment again with autumn foliage. You may see colors that weren't there before because the green pigment (chlorophyll) may be changed into other forms. Some of the fall color pigments were present before, but were concealed by the chlorophyll. Try to distinguish one species from another by comparing the colored bands. These strips, called *chromatographs,* will make an interesting, colorful bulletin-board display, along with the leaves from which they were created.

Important Note: Liquid nail polish remover contains *acetone,* a solvent which will dissolve the pigments in leaves. Exercise caution with acetone; be careful to avoid spills. Allow the strips to absorb the liquid overnight, or in a well-ventilated area away from students. Use small jars to conserve the liquid, pouring in just enough to cover the leaf material.

Name ______________________________

Forests Of The World

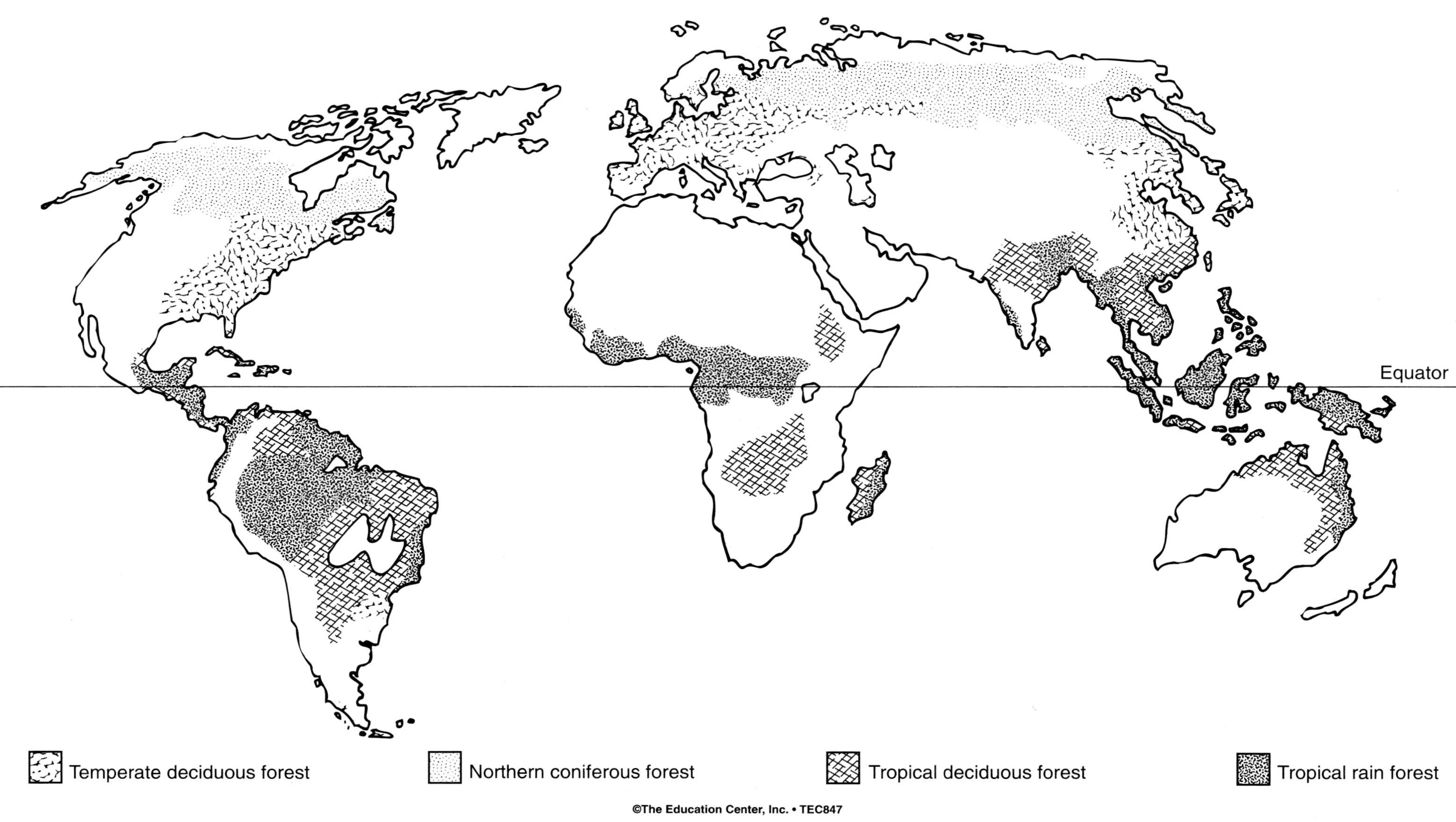

Note To Teacher: Use this map with "World Forests Activities" on page 34.

Name ____

World Forests Activities

Use the world forests map (page 33) and a world atlas, map, or globe to help you complete the following activities.

1. Name the two countries with the largest northern coniferous forests. ______________________________

2. What country in South America has a very large tropical rain forest?
____

3. Name three countries in each area listed below that have tropical rain forests.

Central and South America	Africa	Asia
____________	____________	____________
____________	____________	____________
____________	____________	____________

4. What kind of forests are found in the eastern United States, northern Europe, and eastern China? ______________________________

5. Use crayons, watercolor markers, or colored pencils to color your map according to the following key:

   tropical rain forest—green
   northern coniferous forest—orange
   temperate deciduous forest—blue
   tropical deciduous forest—yellow

6. The following animals may lose their homes if forests continue to be destroyed. Cut out their pictures and glue them to the map near their homes. Use maps and reference books for help.

a. gorilla	central Africa	e. chimpanzee	central Africa
b. orangutan	Indonesia	f. capybara	Brazil
c. spotted owl	Pacific Northwest, USA	g. jaguar	Central America
d. Indian tiger	India	h. three-toed sloth	Ecuador

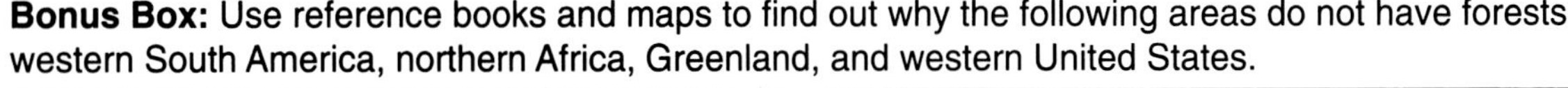
Bonus Box: Use reference books and maps to find out why the following areas do not have forests: western South America, northern Africa, Greenland, and western United States.

 Note To Teacher: Use the reproducible map on page 33 to complete this page.

Name ______________________________

Paper! Paper! Paper!

Do you know where the sheet of paper you're holding came from? More than likely, it was made in the United States. The USA is the leading producer of paper in the world! Use the information in item 1 to complete the graph. Then use the graph to complete the other activities.

1. Complete the bar graph with the following information. The bar for the USA has been done for you.

USA	55.1 million
Japan	17.3 million
Russia	9.1 million
Canada	8.1 million
China	6.3 million

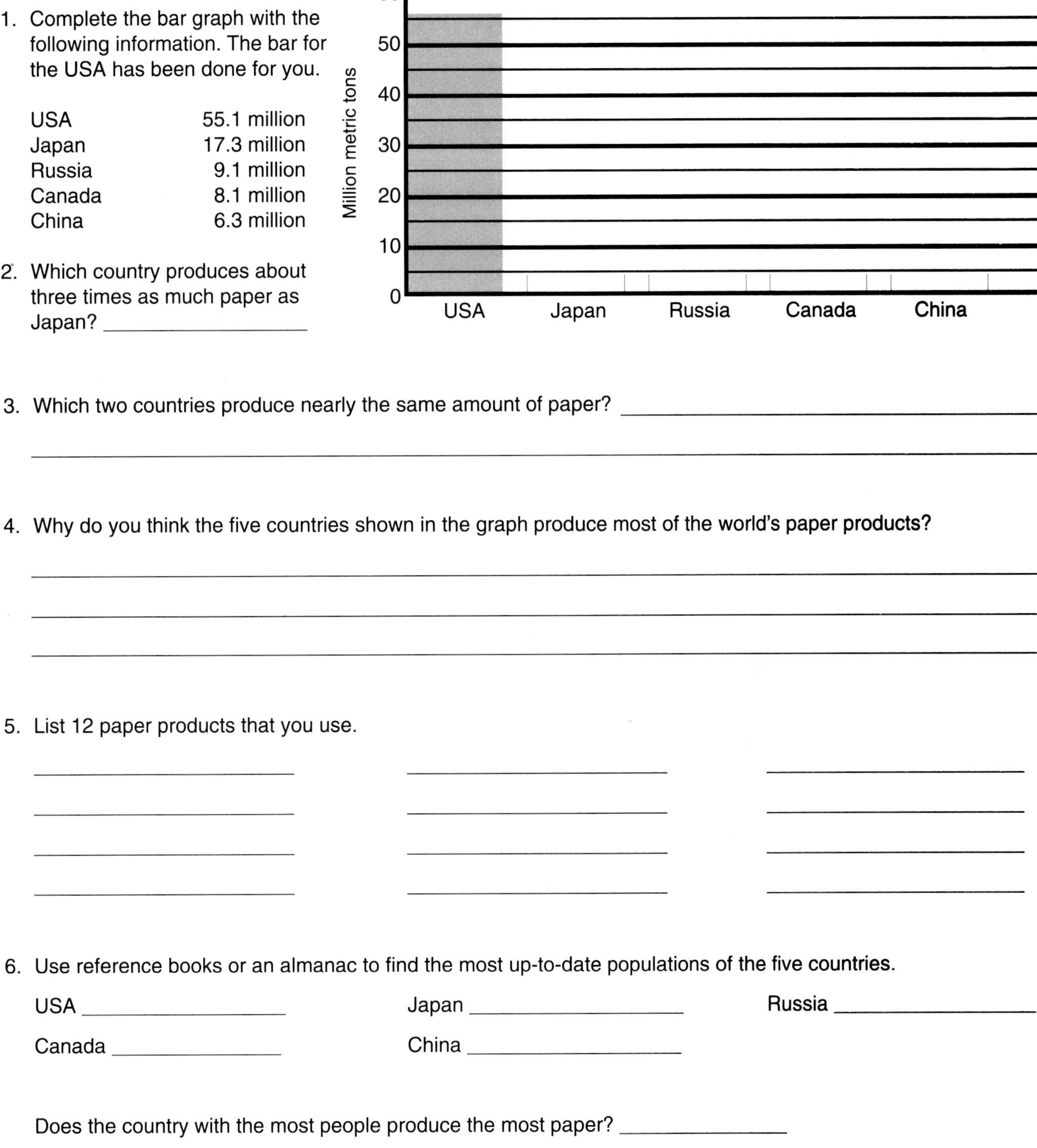

2. Which country produces about three times as much paper as Japan? ______________

3. Which two countries produce nearly the same amount of paper? ______________

____

4. Why do you think the five countries shown in the graph produce most of the world's paper products?

____

____

____

5. List 12 paper products that you use.

________	________	________
________	________	________
________	________	________
________	________	________

6. Use reference books or an almanac to find the most up-to-date populations of the five countries.

USA ______________ Japan ______________ Russia ______________

Canada ______________ China ______________

Does the country with the most people produce the most paper? ______________

What can you conclude from your answer? ______________

____

Bonus Box: Find the area of each country. Make a bar graph to show your information.

Name ______________________________ Science experiment

Grow A Tree!

Start your own oak seedlings!

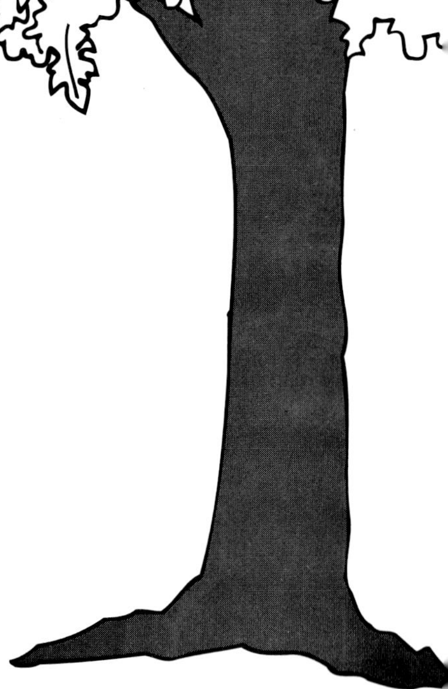

Materials: several acorns, water, soil, planting containers, black paper, freezer, two containers for soaking acorns, marker or pencil

Procedure:

1. Inspect the acorns and remove any that have small holes in them. (If you open these, you'll probably find insect larvae.)
2. Place half the remaining acorns in a freezer for two weeks. Keep the other half in a dry place.
3. After the two weeks are over, soak all the acorns in water overnight. Keep them in two separate, labeled containers *(frozen* and *unfrozen).*
4. Plant each acorn in an individual container. Be sure to label each container *frozen* or *unfrozen.* (Clear containers, if wrapped in black paper, will allow you to observe root development.)
5. Keep records of the growth of each kind of acorn.

Observations and Conclusions: (Write your answers on another piece of paper.)

1. How many acorns did you collect? How many had insect damage?
2. How are the acorns with insect larvae useful?
3. What did you notice about the water the acorns were soaked in?
4. Did freezing the acorns affect them in any way?
5. Which part of the oak plant grew first?
6. After your plants start to grow, choose one to observe. Draw a picture of it each week for eight weeks.

Name ______________________________ Science experiment

A Leaf's Hidden Colors

What colors are hiding in green leaves?

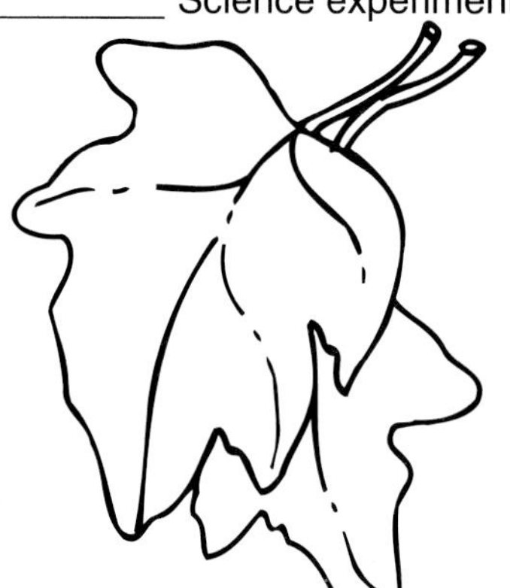

Materials: fresh green leaves, glass jars with covers, spoon, coffee filters or newsprint, clear nail polish remover (provided by your teacher), pencils or paper clips, tape

Procedure:

1. Tear up a leaf or two, place in a small glass jar, and crush completely with a spoon.
2. Your teacher will pour liquid nail polish remover into the jar, covering the leaf.
3. Cover the jar and let it stand overnight.
4. Carefully pour the liquid into another jar.
5. Cut a strip of filter paper or newsprint about 2 cm wide and longer than the jar's height.
6. Place the strip of paper in the jar so that it just touches the liquid. Push a straightened paper clip through the paper and place it across the top of the jar to hold the paper in place. Or you can tape the paper to a pencil.
7. Leave the jar uncovered overnight.

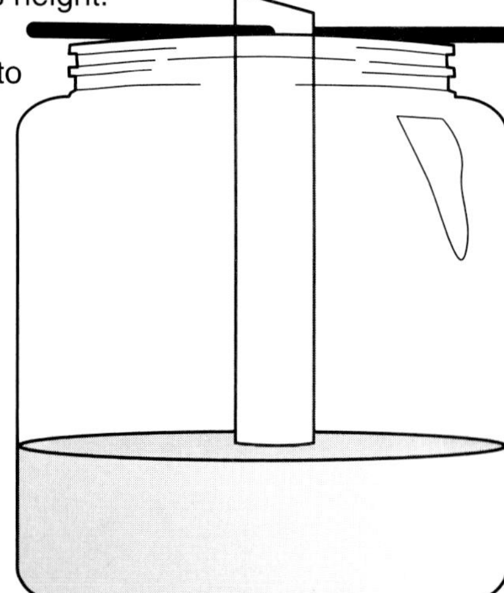

Observations and conclusions: (Write your answers on another piece of paper.)

1. What do you see on the paper?
2. Do you think there was more than one color in the leaf? How many colors?
3. What colors, other than green, do you observe?
4. What do you think would happen if you tried the experiment again with red, yellow, orange, or purple leaves? Wait until the leaves turn colors in the fall and try it!

Adopt A Tree!

Choose a tree near your home to adopt. Observe your tree beginning __________ and continue until ____________. Attach this sheet to the inside of a folder. Store your writing, artwork, observations, and data inside the folder. When complete, make a booklet with all your materials.

1. What kind of tree did you adopt? What is its scientific name?
2. Describe your tree. Try to determine its height and the circumference of its trunk. What shape are your tree's leaves? Describe the color and texture of the bark. Crush a leaf or a twig and describe its smell.
3. Write the life story of your tree. How did the tree get to where it is? How might new trees come to join it? What does your tree need for its survival? How old do you think your tree is? How long might it live?
4. What other living things depend on your tree? Make a list of any creatures you observe living on or visiting your tree, such as insects, birds, and small mammals. Why is the tree important to each of them?
5. Put yourself in your tree's place. Use descriptive sentences to tell how you would feel when there is:
   - a person planting you
   - a snowstorm
   - a violent windstorm
   - a gentle rain falling
   - a thunderstorm with lightning
   - a forest fire raging in the distance
   - a squirrel scampering up your trunk
   - a treehouse being built in you
   - a bird building a nest in your branches
   - a child climbing your branches
   - someone carving into your bark
   - a gentle breeze blowing through your branches
6. Draw a picture of the shape of your tree.
   Draw a detailed picture of a leaf from your tree.
   Draw a picture of a leafless branch in winter (if your tree loses its leaves).
   Make a leaf rubbing.
   Make a bark rubbing.
   Make a map showing the location of your tree.
7. Each month, on the same date, make the following observations of your tree and its environment. Record your data on index cards.
   - date
   - time
   - temperature
   - weather conditions
   - changes in the tree since your last observation

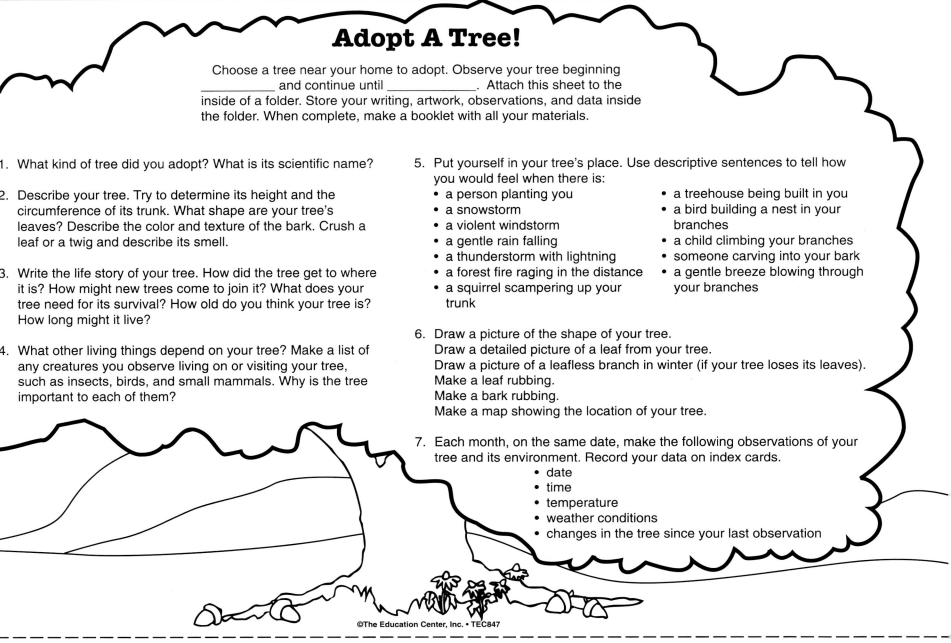

Note To Teacher: Fill in the beginning and ending dates for the tree observation activities before duplicating. See more information about this activity on page 31.

Air, Arteries, And A Whole Lot More!

A CLOSER LOOK AT THE CIRCULATORY AND RESPIRATORY SYSTEMS

Journey with your students through two of the body's transport systems with these fascinating facts, activities, and reproducibles.

by Barbara Sumpter and Becky Andrews

Our Incredible Insides

Grab your students' attention early with an easy-to-make bulletin board. On white construction paper, duplicate several copies of the pattern on page 41. Have student volunteers color faces on the patterns before cutting them out. Write one of the fascinating facts listed below on each cutout.

A week before beginning your unit, post several of the cutouts on a bulletin board with the title "Our Incredible Insides." Add some newly labeled cutouts to the board each day, and watch the excitement about your upcoming unit reach a fever pitch! (Provide extra copies of the pattern for students who want to add their own fascinating facts.)

Fascinating Facts

- The heart circulates your blood through your body at least 1,000 times every day.
- If all the blood vessels in your body were laid end to end, they would measure about 100,000 miles and could encircle the equator about four times.
- The heart beats about three billion times in an average lifetime (75 years).
- A single drop of blood contains about four to six million red blood cells.
- About two million red blood cells die every second.
- At birth, your heart weighed only about 2/3 of an ounce.
- Capillaries are blood vessels that are 50 times thinner than the thinnest hair.
- It takes the blood less than one minute to move through the body, to the right side of the heart, to the lungs, and back to the left side of the heart.
- If you run a 100-yard dash, you'll need about seven quarts of oxygen.
- Your lungs are the only organs in the body that are light enough to float on water.
- The blast of air from a cough can reach speeds of up to 70 miles per hour.
- Your lungs contain about 600 million small air chambers called *alveoli.*

About two million red blood cells die every second.

Let Me Hear Your Heart Beat!

The *pulse,* caused by blood stopping and starting as it rushes through the arteries, indicates the rate at which the heart is beating. Give students the chance to observe the effects of age and activity level on heart rates. Demonstrate to students how to find pulse points in their necks or wrists. Duplicate the mini-worksheet on page 41 for each student. Acting as the official timekeeper, have each student sit at his desk and count the number of beats during a 15-second time period. Students multiply the number of beats by four to find their resting heart rates. Have them chart this on their worksheets.

Next have students walk around the room for two minutes, stop, and count their pulse rates for one minute. Rest for five minutes; then have students run in place for two minutes, stop, and check their rates. Discuss reasons for the differences in the resting, walking, and running rates. Then challenge students to enlist the aid of family members, friends, or neighbors to complete the rest of the chart. (Caution students that anyone with heart or respiratory problems should not be used as a subject in this project.)

The Muscle That Never Sleeps

Try this simple experiment to demonstrate the hard work of the heart. Provide a tennis ball for each student. Instruct each pupil to squeeze the ball, relax his hold, squeeze again, relax, and so on, for a full minute. If students will squeeze 70 times per minute, which is the normal pulse, their tired hands will give them a clearer picture of how hard the heart works. Explain to students that the force needed to squeeze a tennis ball is about the same force the heart exerts to pump blood through the body.

It Must Be Crowded In There!

There are lots of interesting things packed into one tiny drop of blood! Give students a closer look at the four main components of blood: *red blood cells, white blood cells, platelets,* and *plasma.* Enlarge the pattern and mount it on a bulletin board. Divide the class into four groups, one for each component. Have the groups research their blood components and add their facts to the bulletin board.

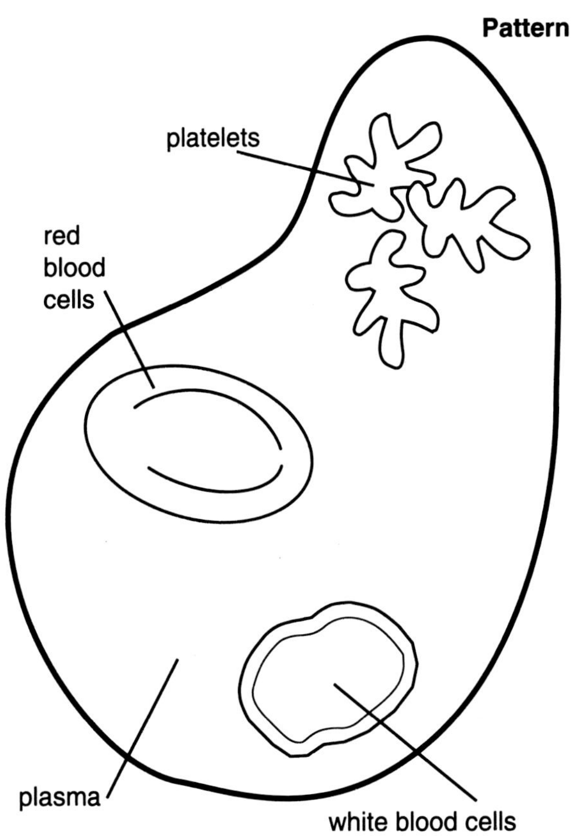

One For The Books

Familiarize students with the parts of the respiratory system with a creative project. On separate sheets of paper, have each student draw detailed pictures of the parts of the respiratory system: nose, mouth, rib cage and muscles, lungs, bronchial tubes, larynx, trachea, pharynx, diaphragm. Students should leave space on each picture for writing interesting facts about the body part. For example: "If you could spread all the tissue in your lungs out flat, it would cover half a tennis court." Collect the completed pages and bind them into class books, with titles such as "Our Lungs: A Matter Of Life And Breath" and "Tracking Down Trachea Facts." Or have each student bind all of his pages together to make a personal study guide on the respiratory system.

A Fantastic Voyage

Anything that you do 15 to 20 times a minute (21,600 times a day) must be important—and breathing is! To help students understand the exchange of oxygen and carbon dioxide wastes which takes place 24 hours a day, send them on an investigative trip to the lungs. Divide students into small groups. Have each group write and perform a short skit describing a visit to the lungs. Each skit should explain how the travelers got to the lungs in the first place, what they saw on the way, and what they viewed once they reached their final destination. Your students will never forget this creative project or what it taught them about the lungs.

Take A Deep Breath

How much air can the lungs hold at one time? To test breath volume, give each child a balloon. Instruct students to blow as much as they can into their balloons, using just one breath. Have students compare the sizes of their balloons. Discuss whether students think size or height of the person affects lung capacity. Can girls hold more air than boys? Students will be amazed to know that, in an average day, their lungs move enough air to blow up over 1,000 balloons!

Breathing And Smoking

Smoking makes the lungs work less efficiently, and many smokers will admit that they feel the effects of smoking as they move around. Challenge students to interview people who have quit smoking. Instruct them to find out why the person started smoking, why he quit, how he was able to quit, what effects smoking had on his life, how much money he spent on cigarettes each week, and whether smoking created any problems for him. Discuss the interviews in class; then have students design posters, badges, or bumper stickers to convince kids not to start smoking.

Math Mini-Sheet

Duplicate the mini-sheet below to add a little math practice to your science unit.

Name ______________________________ Respiratory system: math word problems

Inhale The Information, Exhale The Solution!

Most people breathe about 15 times every minute at rest. Use this information to solve the following problems. Show your work on the back of this sheet.

1. Juan was stretched out on the couch watching TV. How many times did he breathe during the first ten minutes of the program? ________________

2. Jerry played basketball with his sister. He played for one hour and took 2,940 breaths. How many breaths per minute did Jerry average? _________

3. Jenny was chasing her dog, Bozley, around the house. She was breathing 12 times faster than her resting rate. How fast was she breathing? ______________________

4. Jim took 25 breaths per minute while playing tennis. Jo took 28 breaths per minute while playing against Jim. How many more breaths did Jo take in an hour? __________________

5. Joan's heart rate is about five times her breathing rate when she is running the 100-meter dash. What is Joan's heart rate if she is breathing 30 times per minute? _________________

Bonus Box: Write a conversation you just had with your lungs after running across the playground to catch a fly ball.

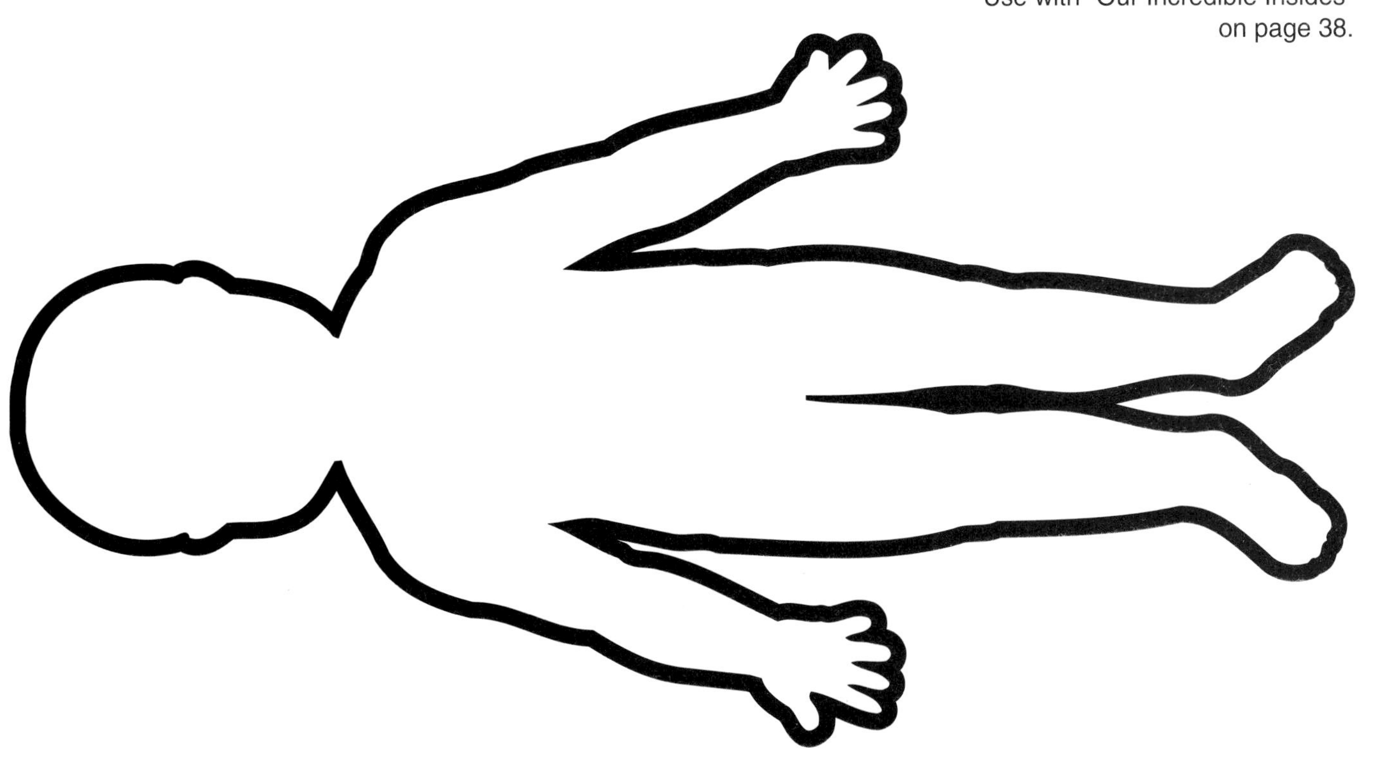

Let Me Hear Your Heart Beat!

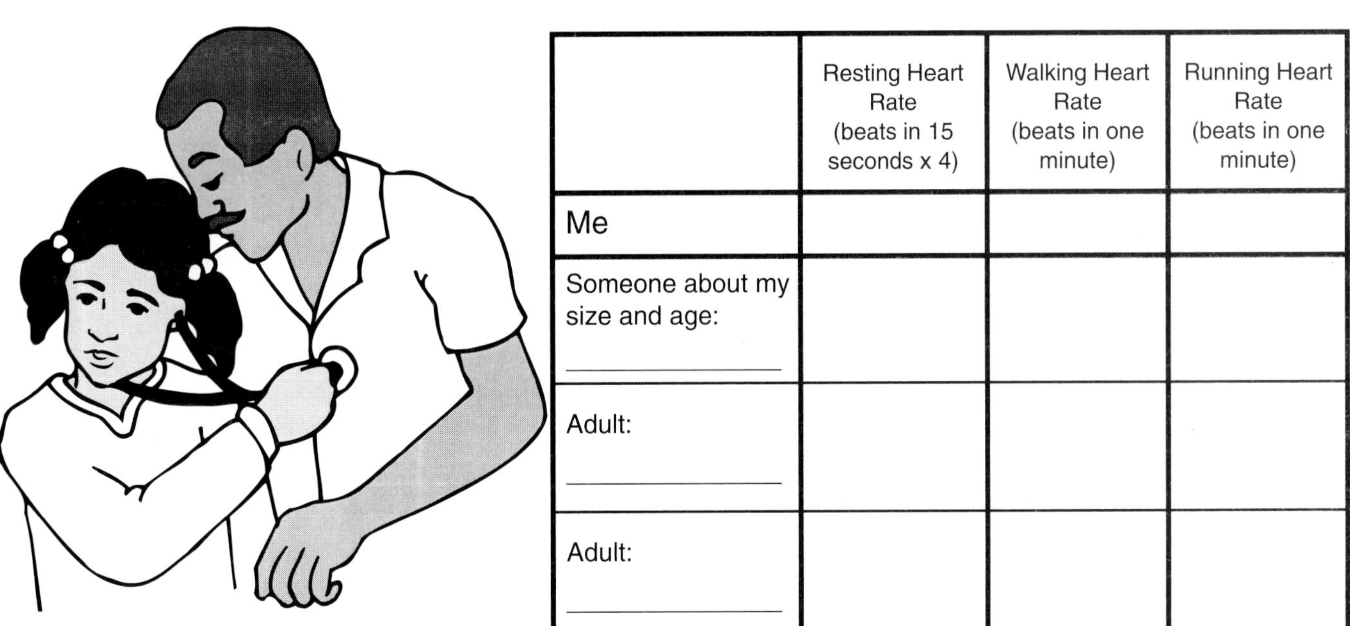

	Resting Heart Rate (beats in 15 seconds x 4)	Walking Heart Rate (beats in one minute)	Running Heart Rate (beats in one minute)
Me			
Someone about my size and age: ______________			
Adult: ______________			
Adult: ______________			

Observations: What conclusions can you make from your observations about heart rates? What difference does age make? Activity level? Size? Write your conclusions on the back of this chart.

Name: ____ Date: ____________________

Note To Teacher: See instructions for use on page 38.

Name ______________________________ Circulatory system: route of blood

Traveling Through: The Journey Of Blood

The flowchart shows the route that blood takes through your heart.
Use the chart to fill in the blanks below with the words written in **bold** type.

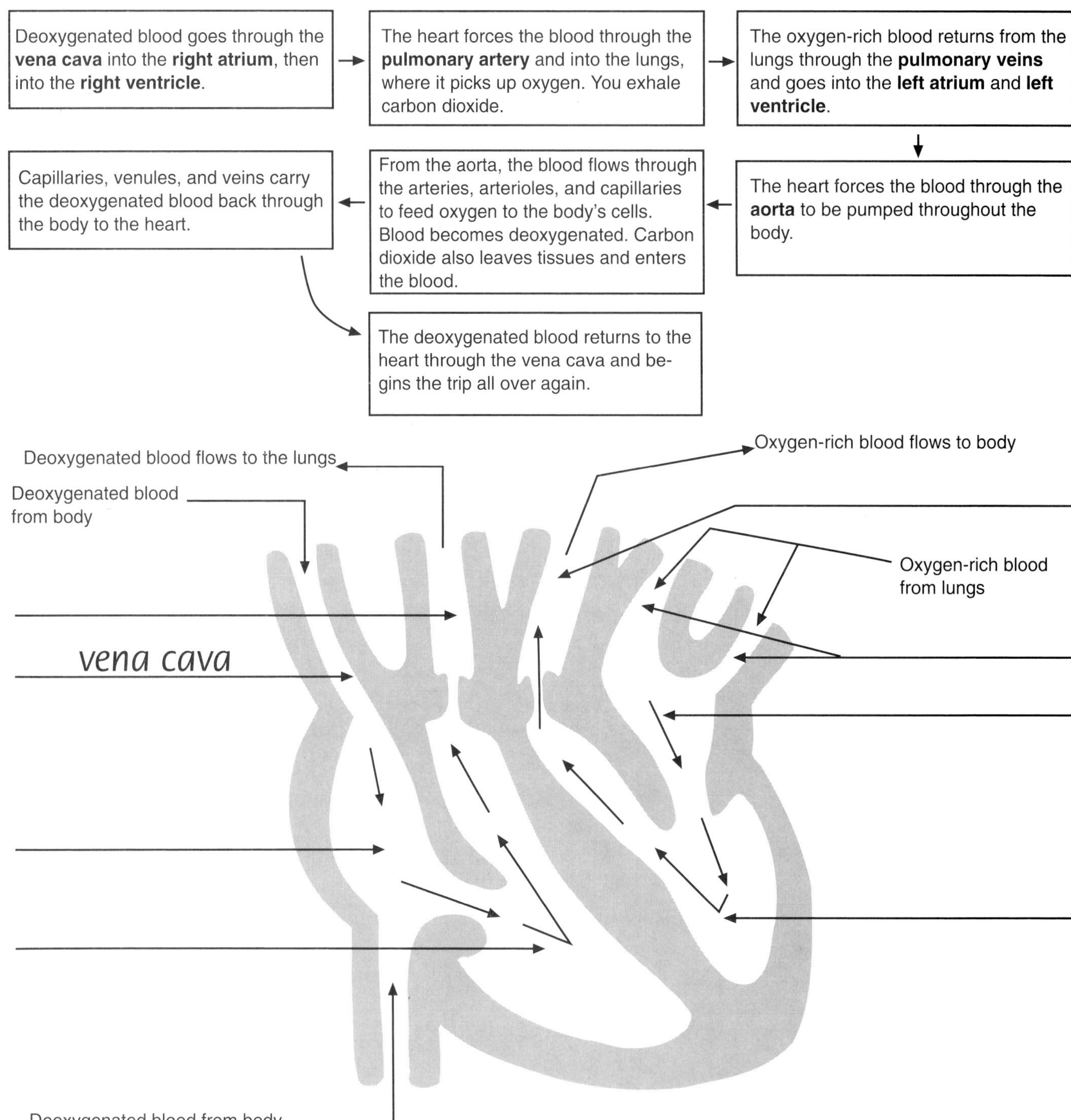

Deoxygenated blood goes through the **vena cava** into the **right atrium**, then into the **right ventricle**.
The heart forces the blood through the **pulmonary artery** and into the lungs, where it picks up oxygen. You exhale carbon dioxide.
The oxygen-rich blood returns from the lungs through the **pulmonary veins** and goes into the **left atrium** and **left ventricle**.
The heart forces the blood through the **aorta** to be pumped throughout the body.
From the aorta, the blood flows through the arteries, arterioles, and capillaries to feed oxygen to the body's cells. Blood becomes deoxygenated. Carbon dioxide also leaves tissues and enters the blood.
Capillaries, venules, and veins carry the deoxygenated blood back through the body to the heart.
The deoxygenated blood returns to the heart through the vena cava and begins the trip all over again.
Deoxygenated blood flows to the lungs
Oxygen-rich blood flows to body
Deoxygenated blood from body
Oxygen-rich blood from lungs
vena cava
Deoxygenated blood from body

Color the vena cava, right atrium, right ventricle, and pulmonary artery blue.
Color the aorta, left atrium, left ventricle, and pulmonary veins red.

Bonus Box: Look in an encyclopedia or resource book for information about one of the following topics: blood transfusions, blood types, capillaries, bone marrow, heart transplants, open-heart surgery, heart murmurs, hypertension, arteriosclerosis. Share your information in a report or poster.

Name____________________

Are There Any Volunteers?

Most of the muscles in your body "volunteer" to work for you. In other words, you can consciously control them. That's why these muscles are called *voluntary* muscles. When you want to run, walk, lift something, or smile, you can consciously send a message to the brain. The brain tells your muscles to work, and they do!

There are some muscles in your body that work for you without your conscious control. These are called *involuntary* muscles, and they do their jobs automatically. The walls of the heart, for example, are made of involuntary muscles. The muscle cells of the heart automatically contract and push blood out of the heart and into the arteries. You can't tell your heart to slow down or stop beating. Try it—but don't worry! It won't listen to you but will keep right on beating.

The muscle that controls your breathing is called the *diaphragm.* It is both a voluntary and an involuntary muscle. Breathing is mostly automatic. You can tell your diaphragm to stop by holding your breath, but only for a short time. An angry little child will sometimes threaten to hold his breath. What he may not know is that involuntary control will cause him to faint and begin breathing again. So, no matter how hard he tries, he can't hold his breath for long!

Every now and then your diaphragm gets the jitters and goes into contractions. As the diaphragm contracts, air rushes into your lungs. To stop the rush, the *epiglottis* (the flap covering your windpipe) slams shut. This stops the air flow so quickly that the body is jolted. This action is a hiccup. The "HIC" is the sound of air rushing in. The "CUP" is the slamming of the epiglottis.

Write your answers on the back of this sheet.

1. What is the difference between involuntary and voluntary muscles?
2. Name two examples of involuntary muscles.
3. Why can't you hold your breath for a long period of time?
4. What muscle is involved in hiccuping?
5. What causes hiccups?
6. Can you stop your diaphragm from working? How?
7. What is the epiglottis?
8. Which of these actions do you think are usually involuntary: speaking, sneezing, blinking, running?

Bonus Box: Draw a diagram of the respiratory system. Label these parts: nose, mouth, windpipe (or trachea), epiglottis, bronchi, lungs, air sacs.

Name ______________________________

Diseases Of The Respiratory System

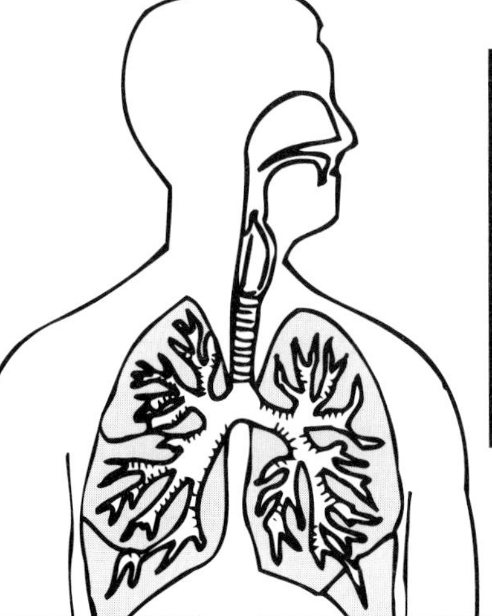

Emphysema is a disease in which the person has difficulty breathing out. With emphysema, the lungs aren't able to pick up oxygen and remove carbon dioxide efficiently. The lungs and heart become overworked. Many doctors blame air pollution and cigarette smoking for emphysema.

Bronchitis is a disease of the bronchial tubes. The lining of the tubes becomes filled with mucus, which is coughed up. Someone suffering from bronchitis will also have a fever and chest pains. If not treated properly, pneumonia may follow. The most common cause of long-lasting bronchitis is cigarette smoking.

Pneumonia is a disease in which the lungs become inflamed and filled with fluid and white blood cells. In some cases, the person will have a sudden attack of chills, high fever, chest pains, and painful coughing. Even though most cases clear up in a few days or weeks, pneumonia is a leading cause of death in America.

Sinus trouble, or *sinusitis,* is a disease in which the membranes in the sinuses become swollen. The sinuses are hollow spaces in the front of the skull. The plugged nose causes painful pressure in the sinuses. The sufferer may also have headaches, dizziness, and a runny nose. A common way to get sinusitis is to swim or dive in unclean water.

Fill in the blanks.

1. The ____________ ____________ become inflamed in bronchitis.
2. Sinuses are located in your ____________.
3. Two possible causes of emphysema are ____________ ____________ and ____________ ____________.
4. The lungs of someone with ____________ fill with fluid and white blood cells.
5. A person suffering from a bad case of bronchitis may develop ____________ later on.
6. The lungs of someone with emphysema have difficulty picking up ____________ and removing ____________ ____________.
7. Swimming underwater in water which is not too clean can cause ____________.
8. ____________ ____________ is the most common cause of long-lasting bronchitis.
9. Emphysema overworks the ____________ and ____________.
10. Another name for sinus trouble is ____________.

"Lunar Module Alpha to Earth! We have safely touched down on the Moon's surface! Repeat; we have safely touched down on the Moon's surface....Now let's create a little...

Moon Magic

...with the following hands-on teaching suggestions and reproducible activities." by Bill O'Connor

Background For The Teacher

From the monument called Stonehenge to the pyramids of the ancient Maya, watching the night sky has long been a preoccupation of humankind. Throughout history, people have gazed at the moon, worshiped it, and studied it. Many phenomena, such as eclipses and phases of the moon, were once viewed with suspicion and fear. And moon travel, one of man's dreams for centuries, became a reality on July 20, 1969, when astronaut Neil A. Armstrong of the United States became the first human to set foot on the moon.

Relative Size And Distance Of The Moon

Teaching about an abstract concept such as the moon is quite a challenge; students can neither visit the moon nor touch it! To demonstrate both the moon's relative size and its distance from the earth, use a 12-inch globe to represent the earth and a baseball or tennis ball to represent the moon. Head to the playground or gym; then have one student hold the "moon" 30 feet (9 meters) away from another student holding the "earth." Did students think that the two objects would be closer together than they are? Farther away?

How Do The Earth, Sun, And Moon Move?

Most people don't understand the relative motions of the earth, moon, and sun. Help your class to get a better grip on these concepts with the following group activity. Divide students into groups of three. Instruct each group to act out the motions of the earth, moon, and sun. Explain that the direction of *rotation* (spinning on an axis) and *revolution* (revolving around another body) must be correct. After practicing for a few minutes, have each group act out its motions in front of the class. Award a group one point for each of the following criteria that is met:

- The earth rotates west to east (counterclockwise, as seen from above).
- The earth revolves around the sun counterclockwise.
- The moon revolves around the earth counterclockwise.
- The sun rotates counterclockwise.
- The same side of the moon always faces the earth.

After each group has taken a turn, have the group(s) with the highest score try again. Call on classmates to identify the group's correct and incorrect movements. To encourage careful observation and inference making, have the group determine its correct movements by interpreting its score. (Note that each body rotates and revolves in the same direction.) Some students may point out that the sun also moves through space. Explain to students that although this is true, motions are studied in relation to the sun; therefore the sun is taken as a fixed reference point. Let each group repeat the demonstration until all the groups attain a score of 5.

Moon Watching

Discuss with students their observations of the moon, listing them on a chart. Students probably know that the moon has different "shapes," or *phases,* and that it can sometimes be seen even during the daytime. Encourage students to relate their observations to what they learned in the activity on page 45.

Check an almanac or a newspaper for the date of the next *first quarter moon,* which is about seven days after the new moon and about seven days before the full moon. At that time, the moon is high in the sky at sunset and does not set until midnight. Distribute copies of page 48. Instruct students to complete the page as they observe the moon each evening for the next ten days.

Each morning during the ten days, spend a few minutes sharing students' observations of the night before. If observations contradict each other, let the students reason out why. After the first few days, ask if patterns are observed. Is the moon following or leading the sun? Near the end of the ten days, see if students can predict where the moon will be at a given time and what phase it will have. After the ten days, ask students why the moon can no longer be observed in the evening. Encourage them to continue looking for the moon and to report to the class when they are able to observe it.

Phases Of The Moon

Use a ball, a projector, and the help of two students to demonstrate the phases of the moon. One student represents the earth while the other holds the moon (a playground ball) over his head. Set up the projector to illuminate both students; then darken the room. The student holding the moon faces the projector. The earth is positioned between the moon and the projector but is not blocking the light (see Point A in the diagram). Have the earth describe the appearance of the moon aloud. (The moon is fully lit, which represents the *full moon.*)

Next have the moon circle counterclockwise one quarter turn, so that the sun, the earth, and the moon form a right angle (see Point B). Again have the earth describe the moon. (It will appear as a half circle lit up on the left side only, which means that the moon is in its *third quarter.*) Repeat this process with the moon moving a quarter turn each time, which demonstrates the *new moon* (Point C) and the *first quarter moon* (Point D). If desired, have the moon stand between the previous locations to represent the *crescent* and the *gibbous* phases.

Make sure that the student describing the moon's phases does so accurately and audibly. Other students will notice that, seen from elsewhere in the room, the phases are not the same as those viewed from the earth. Use this opportunity to point out that the phases of the moon are determined by the relative positions of the sun, moon, and earth. Distribute the activity sheet on page 49 as a follow-up to this activity.

Shadowy Events

Explain to students that when the sun, moon, and earth line up in special ways, *eclipses* occur. Have volunteers demonstrate the eclipses described below. Use the roles described in "Phases Of The Moon" with the earth student holding a globe.

Solar Eclipse: Sometimes the earth, sun, and new moon line up so that the moon passes in front of the sun, blocks the sunlight, and casts a shadow on the earth.

Total Eclipse: The new moon may block out the sun completely. The sky becomes very dark and the stars appear.

Lunar Eclipse: Sometimes the earth, sun, and full moon may align so that the moon moves into the shadow of the earth. Then the moon is in darkness because the earth blocks out the sun's light.

Point out to students that the eclipses don't occur at every new and full moon because the moon's orbit is tilted. The moon usually passes above or below the plane of the earth's orbit.

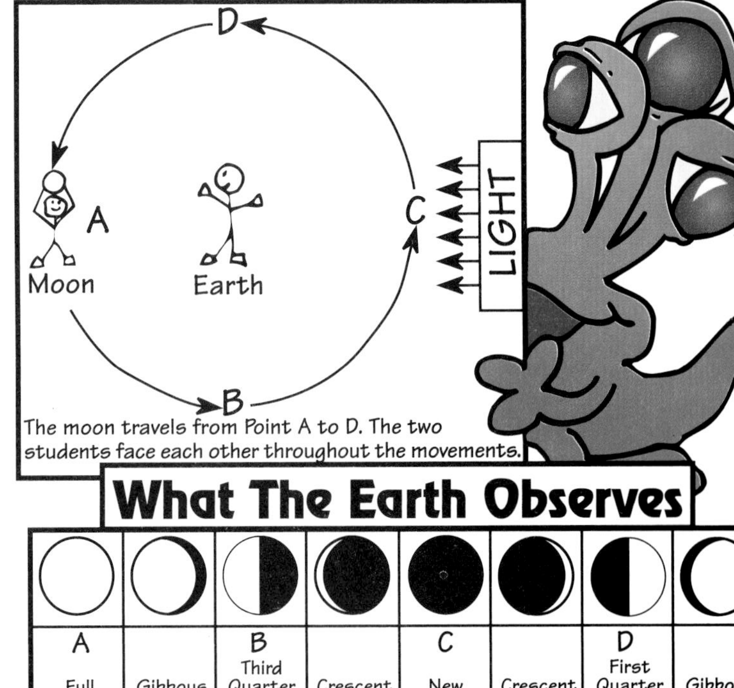

The moon travels from Point A to D. The two students face each other throughout the movements.

What The Earth Observes

A Full	Gibbous	B Third Quarter	Crescent	C New	Crescent	D First Quarter	Gibbou

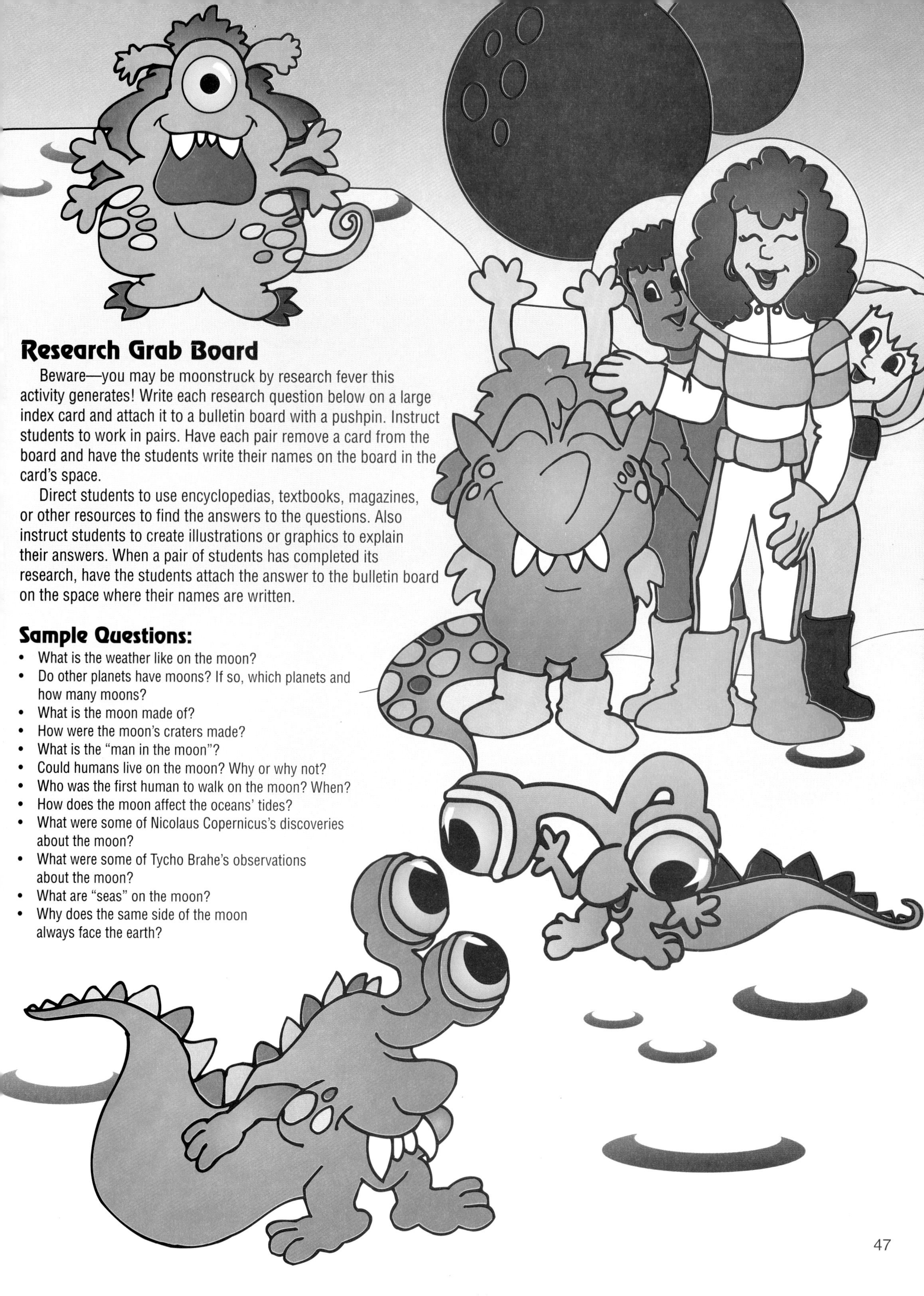

Research Grab Board

Beware—you may be moonstruck by research fever this activity generates! Write each research question below on a large index card and attach it to a bulletin board with a pushpin. Instruct students to work in pairs. Have each pair remove a card from the board and have the students write their names on the board in the card's space.

Direct students to use encyclopedias, textbooks, magazines, or other resources to find the answers to the questions. Also instruct students to create illustrations or graphics to explain their answers. When a pair of students has completed its research, have the students attach the answer to the bulletin board on the space where their names are written.

Sample Questions:

- What is the weather like on the moon?
- Do other planets have moons? If so, which planets and how many moons?
- What is the moon made of?
- How were the moon's craters made?
- What is the "man in the moon"?
- Could humans live on the moon? Why or why not?
- Who was the first human to walk on the moon? When?
- How does the moon affect the oceans' tides?
- What were some of Nicolaus Copernicus's discoveries about the moon?
- What were some of Tycho Brahe's observations about the moon?
- What are "seas" on the moon?
- Why does the same side of the moon always face the earth?

Name ____________________

Moon Watcher

Observe the moon for the next ten nights. Follow the directions below and record your observations each night.

Directions:

1. Record the **date** and **time** that you observe the moon. Try to observe the moon at about the same time each night. If the sky is cloudy or the moon is not visible, try again an hour later. If the moon cannot be observed at all, write "cloudy" or "no moon" on the sheet.
2. Relate your **location** to a landmark (for example: "just above the pine tree when I'm standing on the back porch"). Use north, south, east, or west if you can. Tell if the moon is high or low in the sky.
3. For **appearance**, make a drawing of the moon.

Day 1: Location:	Time:	Appearance:	Day 6: Location:	Time:	Appearance:
Day 2: Location:	Time:	Appearance:	Day 7: Location:	Time:	Appearance:
Day 3: Location:	Time:	Appearance:	Day 8: Location:	Time:	Appearance:
Day 4: Location:	Time:	Appearance:	Day 9: Location:	Time:	Appearance:
Day 5: Location:	Time:	Appearance:	Day 10: Location:	Time:	Appearance:

Note To Teacher: See "Moon Watching" on page 46 for additional information on how to use this reproducible.

Name ______________________________

A Phase Maze

The moon appears to change shape during the month. As the moon revolves around the earth, the amount of its lit surface that we see slowly changes. These changes are called *phases* of the moon.

Directions:

1. Cut apart the boxes at the bottom of the page.
2. Look at the diagram of the different positions in the moon's orbit around the earth.
3. Notice that the side of the moon facing the sun is lit, while the other side is dark.
4. For each position, imagine how the moon would look from the earth.
5. Paste each moon phase in the correct box.
6. In the boxes, label the **full moon, first quarter, third quarter,** and **new moon.**
7. In the boxes, label the two **crescent** phases and the two **gibbous** phases.

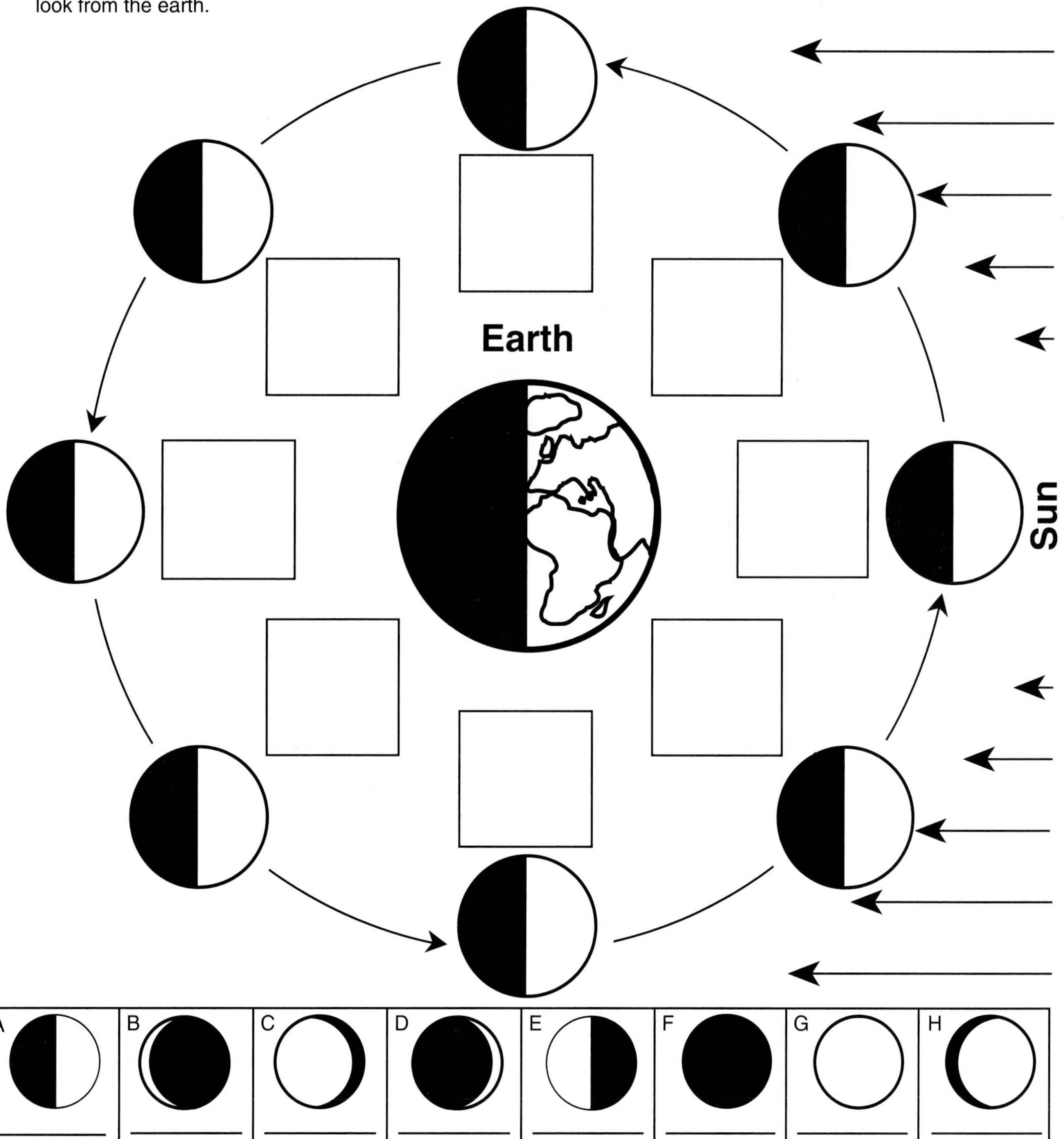

A	B	C	D	E	F	G	H
______	______	______	______	______	______	______	______

Name ______________________________ Number sense

Moon Math

Read the following facts about the moon. Circle the answer that you think is most sensible for each one. Then check encyclopedias and other references to see if your answers make sense!

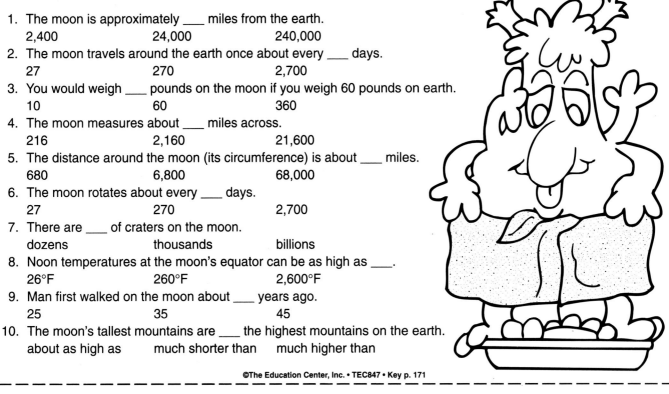

1. The moon is approximately ___ miles from the earth.
   2,400 24,000 240,000
2. The moon travels around the earth once about every ___ days.
   27 270 2,700
3. You would weigh ___ pounds on the moon if you weigh 60 pounds on earth.
   10 60 360
4. The moon measures about ___ miles across.
   216 2,160 21,600
5. The distance around the moon (its circumference) is about ___ miles.
   680 6,800 68,000
6. The moon rotates about every ___ days.
   27 270 2,700
7. There are ___ of craters on the moon.
   dozens thousands billions
8. Noon temperatures at the moon's equator can be as high as ___.
   26°F 260°F 2,600°F
9. Man first walked on the moon about ___ years ago.
   25 35 45
10. The moon's tallest mountains are ___ the highest mountains on the earth.
    about as high as much shorter than much higher than

Name ______________________________ Using a calculator, rounding

Fly Me To The Moon

How long would it take you to walk to the moon, if you *could* walk to the moon? Compute the time that it would take to reach the moon for each form of transportation in the chart. Use a calculator and the following clues:

Clues

The distance to the moon is approximately 240,000 miles. Divide this distance by each rate to find out how many **hours** it would take to reach the moon. Round all quotients to the nearest *tenth.* To find out how many **days** each trip would take, divide the number of hours by 24. Round to the nearest *tenth.*

method of travel	speed	time required to reach the moon hours	days
walking	2 mph		
jogging	8 mph		
bicycle	12 mph		
automobile	55 mph		
passenger jet	550 mph		
Apollo spacecraft	3,300 mph (average)		

Name ____________________

Moon Man's Challenge

For thousands of years, the moon has been studied, worshiped, sung about, written about, and finally even visited by humans!

Research to find answers to the following challenges about the moon. Color the matching part of Moon Man for each answer that you find.

1. What were the *Eagle, Intrepid, Antares, Falcon, Orion,* and *Challenger?* ____________________
2. What does a *selenographer* study? ____________________
3. Who wrote *From The Earth To The Moon,* a book about moon travel published in 1865? ____________________
4. What is the *terminator?* ____________________
5. What is an earthquake on the moon called? ____________________
6. What are *maria?* ____________________
7. What does the word *lunatic* have to do with the moon? ____________________
8. Who was the *second* person to set foot on the moon? ____________________
9. What is meant by *apogee* and *perigee?* ____________________
10. If the moon did have an atmosphere, what would happen to it? ____________________
11. Which nations own the moon? ____________________
12. Who was president of the United States when man first landed on the moon? ____________________
13. What keeps the moon in its orbit? ____________________
14. Name two words that come from Old English words related to *moon.* (Hint: Both words have to do with a calendar.) ____________________

4 5 10 1 13 9 8 7 12 2 5 14 6 3 11

Bonus Box: Some of Galileo's most important observations were about the moon. Research three of these important discoveries by Galileo.

Note To Teacher: Use this activity as an individual or group research project. Or divide students into pairs and provide each pair with a copy of the activity.

Color My World

How do you teach the simple, yet sometimes confusing, concept of color? With fun, hands-on activities!

by Bill O'Connor

Background For The Teacher

Color fills our world with beauty. But to understand how we see color, we must first know something about light. Light is an energy form that acts in some ways like waves. Light waves have a range of wavelengths. A *wavelength* is the distance between any point on one wave and the corresponding point on the next wave. These different wavelengths of light appear as different colors to us. Light that contains all wavelengths in the same proportions as sunlight appears white.

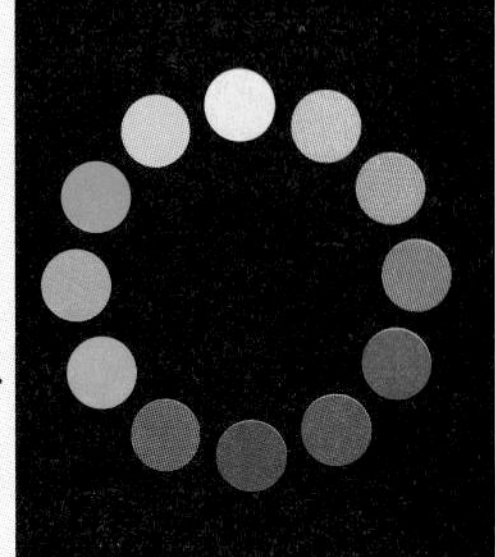

White Light

The "rainbow" produced when white light is broken into different colors fascinates students. Hold a prism in direct sunlight or in the beam of a filmstrip projector. (A narrow band of light is required. Cut a very narrow slit in a piece of dark filmstrip leader and place in the projector.) Move it around until a rainbow (*spectrum*) is visible on a white surface. A spectrum can also be created with a clear glass of water. Set the glass on the edge of a table in direct sunlight. A rainbow will appear on the floor. Discuss with students: What colors appear in the spectrum? What happens if you shine a colored light beam on the prism? What happens if you project the spectrum onto a colored surface?

Make A Color Spinner

Have each student make a color spinner following the directions on page 53. Instruct students to spin their spinners and observe what happens to the colors. The colors will blend and produce a whitish, gray, or neutral color, depending on how the students applied the colors. If a color dominates, the adjacent colors on the wheel need to be darkened.

To create other designs, have students make additional spinners. The spinners should be divided into four equal sections and colored as shown (see illustrations). Ask students to predict how the discs will appear when they are spun.

Creating Afterimages

After staring at a colored image for about one minute, look at a white surface. You'll see an afterimage. An *afterimage* will have the same shape as the original image, but the colors will be different. If the original image was red, the afterimage will be green. If the original image was green, the afterimage will be red. Blue areas become yellow, and yellow areas become blue. Black and white also reverse.

Have each student use a bright color to draw a simple design (an X, circle, square, etc.) on a piece of white paper. Instruct the student to stare fixedly at his drawing for two minutes, then look at a blank white space. An afterimage will appear. If an afterimage is not seen, blinking the eyes a few times will help. List the colors used by students and the colors of their afterimages. Then have students follow the directions on page 53. The afterimage should reveal the flag's actual colors!

Name ____________________

Make A Color Spinner

Directions:

1. Color the circle as labeled.
2. Cut out the circle.
3. Trace the circle onto poster board.
4. Cut out the poster-board circle.
5. Paste the circle to the poster board.
6. Gently push a pencil point through the center of the circle.
7. Spin the circle on your pencil point.
8. What do you observe?

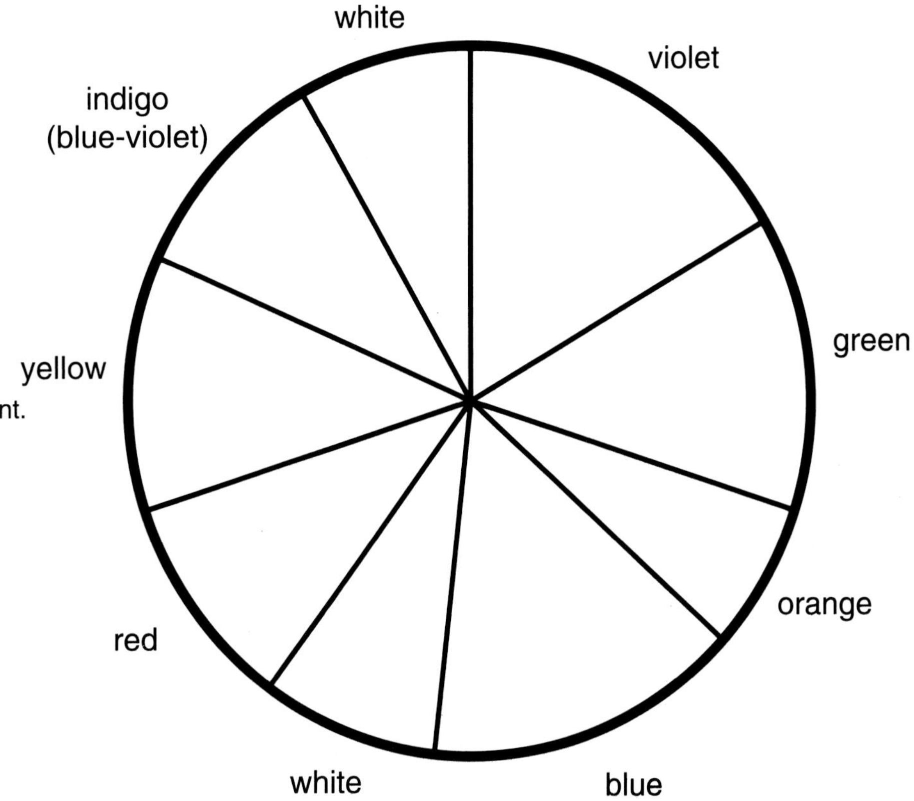

The Flag's True Colors?

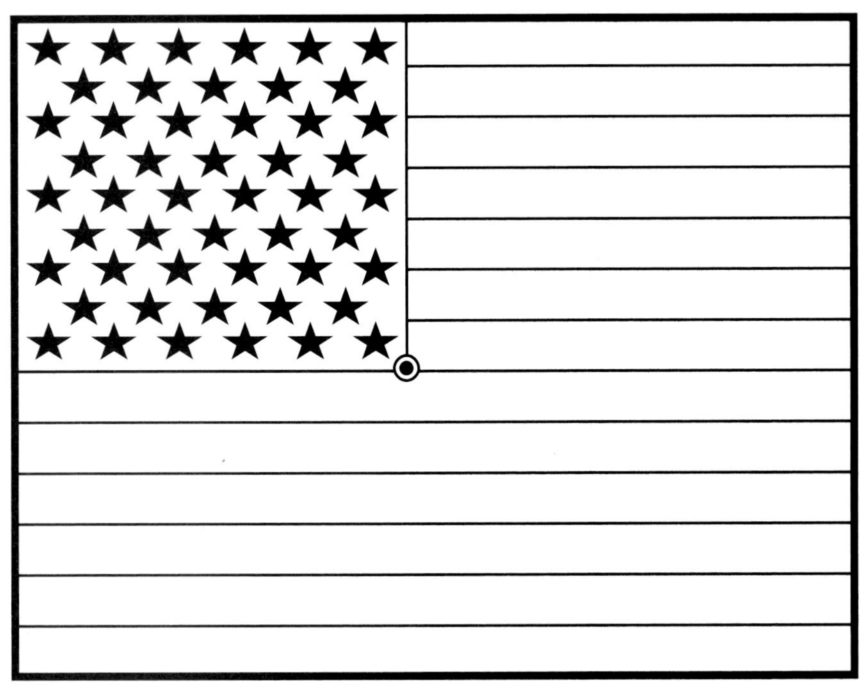

Directions:

1. Color the stripes green and black. (Color the top stripe green; then alternate the colors.)
2. Color the stars' field yellow.
3. When completed, stare at the black dot in the middle of the flag for about 30 seconds.
4. Then look at a blank sheet of white paper.
5. What colors do you see?

Note To Teacher: Provide poster board, glue, scissors, plain white paper, and crayons.

Water, Water, Everywhere

STUDYING THE WORLD OCEAN

Ahoy, landlubbers! It's time to climb on board and study the precious sea that surrounds us. Give your students a truer picture of the ocean and its vital role in the ecological balance of earth with the following ideas and reproducibles. Ready, set, dive!

by Linda D. Rourke

The Water Planet

Water, water, everywhere—the four major oceans (Pacific, Atlantic, Indian, and Arctic) together cover about 71% of the earth's surface. Even though we separate them by name, these oceans are actually connected, forming one large world ocean. Demonstrate this by turning a globe upside down so that the South Pole is at the top. Students will notice that the Pacific, Atlantic, and Indian oceans all come together around Antarctica. Ask your librarian to help you locate photos of the earth shot from space. These pictures dramatically demonstrate why earth is known as "the water planet."

What causes tidal waves?
Why are oceans salty?

Spend a few minutes brainstorming ocean topics such as salt water, sea animals and plants, tides, ocean pollution, currents, and oceanography. Then give each child several large index cards. The student writes a question he has about the ocean on each card. Pin each card on a bulletin board. Encourage students to use resource books to answer their classmates' questions during free time. Have the student write his answer and reference source on the back of the card and repin it on the board, answer-side up for others to read.

The Salty Waters

- Salty seawater is no way to quench one's thirst! Common table salt makes up most of the salty material in the sea. Ask students if it is easier to swim in fresh water or salt water. They may be surprised that it is actually easier to swim in salt water, as demonstrated by the unusual swimming conditions in the Dead Sea. Because salty water is more dense than fresh water and therefore will support a greater load, a person can hardly *sink* in the Dead Sea! This explains why ships float higher in salt water. To further understand this principle, let students complete the reproducible experiment on page 57.
- Need fresh water? Just tow an iceberg to where the water is needed! This idea isn't as crazy as it sounds. Icebergs that form in the Antarctic waters contain no salt. Why? The extreme cold of the Antarctic freezes the water. As it turns to ice, the water expands, and the salt is left behind. Pure water freezes at 0°C, but water with salt mixed into it freezes—as salt and pure water—at a lower temperature. To better understand this concept, have students try the experiment on page 57. (Here's an "icy" fact: one of the biggest icebergs ever seen, twice the size of Rhode Island, floats in Antarctica's waters. If somehow shipped to California, this iceberg could supply millions of people in Los Angeles with drinking water for 1,000 years!)

A Classroom Aquarium

Bring a piece of the ocean right into your classroom by setting up an aquarium. Your students will not only get a firsthand look at the underwater life of some smaller sea creatures, but also learn valuable lessons in responsibility as they work together to maintain the aquarium. Here are some aquarium tips suggested by the Virginia Institute of Marine Science:

- A ten-gallon tank can hold about five invertebrates (such as a hermit crab, sea urchin, shrimp, snail, starfish) and five small (2–2 1/2") marine fish. A 20-gallon tank can support five more fish.
- An air pump and subgravel filter are necessary. They act as ocean wind and currents would, bringing the water to the surface where it can pick up oxygen from the air.

- Two to three hours of indirect sunlight are needed. The water temperature should be in the 68–75°F range.
- Fill the tank with salt water. Use artificial ocean salt to create the right level of salinity. Table salt should never be used.
- Include rocks, gravel, and shells to help the animals feel at home.
- Most marine fish will eat dried fish food. Don't make the mistake of overfeeding the animals. Feed them once a day and at the same time each day. Any food that is left in the tank after ten minutes should be removed.
- A trip to your local pet or tropical fish store should provide you with the help you may need to properly set up and maintain a marine aquarium.

Sea Life

Frightening sharks, awesome whales, mysterious rays—animals of the sea are of particular interest to intermediate students. Since a study of the ocean encompasses such a wealth of material, why not let your students investigate on their own? Duplicate the sea-life cards on pages 59 and 60 to use as springboards for the following research activities:

- Have the student cut out each card and glue it to the unlined side of an index card. After researching the animals, have him write down five facts about each on the lined side of the appropriate index card. Set aside time so that students can share their information with each other.
- Duplicate the cards on white construction paper. Punch a hole in the left-hand corner of each. Attach all cards with a plastic tie to make a sea-life booklet. Encourage students to add a cover and other sea animal or plant cards to their collections.
- Have the class create an underwater seascape incorporating the animals into the picture. Cover a large bulletin board with blue paper. Using what they've learned about sea life, have students use chalk to lightly sketch the surroundings as well as the size and placement of the animal and plant life. Have small groups of students work together in shifts to add color and details to the scene.
- Have groups or individual students cut out the creatures and use them in dioramas of the ocean environment. Try taping blue-tinted cellophane or plastic wrap across the fronts of the boxes to give the appearance of water.

"Tell Me A Tale About The Sea"

Use your study of the ocean to build student interest in reading novels about the sea. Be sure to include Armstrong Sperry's *Call It Courage,* the award-winning tale of a boy's struggle with the sea. Other great books with ocean settings include *The Cay* by Theodore Taylor, *Island Of The Blue Dolphins* by Scott O'Dell, *20,000 Leagues Under The Sea* by Jules Verne, and *Storm Boy* by Colin Thiele.

Oil Spills

On March 24, 1989, the tanker *Exxon Valdez* spilled almost 11 million gallons of crude oil into the pristine waters of Prince William Sound in Valdez, Alaska. Oil spills have happened in the past. (In fact, Coast Guard records show that the ten largest spills between 1984 and 1988 dumped 83.4 million gallons of gas and oil into American waters.) But never before had a spill of this magnitude occurred. It threatened plant and animal life along the 1,090 miles of contaminated shoreline. What scientists don't know are the long-term effects of oil below beach surfaces and deep-water oil on bottom-feeding fish.

Talk about the dangers of an oil spill in a marine ecosystem; then have students try a simple experiment to demonstrate the difficulty of cleaning up oil. Divide your class into small groups. Have each group fill the bottom of an aluminum pie pan with small amounts of sand and rocks. Press small plants into the sand; then fill the pan about half full of water. Put about five drops of used motor oil into the pan. Have students try different methods of removing the oil from the water (using spoons, wind, additional water, paper towels, cotton balls, strings, etc.). Have students record the amount of oil cleaned by each material and how quickly it worked. Encourage creative solutions for cleaning up the oil.

Protect The Ocean

- Massive fish kills. Devastating oil spills. Mysterious burn holes in shellfish. Hypodermic needles and blood vials washed up on our nation's beaches. Declarations of "dead zones" in harbors. Routine dumping of toxic wastes. These are all signs of the times. Fortunately, they are also outrages that are raising public consciousness over the ocean's ills. Have students gather articles from newspapers and magazines about the ocean and pollution. Compile the information into a classroom notebook that chronicles the problems.
- Can you and your students make a difference and work toward solving the problems? Absolutely! Have students brainstorm ways in which the class can help. Include any of the following on your list:

1. Check a phone book or ask a librarian for the names and addresses of any local or national organizations that are addressing these ocean pollution problems. Write for information on each organization and its programs.
2. Obtain addresses of your representatives in Congress. Write letters to express your concerns and encourage these lawmakers to promote legislation to protect the ocean.
3. Encourage your town to practice environmentally sound methods of sewage treatment by writing to the mayor or board of commissioners.
4. Help educate others by making posters about the benefits of recycling.

- Duplicate the take-home poster on page 58. Encourage students to take the time to educate their families and neighbors about pollution solutions. Have each student post this reproducible in his home as a reminder that every family can make a difference.

Victims Of Plastic Pollution

Plastics—the buzzword of the '50s and '60s. This modern-day synthetic, found in most households, has created a huge disposal problem. Plastics don't break down in the environment but can remain in their original form for *hundreds* of years. Marine animals have become victims of plastic pollution too. Six-pack rings can be deadly to seabirds and fish. Turtles will eat plastic bags which they mistake for their favorite food, jellyfish. Seals and sea lions become entangled in plastic netting and packing bands. Balloons can prove fatal to whales and dolphins who ingest them thinking they are eating squid. Discuss the problems of plastic pollution with your class. Brainstorm ways in which people can help. Here are a few suggestions:

- Avoid buying plastic disposables when biodegradable alternatives exist. For example, ask for paper bags instead of plastic ones at the grocery store.
- Avoid plastic disposables at the beach or while boating.

- Discourage organizations from holding balloon launches.
- Encourage plastic recycling in your community.

Have each student create a poster to educate others about the dangers of plastic pollution or the ways in which this problem can be alleviated. Get the word out about plastic pollution by displaying the posters in your school and community.

The Ocean Experts Expo

With an interesting topic and a little bit of time, your students can become experts about ocean topics. Have each student choose an ocean topic (see list) to research. To present his information, have the student glue art paper on both sides of a piece of cardboard. He then decorates both sides of the cardboard with facts and drawings about his topic.

When it comes time to share research findings, hold an exciting Ocean Experts Expo. To display the posters on the big day, provide each student with a small amount of modeling clay or Play-Doh. The student divides the clay into three or four portions and sets his poster on the clay as shown to make a freestanding display. Have students set up their displays on their desks. Divide the class in half; let one half visit displays while the other students stand by their desks to answer questions. After 10–15 minutes, have students switch roles. End the expo with a snack of goldfish crackers and "seaweed punch" (sweetened limeade or green Kool-Aid®).

Topics for research: seaweeds, waves, tides, ocean currents, icebergs, the ocean floor, coral reefs, plankton, coelenterates, the continental shelf, crustaceans, echinoderms, the water cycle, mollusks, phytoplankton, scuba, tsunamis, zooplankton, Jacques Cousteau, William Beebe, diatoms, the Gulf Stream, lighthouses, navigation aids, sponges, submersibles, composition of seawater, sea mining, becoming an oceanographer, products of the sea

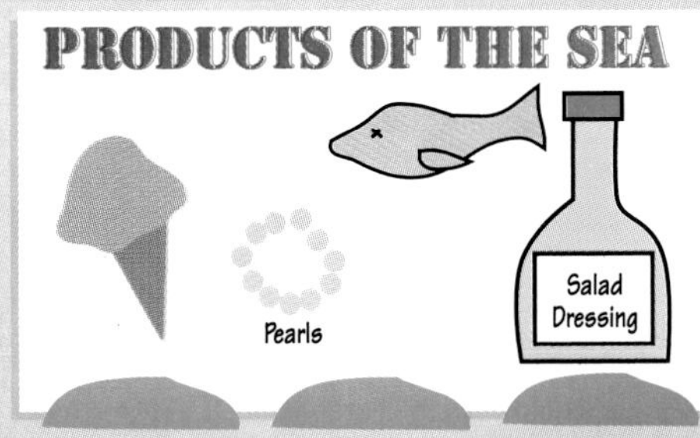

Name ______________________________ Science experiment

Float Or Sink?

Does salt water help an egg to float? Try this simple experiment by following the steps below.

1. Put the same amount of water in two identical cups. Label them Cup A and Cup B.
2. Dissolve ten teaspoons of salt in Cup B.
3. Carefully place an egg in Cup A and an egg in Cup B.
4. What do you observe? ______________________________
5. What can you conclude? ______________________________
6. Based on your conclusion, what does this experiment tell you about a ship in the ocean?

See activity on page 54.

Name ______________________________ Science experiment

Is It Ice Yet?

Does salt water freeze? Try this simple experiment by following the steps below.

1. Put 1/2 cup of water in each of three identical paper cups. Label them Cup A, Cup B, and Cup C.
2. Dissolve eight teaspoons of salt in Cup B. Dissolve three teaspoons of salt in Cup C.
3. Store all three cups in a freezer overnight.
4. Take the cups out of the freezer. What do you observe? ______________________________
5. What can you conclude? ______________________________

Ice is an unusual substance. It is very hard. People construct shelters out of it in northern Alaska. During World War II, even ships made of ice were tested. Write three more uses for ice. ______________________________

See activity on page 54.

Name ______________________________

12 Ways To Save Our Ocean

Check off each item that you and your family try in each of the next four weeks. **You** can make a difference!

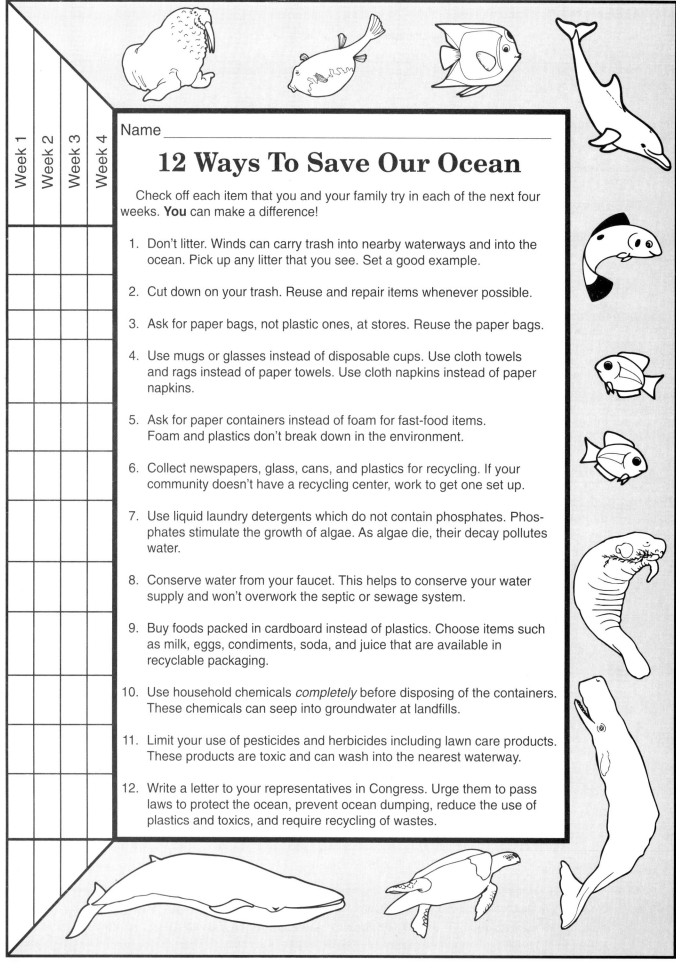

Item	Week 1	Week 2	Week 3	Week 4
1				
2				
3				
4				
5				
6				
7				
8				
9				
10				
11				
12				

1. Don't litter. Winds can carry trash into nearby waterways and into the ocean. Pick up any litter that you see. Set a good example.
2. Cut down on your trash. Reuse and repair items whenever possible.
3. Ask for paper bags, not plastic ones, at stores. Reuse the paper bags.
4. Use mugs or glasses instead of disposable cups. Use cloth towels and rags instead of paper towels. Use cloth napkins instead of paper napkins.
5. Ask for paper containers instead of foam for fast-food items. Foam and plastics don't break down in the environment.
6. Collect newspapers, glass, cans, and plastics for recycling. If your community doesn't have a recycling center, work to get one set up.
7. Use liquid laundry detergents which do not contain phosphates. Phosphates stimulate the growth of algae. As algae die, their decay pollutes water.
8. Conserve water from your faucet. This helps to conserve your water supply and won't overwork the septic or sewage system.
9. Buy foods packed in cardboard instead of plastics. Choose items such as milk, eggs, condiments, soda, and juice that are available in recyclable packaging.
10. Use household chemicals *completely* before disposing of the containers. These chemicals can seep into groundwater at landfills.
11. Limit your use of pesticides and herbicides including lawn care products. These products are toxic and can wash into the nearest waterway.
12. Write a letter to your representatives in Congress. Urge them to pass laws to protect the ocean, prevent ocean dumping, reduce the use of plastics and toxics, and require recycling of wastes.

Note To Teacher: Use this page with the activities listed on page 55.

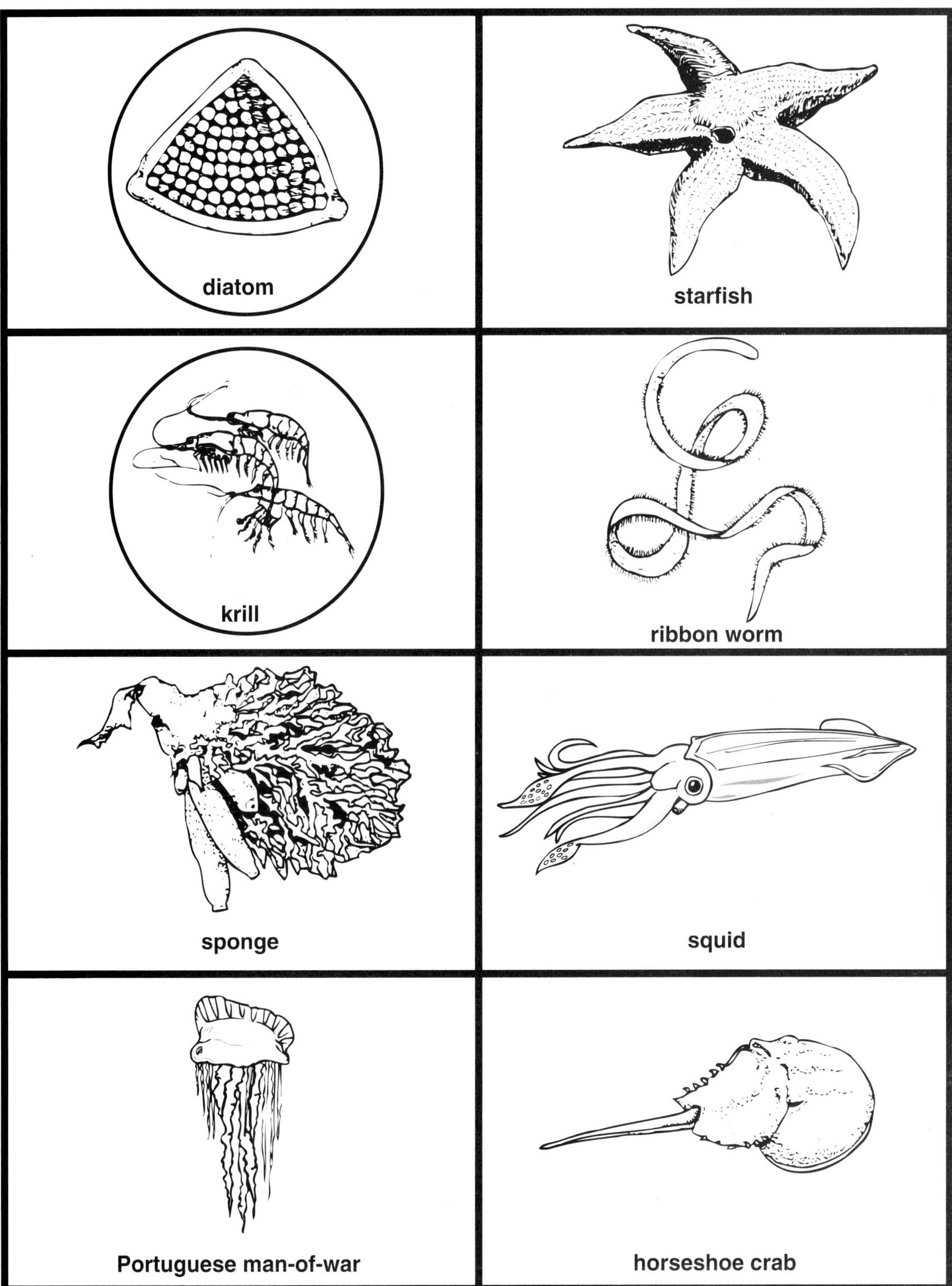

Note To Teacher: Use this page with the activities listed on page 55.

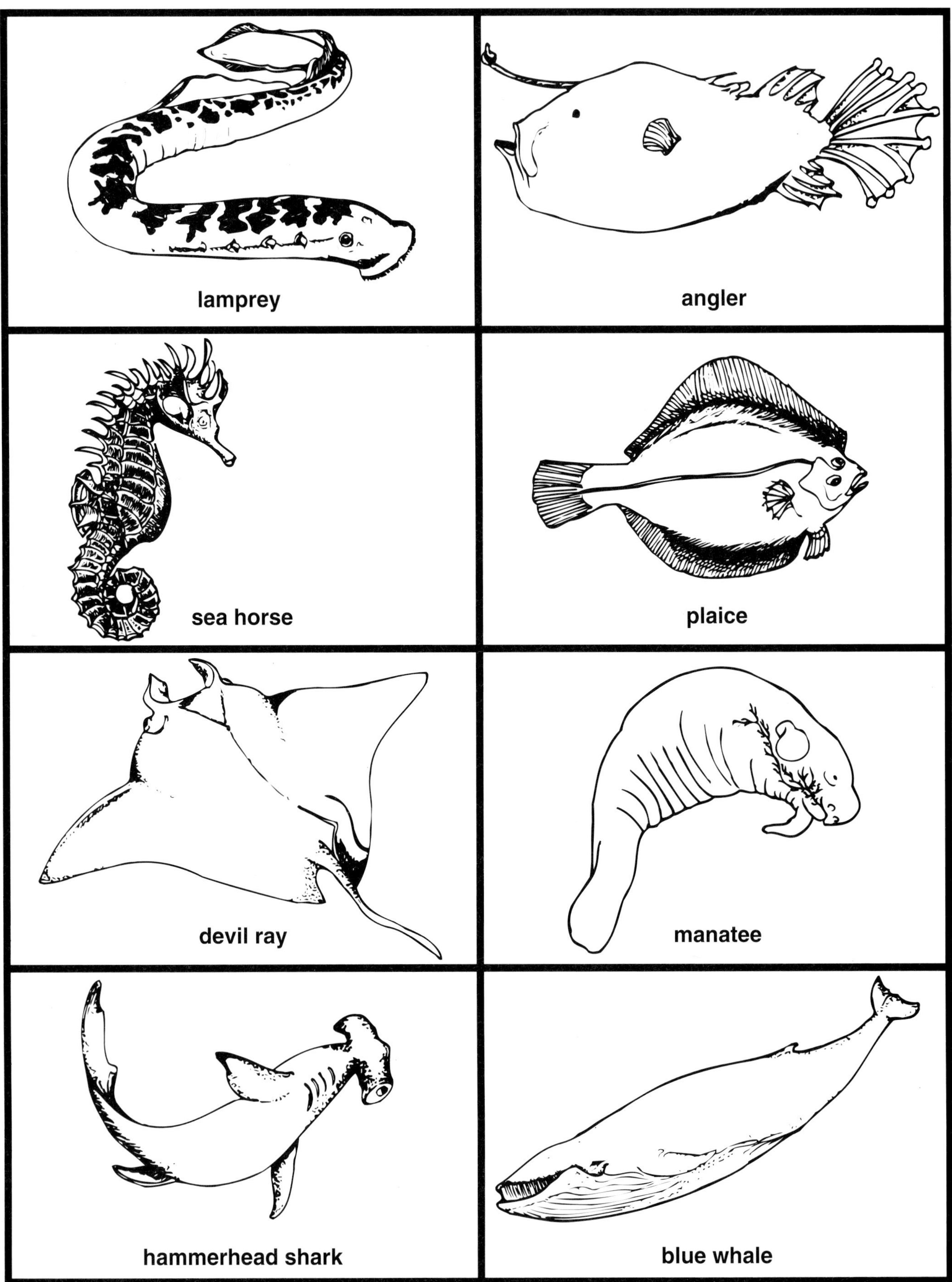

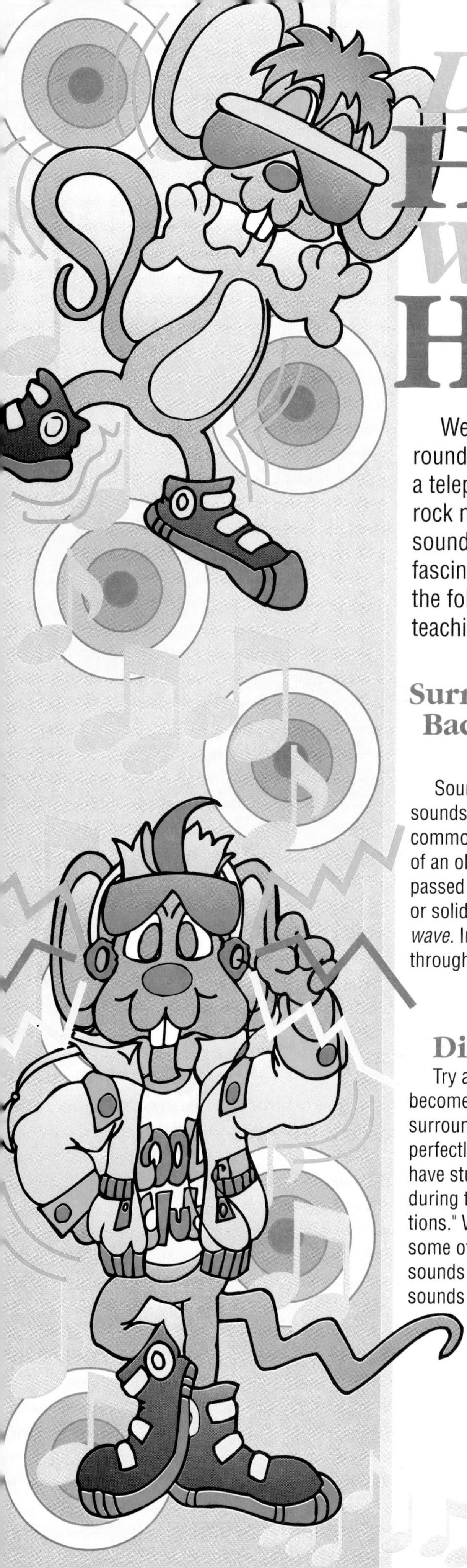

Do You HEAR What I HEAR?

We can't see it, but we're surrounded by it! From the ringing of a telephone to a distant siren, from rock music to talking with friends, sound fills our lives. Explore this fascinating form of energy with the following hands-on, creative teaching activities. *by Bill O'Connor*

Surrounded By Sound: Background For The Teacher

Sound is a form of energy. All the sounds that we hear have one thing in common: each one is caused by *vibrations* of an object. These vibrations can be passed from one molecule of a gas, liquid, or solid, to the next. This is called a *sound wave.* In general, sound travels faster through liquids and solids than through air.

Did You Hear *That*?

Try a simple activity to help students become more aware of the sounds that surround them. Ask the class to remain perfectly quiet for one full minute. Then have students list all the sounds they heard during the minute. Discuss their "observations." Why do they normally not hear some of these particular sounds? Which sounds were important to hear? Which sounds were pleasant? Unpleasant? Encourage students to try the activity at home.

On Sound Terms

Create a colorful display that will help students understand the sometimes-confusing vocabulary of sound. Ask volunteers to copy the terms and definitions below on large index cards. Then have students collect pictures from magazines that portray various sounds in our world: a jet taking off, a barking dog, a busy city street, a cheering crowd, etc. Cover a bulletin board with a collage of pictures; then post the vocabulary cards. Add the title "Hear Ye, Hear Ye!"

acoustics: the science of sound and its effects on people
amplitude: the distance that a vibrating object moves from its position of rest as it vibrates
frequency: the number of vibrations made by a vibrating object per second
intensity: relates to the amount of energy flowing in sound waves
decibel: the unit used to measure the intensity level of a sound
hertz: the unit used to measure frequency
loudness: refers to how strong the sound seems to us when it strikes our eardrums
pitch: the degree of highness or lowness of a sound
noise: sound with many random frequencies

Name That Sound!

Tape-record various sounds from around your home or school. Make the sounds even more interesting by holding the microphone very close to a sound's source. Play the tape in class and ask students to guess the source of each sound. Discuss what helped students guess each sound. Encourage them to describe the sounds using words like *loud, soft, high-pitched, low-pitched, regular, pleasant,* and *unpleasant.* Have interested students make and bring their own tapes of mysterious sounds to class.

Make A Sound Center

Let's hear it for a sound center! The following activities are perfect for a student to try on her own or with a buddy. Demonstrate each activity for the entire class; then place the materials in your sound center. Watch the sound center become the hit of the classroom!

How Are Sounds Produced?

— Use a tuning fork or a heavy dinner fork with the following activities. For best results, strike the fork against the hard rubber sole of a shoe.

- Tie or glue a piece of puffed cereal to a length of thread. Strike a tuning fork and place one of its tines in contact with the hanging cereal. The cereal will fly up and dance around, showing that the fork is vibrating.
- Place a vibrating tuning fork in contact with the rim of a glass. The vibration will be transmitted to the glass.
- Touch the base of a vibrating tuning fork to a hollow object, such as a desktop. The vibrations will be transmitted to the desktop, and the sound will be amplified.
- Try "throwing" the sound from a tuning fork into a glass or into a student's open mouth! As you place the tuning fork in contact with a tabletop, use your other hand to "scoop up" the sound and throw it.

— Remove both ends from a round oatmeal box or coffee can. Cover one end with rubber from a balloon and secure it with tape. Sprinkle salt on the rubber surface. Holding the box level, have a student hum loudly into the open end. Notice the patterns formed by the vibrating salt grains. Are the patterns different for high and low notes? What do you think would happen if a loud instrument, such as a trumpet, were used as the sound source?

— Try another activity with the oatmeal box mentioned in the preceding idea. Glue a small mirror or a piece of aluminum foil to the rubber surface. Hold the box in direct sunlight (or the light from a filmstrip or slide projector) so that a light beam is reflected onto the wall or ceiling. When sounds are introduced into the box, the spot of light will vibrate. See what happens with high, low, soft, and loud sounds.

How Is Pitch Related To Vibration?

— Hold a 12-inch ruler firmly on the top of a desk with about half of it extended over the edge. Pluck the free end sharply. The ruler will vibrate up and down and produce a sound. Move the ruler so that different lengths extend over the edge of the table. Which position produces the lowest-pitched sound? The highest-pitched sound?

— To demonstrate the concept of the relationship of length to frequency, use a thin meter stick, or a long piece of lath obtained from a lumber dealer. If a long section is extended from the tabletop and allowed to vibrate, you can see that the frequency is much lower. It may be too low to even produce an audible sound.

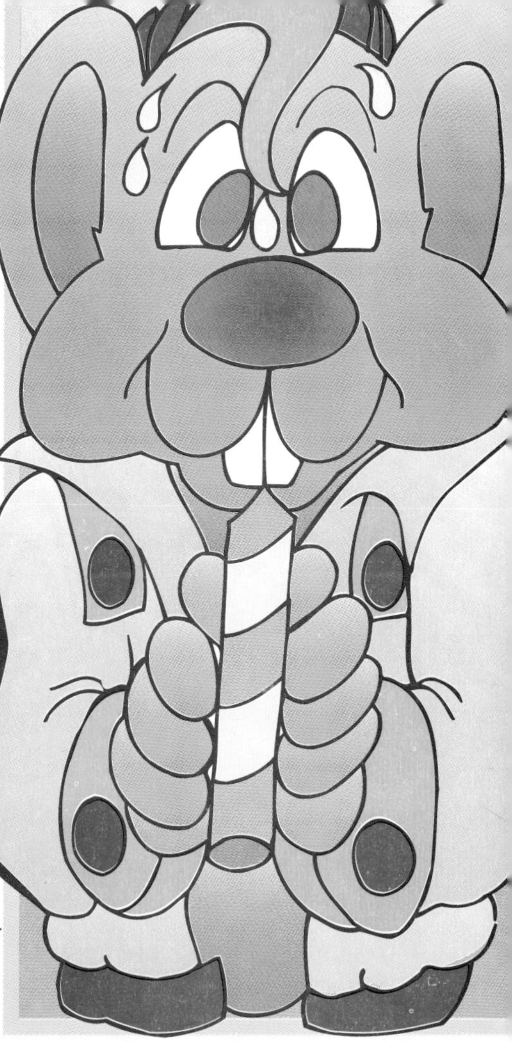

— Provide the class with paper drinking straws. Have each student flatten one end of his straw and cut off the corners as shown. The student then places the flattened end of the straw between his teeth and, pressing down slightly with his lips, blows. After some practice, sounds will come from the straws. (Practice beforehand so that you can motivate students by demonstrating the technique.) If a student can't get a sound, have him cut off the end of the straw and try again. Ask students what is vibrating in this noisemaker? Can they change the pitch of this "instrument"?

— Have students cut their straws (see above idea) shorter. Instruct each student to make a hole halfway down his straw by squeezing and notching it with scissors. He then covers and uncovers the hole while he blows into the straw. If straws of two different diameters are available, slip one over the other to make a "slide strawbone." A small funnel made of paper and taped to the end of the straw will dramatically amplify the sound.

Can Sound Travel Through Solids?

— Demonstrate the nature of sound waves with dominoes. Stand the dominoes in line and tip over the first one. Explain that sound is transmitted through air by molecules colliding with each other, just like the dominoes. Do the activity again with the dominoes closer together, and then with them farther apart. Which way does "sound" travel faster? Which molecules are closest—those of a solid, liquid, or gas? (solid)

— Ask students to scratch the end of a ruler with a fingernail. How loud is the sound? Then ask each student to hold one end of the ruler against an ear, then scratch the other end. Is the sound louder now? Does sound travel better through solids or gases? Have students place one of their ears against their desks while tapping the desks with their pencils. Is sound transmitted through the desk?

— Make string telephones, which are perfect for illustrating the transmission of sound vibrations. Use paper or plastic cups, and thin string or nylon fishing line. Thread the ends of the string through small holes in the bottoms of the cups and tie the thread around toothpick halves. When the string is stretched taut, a student speaking into one cup can be heard by someone listening in the other. Have students use string telephones to investigate the following:

- What happens if someone holds the string in the middle?
- Which works best—thin or thick string? Fishing line? Thin wire? Another material?
- What is the longest string on a string telephone you can use that works?
- Can you make a string telephone that works around corners?
- Can you find a transmitter/receiver that works better than a cup?

— Challenge students to create a container that will muffle the sound of an alarm clock. Provide cardboard boxes, old newspaper, scraps of cloth, and any other materials students wish to bring from home. See which group of students can design something to silence the alarm clock most effectively. What does this tell students about sound waves?

"Pop Music"

Follow the directions below to create your own "pop music."

Materials: eight soda-pop bottles, all the same type; water

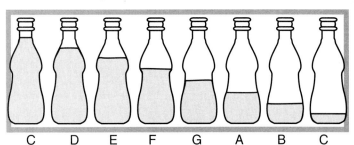

C D E F G A B C

Procedure:

1. Fill one bottle nearly to the top with water.
2. Fill the second bottle with water until the next tone of the music scale can be obtained.
3. Continue filling the bottles, but lower the level of water each time by about an inch (see diagram).
4. You should end up with the eight notes of the scale. Test them by blowing across the bottles.
5. Add or remove water until each bottle has the correct pitch.
6. Now blow across the bottles and play a simple tune.

Observations: Write your answers in the blanks.

1. What causes the pitch and tone to be different in each bottle? ____________________

   ____
2. What other factors could affect tone and pitch? ____________________

   ____
3. Why does enlarging the air space change the pitch? ____________________

   ____
4. Would a larger container make a lower or higher pitch than the pop bottle? ____________________

   Why? ____________________

A Rubber-Band Band

What makes sounds different from each other? Make the following shoebox guitar to find out.

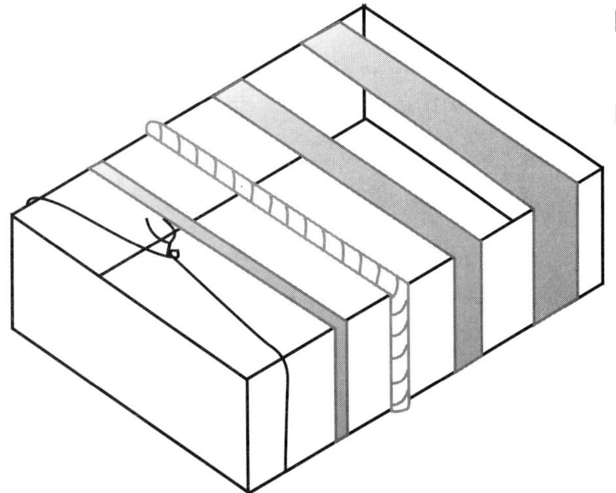

Materials: sturdy shoebox, rubber bands of different lengths and widths, string, wire

Procedure:

1. Place several rubber bands of the same width but different lengths around the box and pluck each one.
2. Place only one rubber band on the box and pluck it. Tighten the band by pulling on it from the bottom. Pluck it again.
3. Place rubber bands of the same length but different widths around the box and pluck each one.
4. Tie the string and wire around the box, along with one rubber band. Pluck each one.

Observations: Write the correct word in each blank.

1. __________ rubber bands will have a higher pitch than __________ ones. (long, short)
2. __________ rubber bands will have a higher pitch than __________ ones. (tight, loose)
3. __________ rubber bands will have a higher pitch than __________ ones. (wide, narrow)
4. __________ materials will have a higher pitch than __________ materials. (light, heavy)

Name ____ Using a calculator

Music To My Ears

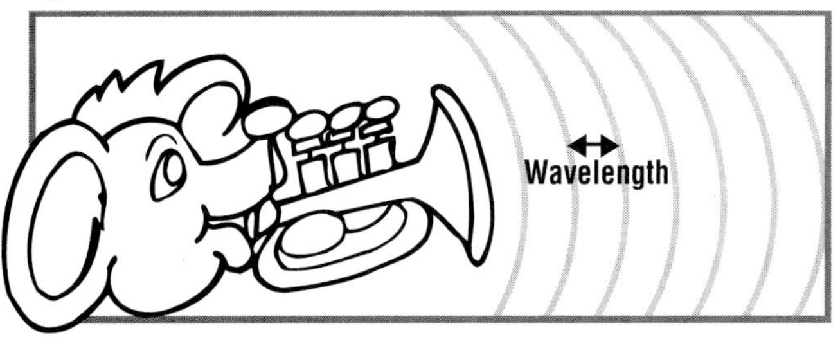

Sound waves travel through the air. In ordinary air, these waves travel at the speed of 1,125 feet per second (344 meters per second)! The distance between one wave and the next is called a *wavelength*.

Sound waves are produced by vibrating objects. The faster something vibrates, the more waves it makes in one second. The number of waves produced in one second is called the *frequency*. One wave produced per second is called one *hertz* (Hz).

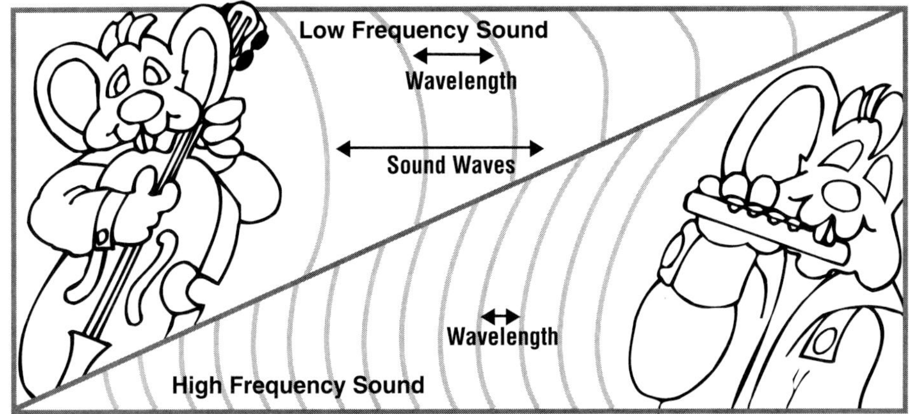

An object vibrating at a higher frequency (faster) makes shorter waves than an object vibrating at a lower frequency (slower). Since it makes more waves in less time, the waves are more crowded.

Since they are related, you can find a sound's wavelength if you know the frequency. Simply divide the speed of sound by the frequency:

$$\text{wavelength} = \frac{\text{speed of sound}}{\text{frequency}}$$

Directions: Use a calculator to find the wavelength of each sound in the chart below. Find the wavelength in both meters and feet. Round off each quotient to the nearest hundredth.

sound	frequency	speed of sound (meters per second)	wavelength (meters)	speed of sound (feet per second)	wavelength (feet)
lowest sounds humans can hear	20 Hz	344		1,125	
low G played on a bass violin	98 Hz	344		1,125	
middle C played on a piano	262 Hz	344		1,125	
A played on a clarinet	440 Hz	344		1,125	
F played on a flute	698 Hz	344		1,125	
high C sung by a soprano	1,048 Hz	344		1,125	
highest sounds humans can hear	20,000 Hz	344		1,125	

Bonus Box: If sound travels at the speed of 1,125 feet per second, how far does it travel in a minute? An hour?

Name ______________________________ Contract

Loud And Clear!

We have lots of words that describe sounds. These words help us make mental pictures about the people, places, or things being described. Sometimes a word even names a thing or action by copying the sound associated with it. *Buzz, hiss,* and *zip* are examples of these words, called *onomatopoeia*.

Read the following words that name or describe sounds.

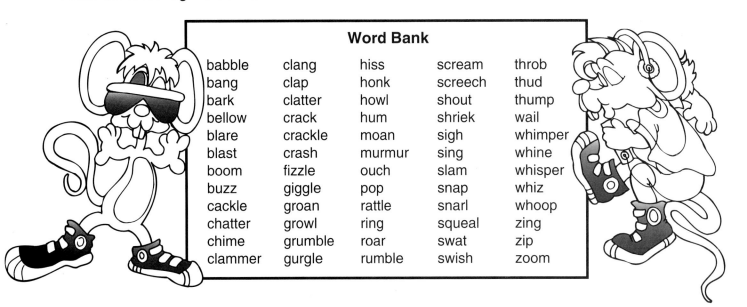

Word Bank

babble	clang	hiss	scream	throb
bang	clap	honk	screech	thud
bark	clatter	howl	shout	thump
bellow	crack	hum	shriek	wail
blare	crackle	moan	sigh	whimper
blast	crash	murmur	sing	whine
boom	fizzle	ouch	slam	whisper
buzz	giggle	pop	snap	whiz
cackle	groan	rattle	snarl	whoop
chatter	growl	ring	squeal	zing
chime	grumble	roar	swat	zip
clammer	gurgle	rumble	swish	zoom

Directions: Complete _____ of the following activities. Use words that are listed in the Word Bank to help you.

1. Choose ten words. Beside each word, write the person, place, or thing that first comes to your mind when you say the word.
2. Find five of the words in the comics section of a newspaper. Cut out the comic-strip frames and glue them to a piece of construction paper.
3. In a paragraph, describe your first attempt at snow skiing. Use at least five words from the Word Bank in your writing.
4. Write five descriptive sentences, each containing a word from the Word Bank. Now rewrite the sentences and replace each Word Bank word with a word that means the opposite. For example: a *whispering* siren instead of a *wailing* siren.
5. In a paragraph, describe the noisiest (or quietest) place you've ever visited. Use at least five words from the Word Bank in your writing.
6. From magazines, cut out two or three pictures that show lots of action. Mount them on a piece of construction paper. Choose words from the Word Bank that describe the action. Write the words on white bubble cutouts; then glue the cutouts to the pictures.

Note To Teacher: Before duplicating, fill in the number of activities that you want your students to complete. Or use any of the activities as whole-class or small-group assignments.

THE TORNADO MACHINE

Create a spectacular, close-up view of a funnel-shaped tornado in action. This tornado machine not only demonstrates a tornado's shape and motion, but also exercises the same principle as that which creates a real tornado.

Dr. Hy Kim—School Of Education
Youngstown State University
Youngstown, OH

What You'll Need:

2 two-liter pop bottles
3 inches of rigid tubing, with same diameter (5/8") as opening of bottles
water

How To Make:

1. Fill one pop bottle with water (to the top of the neck).
2. Insert 3/4" of the tubing into the bottle top. (See diagram 1.)
3. Place the empty bottle on top of the one filled with water. Insert 3/4" of the protruding end of the tubing into the empty bottle. (See diagram 2.)

How To Demonstrate:

Invert the bottles so that the water-filled bottle is now on top of the empty one, as shown in diagram 3. Water from the top bottle will begin to fall into the bottom one. Rotate the water-filled bottle counterclockwise with a shaking motion (diagram 4). The water will begin to whirl, forming a funnel-shaped air column in the center.

Why This Works:

Because the water in the upper bottle is heavier than the air in the lower bottle, the water starts to fall while the air starts to move upward. When the bottle is shaken in a circular motion, the water descends in a circular motion, leaving an air passage in the middle through which the air quickly ascends.

How does this machine demonstrate a real tornado? The water represents a cold air mass which is dry and heavy, and the air in the bottle represents a warm, moist air mass. When a warm air mass and a cold air mass meet, the cold air mass moves under the warm air mass. But under certain conditions, which scientists cannot explain, a cold air mass is sometimes pushed over a warm air mass. The lighter air mass moves up through the cold air mass, aided by strong winds aloft. A low pressure center in the cold air mass becomes a vertex and the funnel-shaped tornado is formed.

Why does a tornado turn counterclockwise? The earth turns on its axis making day and night. If you looked down at the earth from the North Pole, the earth spins counterclockwise. The earth's turning contributes to the swirling action of a tornado. However, if you looked up at the earth from the South Pole, the earth spins clockwise. Therefore, tornadoes in the Southern Hemisphere turn clockwise.

1.

2.

3.
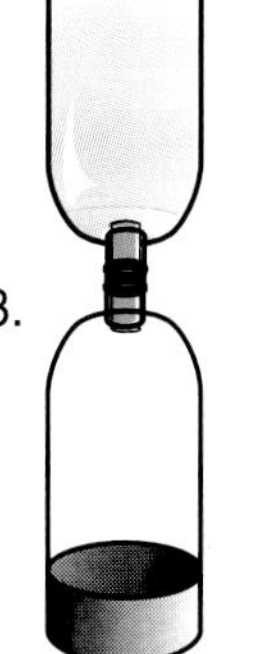

4.

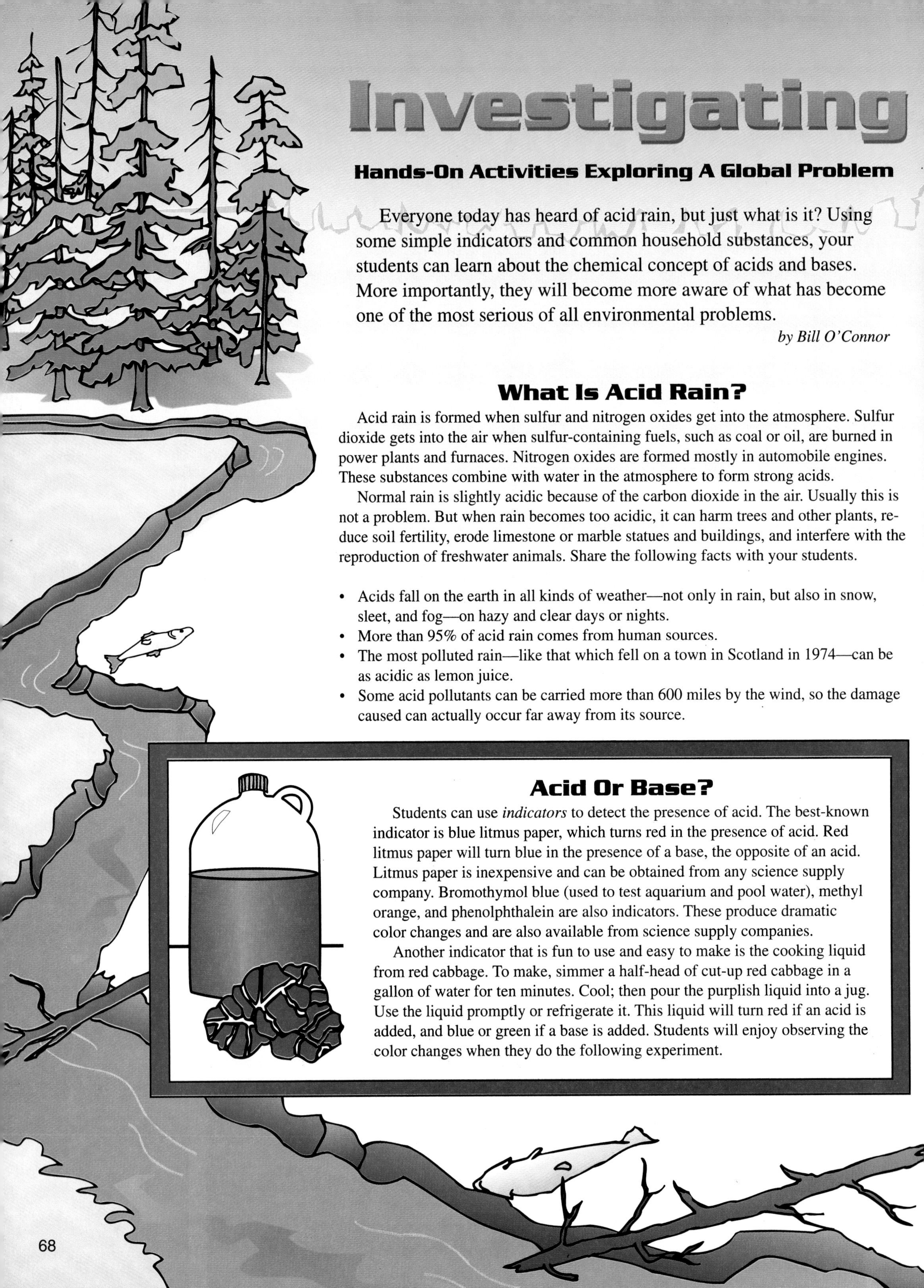

Investigating

Hands-On Activities Exploring A Global Problem

Everyone today has heard of acid rain, but just what is it? Using some simple indicators and common household substances, your students can learn about the chemical concept of acids and bases. More importantly, they will become more aware of what has become one of the most serious of all environmental problems.

by Bill O'Connor

What Is Acid Rain?

Acid rain is formed when sulfur and nitrogen oxides get into the atmosphere. Sulfur dioxide gets into the air when sulfur-containing fuels, such as coal or oil, are burned in power plants and furnaces. Nitrogen oxides are formed mostly in automobile engines. These substances combine with water in the atmosphere to form strong acids.

Normal rain is slightly acidic because of the carbon dioxide in the air. Usually this is not a problem. But when rain becomes too acidic, it can harm trees and other plants, reduce soil fertility, erode limestone or marble statues and buildings, and interfere with the reproduction of freshwater animals. Share the following facts with your students.

- Acids fall on the earth in all kinds of weather—not only in rain, but also in snow, sleet, and fog—on hazy and clear days or nights.
- More than 95% of acid rain comes from human sources.
- The most polluted rain—like that which fell on a town in Scotland in 1974—can be as acidic as lemon juice.
- Some acid pollutants can be carried more than 600 miles by the wind, so the damage caused can actually occur far away from its source.

Acid Or Base?

Students can use *indicators* to detect the presence of acid. The best-known indicator is blue litmus paper, which turns red in the presence of acid. Red litmus paper will turn blue in the presence of a base, the opposite of an acid. Litmus paper is inexpensive and can be obtained from any science supply company. Bromothymol blue (used to test aquarium and pool water), methyl orange, and phenolphthalein are also indicators. These produce dramatic color changes and are also available from science supply companies.

Another indicator that is fun to use and easy to make is the cooking liquid from red cabbage. To make, simmer a half-head of cut-up red cabbage in a gallon of water for ten minutes. Cool; then pour the purplish liquid into a jug. Use the liquid promptly or refrigerate it. This liquid will turn red if an acid is added, and blue or green if a base is added. Students will enjoy observing the color changes when they do the following experiment.

Acid Rain

Testing With Red Cabbage Indicator

What are some common acids and bases? To find out, divide your class into groups of two or three students each and provide each group with a copy of the experiment on page 71. Each group will need a small, plastic cup; a medicine dropper (or spoon); and baby food jars with various liquids for testing. A student places a small amount of red cabbage juice in a cup and then adds the liquid to be tested. After determining whether the liquid is an acid or a base, or is neutral (some liquids are neither an acid nor a base and will not produce a red or blue color), a recorder writes the liquid's name in the appropriate column on the experiment sheet.

Have students test the following liquids. Those marked with an * are neutral.

"pure" water*	baking soda solution	boric acid solution
lemon juice	cream of tartar solution	soda water
milk of magnesia	rainwater*	salt water*
sugar water*		milk*

ammonia water (dilute with an equal amount of water)
vinegar water (dilute with an equal amount of water)

Take-Home Activity

Undoubtedly, students will want to test other liquids. Have students make their own "test paper" by soaking strips cut from coffee filters in red cabbage juice and letting them dry. Students can take these home and test liquids there. Suggest any kind of fruit juice. Most or all of these will be acids. Household cleaners are usually bases. Avoid drain and oven cleaners! Also advise that dark-colored liquids will be difficult to test.

Challenge students to obtain indicator liquids from other sources. Suggest the juice of beets, purple grapes, rhubarb, or petals from red or blue flowers.

Using A pH Meter

The strength of acids and bases is measured by the *pH scale.* The relative strength of acids and bases can be measured by using wide-range pH or pHydrion paper strips, available from science supply companies. This paper varies over a range of colors depending on the pH. After testing a substance, students simply match the paper color to a printed scale to determine the pH.

If you have pH paper, your students can collect rainwater in a clean container and test it to see if your community has acid rain. A narrow range pH paper that covers from pH 4.0 to pH 6.0 will give the most accurate results.

Still more accurate measurements can be made by using an electric pH meter. Ask a high school chemistry teacher or someone from your city's water or environmental department to demonstrate one of these for your class.

Familiarize your students with a pH meter using the reproducible on page 72. The table on the reproducible gives the pH of some common substances. The further the pH is from 7, the stronger the acid or base. The strongest acid has a pH of 1; the strongest base has a pH of 14.

Does Acid Rain Affect Plants?

Damage to soil is the most serious effect of acid rain. Do the following activity with your students to demonstrate how acid rain can affect plants. Place six small flowerpots in each of two dishpans. Fill the pots with soil. Soak 12 large lima beans overnight and plant them in the pots. Water normally until the first pair of leaves has grown. As a rule, not all of the plants may grow. Adjust the dishpans so that they have plants equal in number and vigor. Then duplicate and distribute page 73 for students to record their observations.

Sprinkle one set of plants daily with ordinary water; sprinkle the other set with vinegar water. Make sure the liquid wets the leaves and the soil. Each week, have the students observe and describe any differences between the two sets of plants.

Discuss with students the importance of watering each set of plants with the same amount of liquid, allowing them the same amount of sunlight, etc. After four weeks, discuss the differences between the two sets of plants. Discuss what might happen if acid rain were to affect an entire crop such as soybeans. Remind students that soybeans are a key ingredient in animal feeds.

Acid's Effect On Building Materials

The effect of acid rain on buildings, statues, and monuments around the world has been well-documented. Materials used in building, including marble, limestone, and some types of sandstone, contain large amounts of calcium carbonate. When acid rain falls on these materials, a chemical reaction occurs. The acid reacts with the calcium carbonate to form a substance called *gypsum*—a fine-grained, white material that is soft and readily dissolves in water. Show your students how calcium carbonate reacts with an acid with the following activity.

Place an antacid tablet in a small, clear bowl. The tablet contains calcium carbonate as do marble, limestone, and sandstone. Sprinkle one tablespoon of vinegar over the tablet. Observe bubbles of carbon dioxide form as the tablet partially dissolves. Next place the bowl in direct sunlight so the liquid will evaporate. After a few days, a soft, flaky residue that looks like gypsum will be all that remains. The antacid tablet dissolves when acid (vinegar) is sprinkled on it in much the same way that marble, limestone, and sandstone dissolve in acid rain.

Students can further investigate this concept with the following experiment.

What Is The Effect Of Acid Rain On Rocks?

Have your students do the experiment on page 74 to discover acid rain's effect on various kinds of rocks. Students can work individually, in pairs, or in small groups. Materials needed include two each of several kinds of rocks, cups, vinegar, water, and a copy of page 74.

Have students place the rocks in cups of liquid—one of each kind in vinegar and in regular water. Cups should be labeled to indicate type of rock and type of liquid. Examine the rocks after 24 hours. Examine them again after one week. Students should record their observations on the sheet. Which rocks are affected the most? The least? (Limestone and marble will be dissolved the most by the acid. Some other rocks will disintegrate in the water.) Ask why it is important to place each kind of rock in acid *and* water cups.

Are There Solutions?

Acid rain is a serious global problem. But many methods to bring it under control and reduce the smoke and dust that are causing the damage have been successful. Have students explore and research some of these methods. What are different nations around the world doing to curb acid pollution? Does the United States currently have any policies concerning the problem? What can be done in your own community, or even in your own homes? Energy conservation is one effective and easy method of reducing acid pollution. Have students research the link between energy conservation and acid rain reduction. What part can each individual play in cleaning up our environment for future generations?

Name ____ Experiment

Cabbage Juice Indicator

How can we determine whether a liquid is an acid or a base? Pair up with a friend and do the following experiment.

Purpose: Find out which liquids are acids and which are bases by using red cabbage juice as an indicator.

Hypothesis: Which liquids do you think are acids? ______________________________

____

Materials: small, plastic cup
medicine dropper (or spoon)
red cabbage juice
liquids to test (provided by the teacher)

Procedure:

1. Pour red cabbage juice into cup—about 1/3 full.
2. Add one dropperful (or spoonful) of liquid to be tested to the red cabbage juice in your cup.
3. Observe the color of the cabbage juice:
   a. If the juice turns red, the liquid is an acid.
   b. If the juice turns blue or green, the liquid is a base.
   c. If there is no color change, the liquid is neutral (neither acid nor base).
4. Write the name of the liquid you tested in the correct column below, depending on whether it is an acid, neutral, or a base.
5. After testing one liquid, empty the cup and pour in some fresh cabbage juice.
6. Repeat the procedure until you have tested all of the liquids.

Observations: Which liquids were acid, neutral, or base?

Acid	Neutral	Base
____________	____________	____________
____________	____________	____________
____________	____________	____________
____________	____________	____________
____________	____________	____________

Conclusions: What have you learned about liquids that are acids and bases? ____________

____

____

____

Bonus Box: Test other substances—any which will dissolve in water. Try some foods or drinks from the school cafeteria. On the back of this sheet, list the substances that you test. Tell whether they are acid, neutral, or base.

Note To Teacher: Duplicate this page and use with the activity on page 69. For information on obtaining red cabbage juice, see page 68.

 Name ____________________

Using The pH Meter

Each unit of the pH meter is divided into spaces that equal 0.2 (two tenths). Read and determine the pH value indicated by each pointer. Find that liquid in the table of pH's; then write it beside the appropriate number.

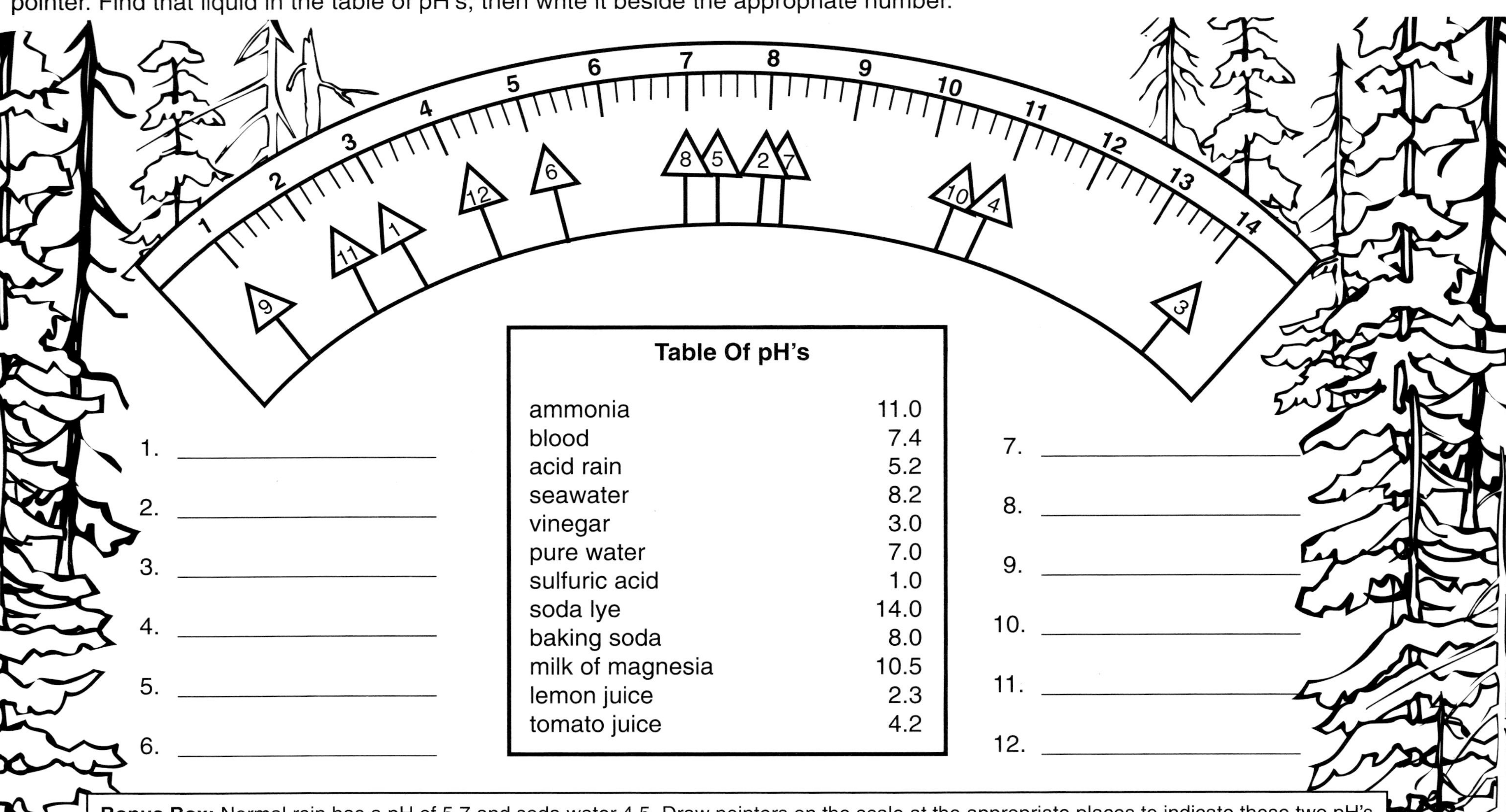

Table Of pH's	
ammonia	11.0
blood	7.4
acid rain	5.2
seawater	8.2
vinegar	3.0
pure water	7.0
sulfuric acid	1.0
soda lye	14.0
baking soda	8.0
milk of magnesia	10.5
lemon juice	2.3
tomato juice	4.2

1. ____________________
2. ____________________
3. ____________________
4. ____________________
5. ____________________
6. ____________________
7. ____________________
8. ____________________
9. ____________________
10. ____________________
11. ____________________
12. ____________________

Bonus Box: Normal rain has a pH of 5.7 and soda water 4.5. Draw pointers on the scale at the appropriate places to indicate these two pH's. Write NR (normal rain) and SW (soda water) on the pointers to designate the two liquids.

Name ______________________________ Experiment

Does Acid Rain Affect Plants?

Each week, write down observations that you make about the two sets of plants. Especially note any differences in size, number of leaves, color, or appearance.

Week	Plants Sprinkled With Water	Plants Sprinkled With Vinegar

Based on your observations over the past four weeks, what are your conclusions? ______________________________

Note To Teacher: Duplicate this page and use with the teacher-directed activity on page 70.

Name ____________________

What Is The Effect Of Acid Rain On Rocks?

What exactly does acid rain do to statues, monuments, and buildings? Try the following experiment to see its effect on simple rocks.

Purpose: Determine the effect of an acid on different types of rocks.

Hypothesis: What do you think will happen when rocks are exposed to plain water and to acid? ____________________

Materials: two each of several kinds of rocks, cups, vinegar, and water

Procedure:

1. Fill each of two cups 3/4 full of liquid—one with vinegar and the other with water.
2. Place two like rocks in the liquids—one in the cup of vinegar and one in water.
3. Label cups (type of liquid and rock).
4. Follow this procedure with each type of rock.
5. List the types of rocks on the chart below.

Observations: Observe the rocks after 24 hours. Describe any changes in the rocks or the liquids. Record your observations on the chart below. Observe and examine again after seven days. Describe the changes on the chart.

Kind Of Rock	In Water		In Vinegar	
	After 24 Hours	After 7 Days	After 24 Hours	After 7 Days

Conclusions: What have you learned about the effects of acid and water on different types of rocks? Write your conclusions on the back of this sheet.

Bonus Box: Test different types of building materials. Try pieces of brick, cinder block, concrete, and stucco. What are the effects of acid and water on each?

Note To Teacher: Use with the activity on page 70. Be sure that the rocks used include limestone or marble. Limestone and marble chips can be found in most garden shops. Check with a local trophy shop to find out if it can donate leftover bits of marble used in making trophy bases. Instruct students to cover the rocks with lots of liquid.

The DISAPPEARING ACT

Now you see it…now you don't! How *does* matter change from one state to another? Further students' understanding of evaporation with this easy-to-organize, hands-on activity.

by Lisa Gentile, Monroe, CT

What You'll Need:

3 test tubes
2 ml water
2 ml rubbing alcohol
2 ml nail polish remover (containing acetone)
3 half-sheets of paper towel
chalkboard
chalk

Discuss With Students:

1. Why do puddles of water disappear?
2. Do all puddles disappear at the same rate?
3. What is *evaporation?* What actually happens when a liquid evaporates?
4. What are some things that might affect evaporation?
5. Does the size of the area that a liquid covers affect evaporation?
6. Give some examples of evaporation.
7. Which do you think would evaporate fastest—water, rubbing alcohol, or nail polish remover?

Do The Activity:

1. Label three wide columns on the chalkboard: Nail Polish Remover, Rubbing Alcohol, and Water.
2. Label the three test tubes: Nail Polish Remover, Rubbing Alcohol, and Water.
3. Pour the three liquids into the labeled test tubes.
4. Choose three student volunteers. Give each volunteer a test tube and a piece of paper towel.
5. On a signal of "Go," each student folds his paper towel, places it over the test tube opening, and empties the liquid into the towel.
6. On a second signal, each student wipes his towel on the board, making a vertical streak in his liquid's column.
7. Instruct volunteers to dispose of the paper towels, wash their hands, and be seated.
8. The class observes the streaks and determines the order in which the liquids "disappear."
9. Repeat the demonstration several times with other student volunteers.
10. Have students discuss possible reasons for the results.

What Happens:

Different substances vary greatly in how fast they evaporate at the same temperature. The nail polish remover will "disappear" first, followed by the rubbing alcohol and water.

The molecules of all substances have a certain amount of *kinetic energy,* or energy of motion. This energy comes from the surroundings and other nearby molecules. The more energy the molecules have, the faster they move. This makes it possible for them to break away from each other. Evaporation occurs when the molecules of a liquid have enough kinetic energy to escape from the surface of the substance as vapor. Of the three substances in the experiment, the acetone molecules in the nail polish remover move fastest; thus evaporation occurs more readily.

Classification Station

Teaching Kids The Scientific Skill Of Classifying

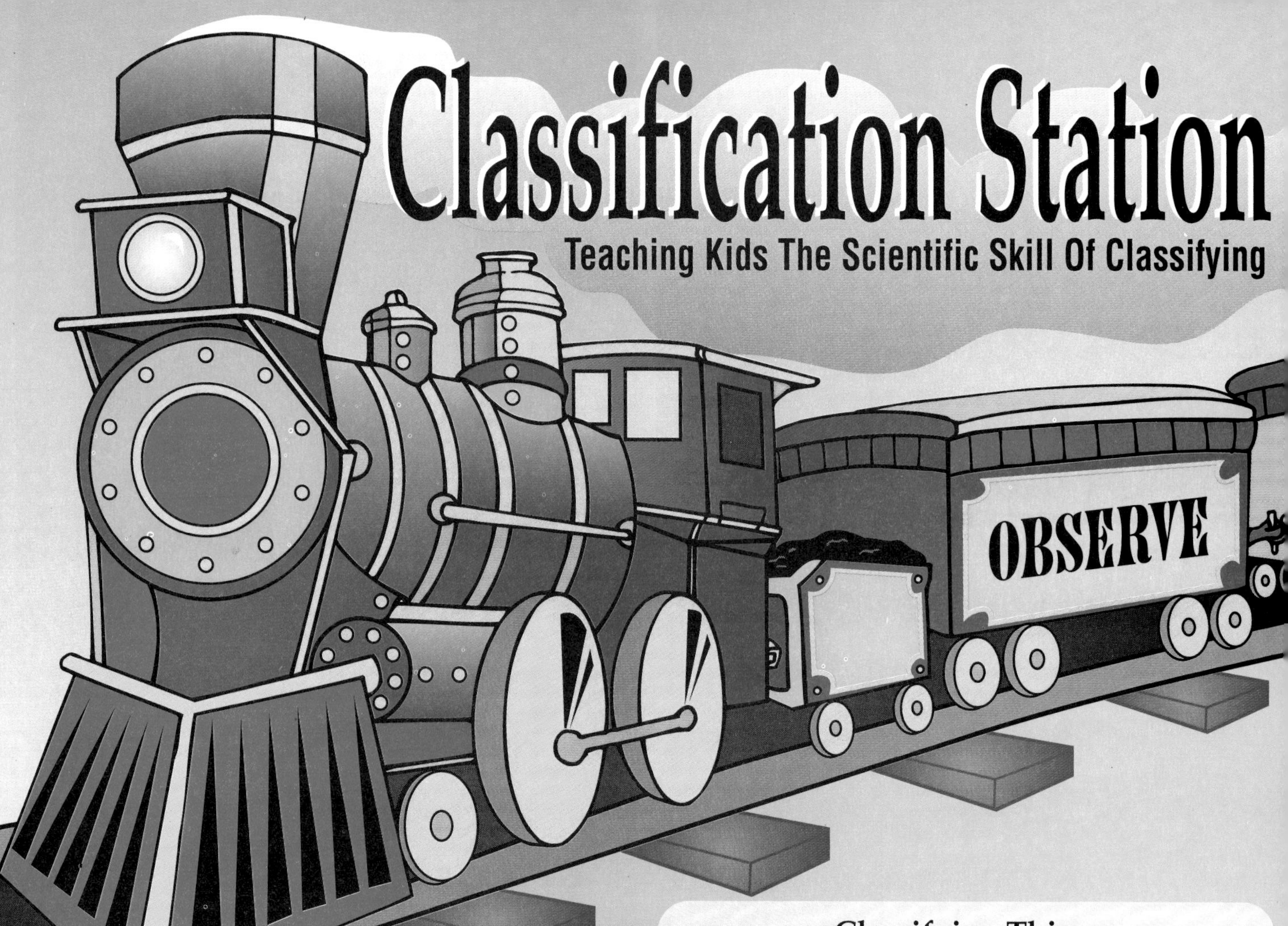

From sorting big and little objects in kindergarten to listing the attributes of geometric shapes in the middle grades, classifying is a lifelong skill. Classifying requires students to observe, compare, research, and use logic. With a few simple objects and the following creative games, activities, and reproducibles, you'll have all that you need to sharpen students' classifying skills.

by Bill O'Connor

In A Class By Themselves

Begin a study of classification with what students know best—each other! Ask students to think about the different ways that they could be divided into two groups. Then have students stand on one side of the room or the other, according to an *attribute* (a natural characteristic or quality) that you specify. At first, keep the attributes simple; for example, divide boys and girls. Then challenge students to think of other ways to divide the class. They might suggest attributes that require interpretation or careful observation, such as eye color or individual skill in a particular game. After several examples, ask students which attributes are the best to use. Point out that easily observable, physical attributes generally work best.

Classifying Things

Discuss with students how common, familiar objects are often classified. Write the general class of an object on the board, such as *shoes*. Then list subsets as children name them. For each subset, write the distinguishing characteristic that sets it apart from the others. You may even list sub-subsets. For example: *Shoes* can be divided into the subsets *men's, women's,* and *children's.* These subsets can be further classified by style, purpose, color, material, etc.

Divide students into small groups and assign each group a familiar topic, such as *vehicles, pets, writing implements*, or *games.* Have each group list subsets and sub-subsets for its topic.

Hands-on Classifying

Provide small groups of students with similar bags of 15–20 common objects (pencil, pen, eraser, sticker, chalk, paper clip, paper cup, safety pin, etc.). Instruct each group to make a list of "rules" for classifying the objects in the bag, based on attributes such as color, material, shape, use, or size. Discourage arbitrary attributes such as "things we like." Have students physically sort the objects into subsets. Ask a recorder in each group to list the characteristic of each subset and its objects.

Have each group present its classification scheme to the class. One fun way to do this is to have the recorder read the objects that his group listed in a subset, then challenge the rest of the class to name the characteristic that was used. Ask if some objects can be classified into more than one set. For example, an object may be both round and red.

Classifying Games

Intermediate kids are familiar with the game 20 Questions. Try some fun variations to help students learn more about classifying. Let students lead the games once they've learned the techniques.

Name That Student!

Secretly choose one student in the class. Have the other students ask *yes* and *no* questions until someone guesses the chosen student's identity. Allow each student only one guess. Challenge the class to use the fewest number of questions possible (no more than a total of five questions from a class of 30 students). List the most productive questions on the chalkboard. What do they have in common?

Welcome To The Club

Announce that you have made a rule about students who belong to your special "club." First decide on an attribute that identifies a group of students. Then call on a volunteer to ask the question, "Does ______ belong to your club?", inserting a classmate's name in the blank. Answer either yes or no. How many questions must be asked before students can determine the rule of the club? (Examples: students wearing short-sleeved tops, students with high-top sneakers, students with pierced ears, etc.)

Draw Me A Picture

Use the reproducible on page 79 for additional classifying practice. Have each student list the members of the class in the top box if there is enough space. Or have students write your name and grade level. As students proceed down each level of the diagram, they will make "rules" for subsets (such as "students who are boys OR students who are girls"). It's okay to use the same rule on both sides of the diagram; for example, both boys and girls may or may not be wearing white socks. A student may be listed in a block only if he is listed in the block directly above.

Duplicate the reproducible for additional practice with other sets of objects or people. Use the activity for classifying science topics (plants, animals, bodies in space) and social studies topics (explorers, presidents, states, regions).

Classifying The Animal Kingdom

There are so many animals in the world that no one could ever count them. Scientists have classified almost a million kinds of animals. And each year, hundreds of new kinds are discovered. Scientists classify animals by two simple methods: by separating them according to their differences and by grouping them according to their likenesses. Use the following games and activities to help students learn more about classifying animals.

Animal House

Obtain pictures of a variety of animals from back issues of *Ranger Rick, National Geographic,* or *Natural History* magazines. Check your library for sets of animal study prints, and collect animal flash cards or animal card games. Try to collect at least one example of each of the major phyla and classes listed in the charts on pages 80 and 81. Display the pictures.

Divide students into small groups. Secretly choose an animal. In turn, each group asks a *dichotomous* question, meaning one that has only two possible answers. For example, the group might ask, "Does the animal have scales?" The two possible answers would be, "The animal has scales" and "The animal does not have scales." After you answer the group's question, allow students to try to guess the identity of your secret animal. Encourage students to ask questions based on the observable, physical characteristics of the animal's phylum or class. Use the game as an opportunity to explain the characteristics of the different animal groups.

Distribute the animal kingdom reproducibles on pages 80 and 81. Have students research and fill in the characteristics of the groups, then list several examples for each group. In most cases, students can look up the phylum or class name in a dictionary or encyclopedia.

What Animal Am I?

Pin a picture of an animal to the back of a student, without letting him or her know the identity of the animal. Have the student ask his classmates dichotomous questions to determine the animal's identity. Encourage students to narrow the animal's classification to a phylum or class first.

Making A Dichotomous Key

Display one picture each of a mammal, bird, reptile, amphibian, and fish. Explain to students that a *key* is simply a way of identifying something—such as determining its name or placing it into a specific category. Discuss the importance of a map key.

Have students help you develop a dichotomous key for classifying a vertebrate in one of the five classes listed above. A *dichotomous key* is a structured set of questions that leads from a general group to a specific subgroup or individual. Stress to students to ask only about visible, physical characteristics observed in the pictures (for example: type of body covering or number of legs). Examples that don't ask about observable characteristics should not be used.

A sample key for determining *amphibian* might include four questions:

1. What kind of body covering does the animal have?
   a. The animal has feathers. The animal is a bird.
   b. It does not have feathers. Go to question 2.

2. Does the animal nurse its young?
   a. The animal nurses its young. The animal is a mammal.
   b. It does not nurse its young. Go to question 3.

3. Does the animal have fins?
   a. The animal has fins. The animal is a fish.
   b. The animal does not have fins. Go to question 4.

4. What kind of body covering does the animal have?
   a. The animal has scales. The animal is a reptile.
   b. The animal has smooth, moist skin.
   The animal is an amphibian.

A number of different keys could have been made that would have achieved the same end. Point out that a dichotomous key can be used to identify a species or even an individual. Have students make up their own keys about various topics and try them out on their classmates. Suggest groups such as teachers in your school, trees, birds, or any other set of familiar objects.

Books About Animals

The following books are great resources to use with your studies of animals and animal classification:

- *Amazing Poisonous Animals* by Alexandra Parsons (Additional titles in Parsons's Eyewitness Juniors series include *Amazing Birds, Amazing Cats, Amazing Mammals, Amazing Snakes,* and *Amazing Spiders.)*
- *Animal Families Of The Wild: A Read-Aloud Collection Of Animal Literature* edited by William F. Russell
- *Insect* by Laurence Mound
- *Spiders* by Alice L. Hopf
- *Seals, Sea Lions, And Walruses* by Dorothy H. Patent
- *Tiger Trek* by Ted Lewin
- *Wolves* by R. D. Lawrence
- *The Hidden Life Of The Desert* by Thomas Wiewandt
- *Near The Sea* by Jim Arnosky
- *Aardvarks, Disembark!* by Ann Jonas
- *Animal Tracks* by Arthur Dorros
- *Big Cats* by Seymour Simon

Name____

A Classroom In A Box

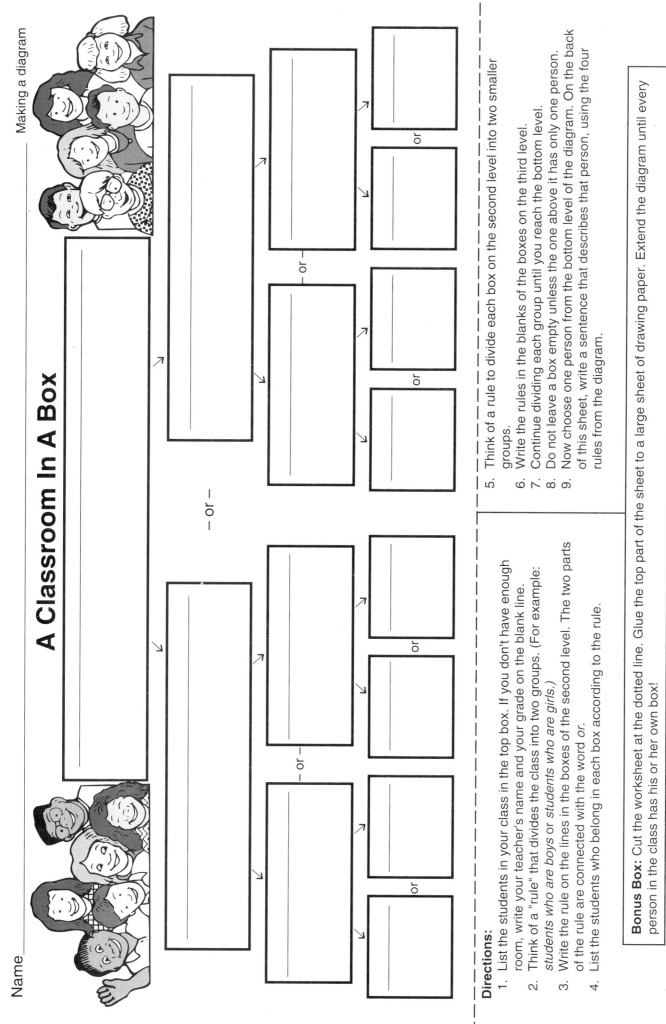

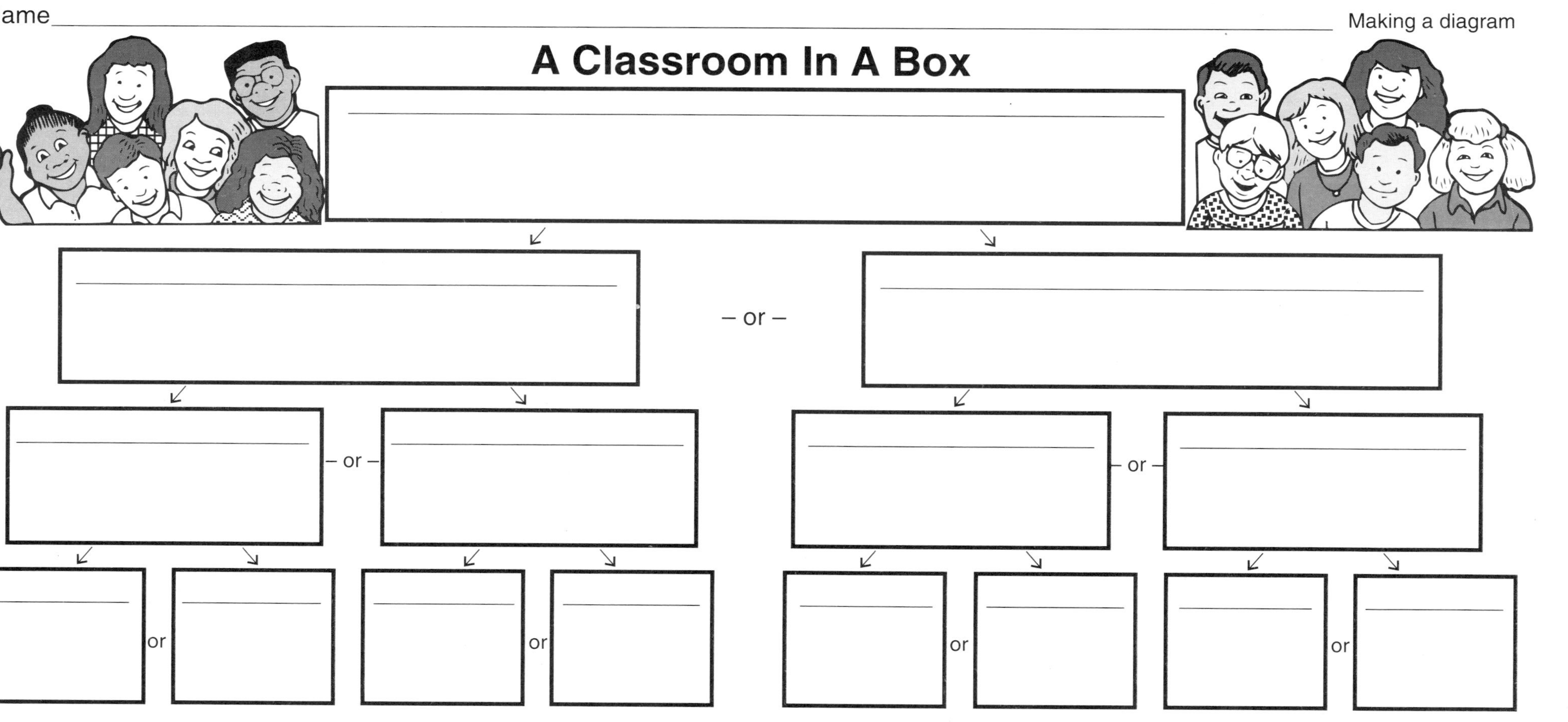

Directions:

1. List the students in your class in the top box. If you don't have enough room, write your teacher's name and your grade on the blank line.
2. Think of a "rule" that divides the class into two groups. (For example: *students who are boys* or *students who are girls.)*
3. Write the rule on the lines in the boxes of the second level. The two parts of the rule are connected with the word *or.*
4. List the students who belong in each box according to the rule.
5. Think of a rule to divide each box on the second level into two smaller groups.
6. Write the rules in the blanks of the boxes on the third level.
7. Continue dividing each group until you reach the bottom level.
8. Do not leave a box empty unless the one above it has only one person.
9. Now choose one person from the bottom level of the diagram. On the back of this sheet, write a sentence that describes that person, using the four rules from the diagram.

Bonus Box: Cut the worksheet at the dotted line. Glue the top part of the sheet to a large sheet of drawing paper. Extend the diagram until every person in the class has his or her own box!

Name____ Completing a chart, research

Charting The Animal Kingdom: Invertebrates

There are more than one million known kinds of invertebrates! *Invertebrates* are animals that have no backbone. Every invertebrate is classified in a large group called a *phylum.* A phylum is subdivided into *classes.* Listed in the chart below are some of the invertebrate phyla.

Use reference books to learn more about each phylum below. First list some characteristics of the phylum. Then list two or three animals that are classified in the phylum. In the last column, illustrate and label one animal in the phylum.

Phylum	Characteristics	Examples	Illustration
Porifera (sponges)			
Coelenterata (animals containing jellylike material)			
Echinodermata (spiny-skinned animals)			
Mollusca (mollusks)			
Platyhelminthes (flatworms)			
Brachiopoda (animals with two-piece shells)			
Annelida (segmented worms)			
Arthropoda (animals with jointed legs) *Crustacea* (crustaceans)			
Arthropoda *Arachnida* (arachnids)			
Arthropoda *Insecta* (insects)			

Bonus Box: Research an invertebrate that you listed in the chart. Find and list the names of the seven chief groups in which the animal is classified: *kingdom, phylum, class, order, family, genus,* and *species.*

Name ______________________________

Charting The Animal Kingdom: Vertebrates

A *vertebrate* is an animal with a backbone and *cranium* (braincase). There are seven living classes of vertebrates, five of which are listed in the chart below.

Research each class. Fill in the chart with some of the characteristics and animals of each class. Use encyclopedias and other reference books to help you. Some boxes have been filled in for you.

class	cold-blooded or warm-blooded	type of body covering	method of reproduction	method of breathing	other attributes	examples
Osteichthyes (bony fish)	• cold-blooded					
Amphibia (amphibians)				• most breathe with lungs • some have gills • some have lungs and gills		
Reptilia (reptiles)		• dry, scaly skin				
Aves (birds)					• all birds have wings	
Mammalia (mammals)						• cats • dogs • cattle • goats • hogs • anteaters • apes • people

Bonus Box: Research to find out the four main groups of reptiles.

Those Amazing Mammals

Mammals are one of the seven classes of vertebrates. There are about 4,000 kinds of mammals. Many of them are among the most familiar of all animals.

Mammals are subdivided into *orders.* Below are ten of the 18 orders of living mammals. Read each order and the description of the animals classified in it. Then study the animals pictured at the bottom of the page. Cut out each animal picture and glue it beside its order.

	1. **lagomorphs**	small mammals with two pairs of upper incisors; no canine teeth; molars without roots; short or absent tail		6. **edentates**	lack teeth or have only molars; forelimbs adapted for digging or for clinging to branches
	2. **rodents**	small, gnawing mammals; one pair of chisellike upper incisors		7. **bats**	only mammals capable of true flight; forelimbs adapted as wings
	3. **cetaceans**	aquatic mammals with streamlined bodies; paddlelike forelimbs; no hindlimbs; horizontally flattened tail; nostrils on top of head		8. **sea cows**	aquatic mammals; paddlelike forelimbs; no hindlimbs; flattened muzzle
	4. **carnivores**	most are meat-eaters; claws; large canine teeth		9. **odd-toed ungulates**	hoofed mammals; one or three toes on each foot
	5. **primates**	most species are tree dwellers; hands have five fingers; feet have five toes		10. **even-toed ungulates**	hoofed mammals; two or four toes on each foot

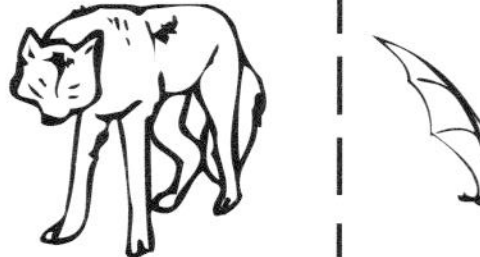

Bonus Box: If you could be a scientist, what animal order would you want to study? On the back of this sheet, write your answer. Be sure to include the animal order's name and your reasons for wanting to study it.

Everybody talks about the weather, but no one does anything about it! But to study weather ...

Just Step OUTSIDE!

The best way to learn about weather is to watch it as it happens. And the best way to watch weather? Just step outside! A study of weather offers unique opportunities for students to make scientific observations and predictions every day. Explore some of the many teachable moments about weather with the following hands-on activities and reproducibles. *by Bill O'Connor*

A Good Chance Of Rain

Rain falls when cloud-forming drops of water combine and become so heavy that the air can't hold them up. Demonstrate this concept by making it "rain" in your classroom! You'll need a hot plate, a saucepan, a cookie sheet or baking pan, and ice. Fill the saucepan with water a few inches deep and bring it to a boil. Fill the baking pan with ice and support it about 18 inches above the hot plate. After a few minutes, water droplets will begin to form on the underside of the baking pan. As the drops grow larger, they will fall off the pan. This shows how raindrops form in a cloud, as warm, humid air rises and cools.

Weather: Background For The Teacher

Weather is the condition of the air that blankets our earth. It is shaped by four "ingredients": the sun, the earth, air, and water. These ingredients work together to make it hot or cold, cloudy or clear, windy or calm. They may produce rain, snow, sleet, or hail.

One universal aspect of weather is that it affects everyone! The type of clothing that we wear each day, how we decide to spend our leisure time, and even our moods are tied to the weather. Weather also has a tremendous impact on farming, industry, transportation, communication, construction, and, sometimes, our very survival.

In A Fog

Humidity is the amount of water vapor in the air. Introduce this concept by asking what happens to mirrors and windows when students take baths or showers. (They "fog" up.) Warm air can hold a great deal of water vapor, but if the air is cooled the water condenses into droplets of liquid.

To demonstrate this concept, place a container of iced water on your desk. Have students observe the condensation that forms on the outside of the container. This condensation is moisture that has been removed from the air when the air is cooled. A cooling of moist atmospheric air also causes moisture to fall to the earth in the form of rain, snow, sleet, or hail.

It's All Relative!

Every television weather report includes the relative humidity. But there are probably few students (and adults!) who understand this concept. *Relative humidity* is the percent of water vapor saturation of the air at a given temperature. If the air contains only half of the amount of water vapor that it can hold when saturated, we say the relative humidity is 50%; if no water can evaporate into the air, the relative humidity is 100%. Help students better understand this concept with the reproducible project on page 88. Divide the class into small groups or pairs to complete the project.

A Cloud In A Bottle

What's fog? A cloud that touches the ground! Gather the following materials to make a cloud in a bottle: a cup of hot water; a large, clear bottle, such as a glass gallon jug; matches; an air pump (a basketball or bicycle tire pump); and a cork or plasticene clay. (Instead of a cork or plasticene clay, ask a secondary science teacher for a #7 one-hole stopper. It will fit most glass gallon jugs perfectly.)

Pour one cup of hot water into the bottle. Light a match, blow it out, and drop it into the bottle. Seal the opening with a cork or with clay, leaving a small opening into which you can insert the air pump tube. Pump up the pressure inside the jar with about 15 to 20 strokes. Then remove the air pump, releasing the pressure. The air inside the bottle will instantly turn to fog! If you pump up the pressure again, the air will clear. This can be repeated many times over and still work.

Why does it work? Increasing the air pressure warms the air inside the jar, allowing it to hold more water vapor. When the pressure is suddenly reduced, the water condenses into tiny droplets that produce fog. The smoke particles act as condensation nuclei, like dust particles in the atmosphere.

A Mini-Greenhouse

The *greenhouse effect* is the warming of the earth as the atmosphere traps heat radiated from the earth's surface—similar to the way that heat in a greenhouse is trapped by its glass walls and roof. A simple demonstration vividly explains this concept. Place a thermometer in each of two identical glass jars. Cover the opening of one jar with plastic wrap. Place both jars in direct sunlight or under a strong lamp. After 15 minutes compare the temperatures. The covered jar will be warmer because the light rays are absorbed inside the jar and converted to heat. These heat (infrared) rays cannot escape through the glass. The plastic wrap covering simulates the *greenhouse gases* (including carbon dioxide and ozone) in our atmosphere that trap infrared rays and send them back toward earth.

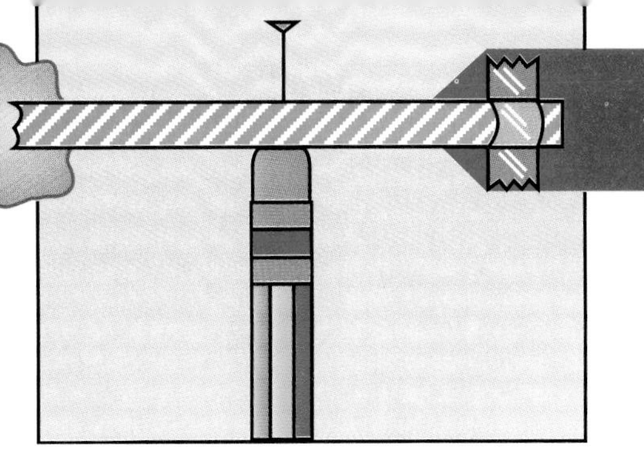

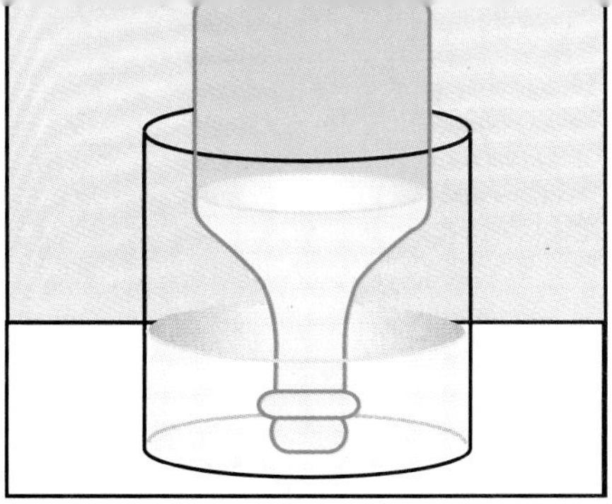

Homemade Weather Instruments

Commercially made weather instruments give best results, but homemade instruments are fun for kids to make and help illustrate weather concepts just as well. Be sure to include the following easy-to-make projects in your weather studies:

Wind Direction Indicator

Materials: a drinking straw, tape, scissors, a straight pin, tagboard, a pencil, plasticene clay, a compass
How to make: Cut a "tail" (see illustration) from tagboard and tape it to one end of the straw. Place a small ball of plasticene clay on the other end. Find the point on the straw at which it balances. Push a straight pin through the straw at this point. To complete the indicator, push the pin into the eraser end of a pencil.
How to use: Go outside to a large, open area. Take along a compass. The clay end of the straw points to the direction from which the wind blows. Try to place a wind direction indicator in a location so that it can be observed from the classroom.

Rain Gauge

Materials: a tall, narrow bottle; a wooden stake; large rubber bands; a permanent marker; a funnel; a container with a diameter about the same as the large end of the funnel; water
How to make: Fill the container with one inch of water; then pour the water through the funnel into the tall bottle. Mark "1 in." on the bottle at this level and divide the distance into tenths. Repeat this procedure for two and three inches of water to make a scale for the rain gauge.
How to use: Drive the stake into level ground in an open area. Set the bottle beside it. Place rubber bands around the bottle and stake to help keep the bottle upright. Place the funnel in the bottle. Take daily readings of the amount of rainfall.

Barometer

Materials: a heavy glass jar; a large, glass bottle that will stand upside down when placed in the heavy glass jar; water
How to make and use: Fill both the jar and bottle about halfway with water. Invert the bottle into the jar so that the water level in the bottle is visible. Observe the water level in the bottle from day to day. It will rise and fall according to the air pressure. Rising air pressure outside will press down on the water in the jar, raising the water level inside the bottle. This barometer is only reliable if the temperature remains constant. Observe it at the same time every day.

BIG Breeze

2
1

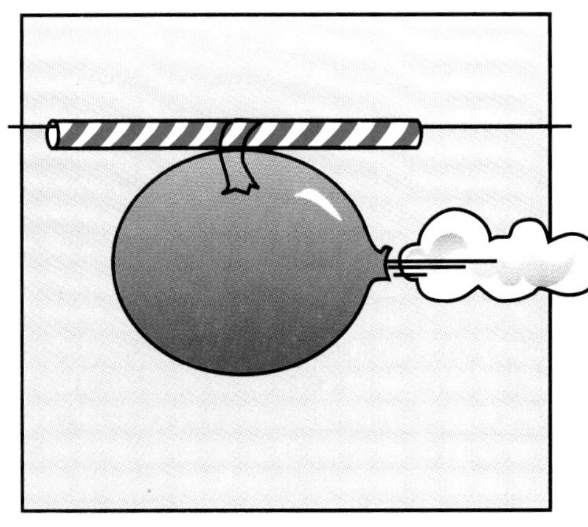

How Does The Wind Blow?

Air on the move—that's what winds are. Here's a quick trick to demonstrate the movement of winds. Slip a six-foot piece of string through a plastic drinking straw. Have two students hold the ends of the string tightly. Blow up a balloon, and hold the end closed. Carefully tape the balloon to the straw; then let the balloon go. Have students hypothesize about what they observe. Explain that as you blew up the balloon, air was forced into a small space, creating an area of pressure higher than that outside the balloon. By releasing the balloon, you caused the high-pressure air in it to escape into the low-pressure air outside, resulting in a rush of air. Winds behave in the same way: air moves from areas of high pressure to areas of lower pressure. The larger the difference in air pressure from one area to another, the stronger the winds. Have students do some free-time research on special winds such as monsoons, jet streams, prevailing winds, and chinooks.

Facts About Fronts

That peppy weather reporter on television is always mentioning fronts, but does anyone know what she's talking about? Help your students understand the movement of air which causes fronts. Fill one baby food jar with hot water and one with cold water. Place several drops of red food coloring into the jar of hot water and several drops of blue food coloring into the jar of cold water. Cover the hot-water jar with an index card and carefully place it over the mouth of the cold-water jar. Slowly slide out the card and observe what happens. (Nothing: the hot water is lighter than the cold water and will remain on top.) Prepare two more jars of water in the same manner, placing the cold-water jar on top of the hot-water jar. Remove the card. Students will observe the colder, heavier blue water sinking down into the warmer, lighter red water. In the same way, a cold air mass will push under a warm air mass to create a cold front. A warm air mass will climb over a colder air mass to form a warm front.

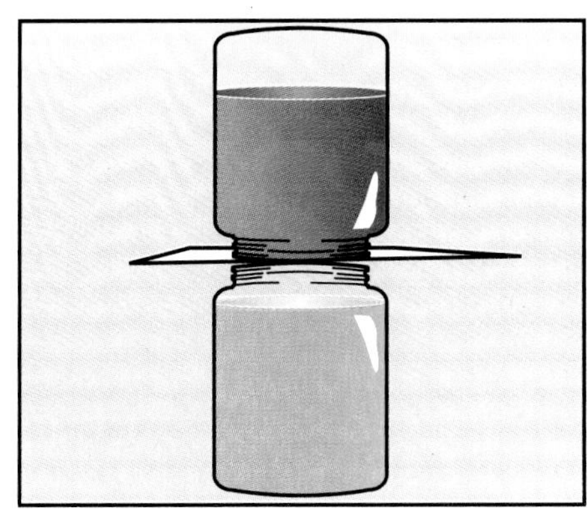

Stormy Weather

Kids are fascinated by tales of twisting tornadoes and blinding blizzards. Alert students to the facts about storms by dividing your class into "disaster teams." Give each team a type of storm to research extensively: thunderstorm, heavy snowstorm, hurricane, tornado. (See "The Tornado Machine" on page 67.) Each team creates a display highlighting the causes, locations, seasons, safety procedures, and other information associated with its storm. Depending on your area, have teams also investigate what local government does to prepare and protect citizens during severe storms. When research is completed, let each team present its display and answer questions from classmates.

Weather Folklore

If sheep huddle together, does that mean rain is on the way? Before modern technology and communication, people looked for signs in nature to predict the weather. Many of these signs accurately forecasted weather much as modern meteorologists do today. For example, sheep's wool traps air as insulation. Since they huddle together to keep warm, sheep may reliably predict approaching cooler air and rain. Have students survey parents, other older relatives, or neighbors to collect weather sayings or superstitions. List these on a bulletin board or class chart. Discuss whether students believe they are accurate predictors of weather. A good resource book is *A January Fog Will Freeze A Hog And Other Weather Folklore* compiled and edited by Hubert Davis (Crown Publishers, Inc., New York, 1977).

Books About Weather

—*Weatherwatch* by Valerie Wyatt
—*It's Raining Cats And Dogs* by Franklyn M. Branley
—NatureScope's *Wild About Weather* (National Wildlife Federation, 1986)
—*Weather Forecasting* by Gail Gibbons
—*Weather Words And What They Mean* by Gail Gibbons
—*The Usborne Book Of Weather Facts* (Usborne, 1987)
—*Global Warming* by Laurence Pringle
—*The Greenhouse Effect* by Rebecca L. Johnson

Name(s) ____________________

Directions: Work with a partner to complete the daily weather report below. Write your names and today's date in the blanks. Then cut out the report and post it in the classroom. Follow the steps below to complete the report.

1. Record temperatures at three different times: morning, midday, and the end of the school day.
2. Estimate the wind speed. Use the Beaufort Wind Scale in the chart to help you.
3. Use a weather vane to determine wind direction.
4. Record the barometric pressure. If you don't have a barometer, call a local weather station for a reading.
5. Describe any clouds in the sky. Use a cloud chart from your science book or an encyclopedia to help you.
6. Describe the present weather conditions. Tell whether it is sunny, rainy, windy, cloudy, clear, etc.
7. Record the amount of precipitation that has fallen in the last 24 hours.
8. Make a forecast for tomorrow based on your observations of today's weather.

The Beaufort Wind Scale

mph	description	observation
less than 1	calm	smoke rises vertically
1–3	light air	smoke drifts slowly
4–7	light breeze	leaves rustle; wind felt on face
8–12	gentle breeze	leaves and small twigs move
13–18	moderate breeze	small branches move
19–24	fresh breeze	small trees sway
25–31	strong breeze	large branches sway
32–38	moderate gale	whole trees sway; difficult to walk against wind
39–46	fresh gale	twigs break off trees
47–54	strong gale	shingles blown off roof
55–63	whole gale	trees uprooted
64–73	storm	widespread damage
74 and above	hurricane	extreme damage

TODAY'S WEATHER

date: completed by:

daily temperatures:	estimated wind speed:	barometric pressure:
______ at ______ A.M. ______ at midday ______ at ______ P.M.	______ mph wind direction: from ________________ observations:	______ in. ☐ rising ☐ steady ☐ falling
clouds:	present conditions:	precipitation in the last 24 hours:

our forecast for tomorrow:

Note To Teacher: Duplicate one copy of this page for each pair of students. Assign one pair of students to be "Today's Weather Watchers" for each day of the week. For a homemade weather vane to use to complete step 3, see "Wind Direction Indicator" on page 85. To complete step 7, see "Rain Gauge" on page 85.

What's The Relative Humidity?

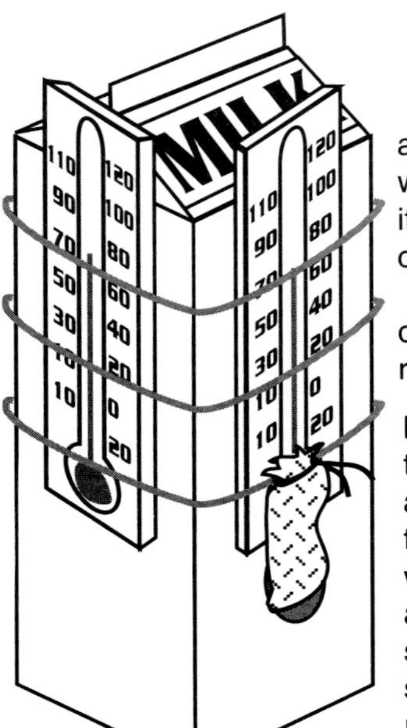

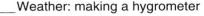

A *hygrometer* is an instrument used to measure the amount of water vapor in the air. People who study the weather use a hygrometer to determine the relative humidity. *Relative humidity* is the amount of water vapor in the air compared to the amount required for saturation.

Work with a partner to make a hygrometer. Follow the directions below. Then use your hygrometer to measure the relative humidity for the next five days.

Materials:
two Fahrenheit thermometers
an empty, quart-sized milk or juice carton
three rubber bands
water
a piece of scrap cloth (muslin works well)
scissors
string
ruler

dry-bulb temperatures °F. (columns) / wet-bulb temperatures °F. (rows)

wet-bulb °F.	56	58	60	62	64	66	68	70	71	72	73	74	75	76	77	78	79	80	82	84	86	88
38	7	2																				
40	15	11	7																			
42	25	19	14	9	7																	
44	34	29	22	17	13	8	4															
46	45	38	30	24	18	14	10	6	4	3	1											
48	55	47	40	33	26	21	16	12	10	9	7	5	4	3	1							
50	66	56	48	41	34	29	23	19	17	15	13	11	9	8	6	5	4	3				
52	77	67	57	50	43	36	31	25	23	21	19	17	15	13	12	10	9	7	5	3	1	
54	88	78	68	59	51	44	38	33	30	28	25	23	21	19	17	16	14	12	10	7	5	3
56		89	79	68	60	53	46	40	37	34	32	29	27	25	23	21	19	18	14	12	9	7
58			89	79	70	61	54	48	45	42	39	36	34	31	29	27	25	23	20	16	14	11
60				90	79	71	62	55	52	49	46	43	40	38	35	33	31	29	25	21	18	15
62					90	80	71	64	60	57	53	50	47	44	42	39	37	35	30	26	23	20
64						90	80	72	68	65	61	58	54	51	48	46	43	41	36	32	28	25
66							90	81	77	73	69	65	62	59	56	53	50	47	42	37	33	30
68								90	86	82	78	74	70	66	63	60	57	54	48	43	39	35
70									95	91	86	82	78	74	71	67	64	61	55	49	44	40
72											95	91	86	82	79	75	71	68	61	56	50	46
74													96	91	87	83	79	75	69	62	57	51
76															96	91	87	83	76	69	63	57
78																	96	91	84	76	70	64
80																			92	84	77	70
82																				92	84	77
84																					92	85
86																						92

Procedure:
1. Cut a round hole about three inches from the bottom of the carton.
2. Wrap and tie the cloth around the bulb of one thermometer (this is your *wet-bulb thermometer).* Leave about four to five inches of cloth hanging below the bulb.
3. Use rubber bands to attach the thermometer to the side of the carton with the hole. The bulb should be placed right above the hole. Push the leftover cloth through the hole in the milk carton.
4. Pour water into the carton up to the hole. Make sure the cloth is in the water.
5. Slide the other thermometer (your *dry-bulb thermometer)* under the rubber bands on another side of the carton. See the illustration.

To use the hygrometer:
1. Make sure that the wet-bulb thermometer's bulb is saturated with water.
2. Place the hygrometer in a breeze, out of direct sunlight.
3. Leave the hygrometer there for about 20 minutes.
4. Read both thermometers and record the temperatures in the chart.
5. Determine the relative humidity by using the chart of wet-bulb and dry-bulb temperatures. Read across from the wet-bulb reading; read down from the dry-bulb reading. Record the percent in the chart. An example has been done for you.
6. Determine the relative humidity twice a day for five days.

time	wet-bulb temperature	dry-bulb temperature	relative humidity
example	66°	72°	73%
day 1			
day 1			
day 2			
day 2			
day 3			
day 3			
day 4			
day 4			
day 5			
day 5			

Name ____

Collection Of Clouds

Clouds can be grouped according to where they are found in the sky:

low-sky clouds (form from ground level to 5,000 feet): fog, cumulus, stratus, stratocumulus, nimbostratus, cumulonimbus

middle clouds (form from 5,000 to 20,000 feet): altocumulus, altostratus

high clouds (form from 20,000 to 40,000 feet): cirrus, cirrocumulus, cirrostratus

Clues about clouds can also be found in their names. For example, the Latin word *cumulo,* meaning "pile," describes cumulus clouds. Cumulus clouds look like puffy piles of cotton. Other Latin words which describe clouds are:

cirro ("curl") *nimbus* ("rain")
stratus ("layered") *alto* ("middle")

Directions: Use the information above to write the number of the matching definition in each cloud.

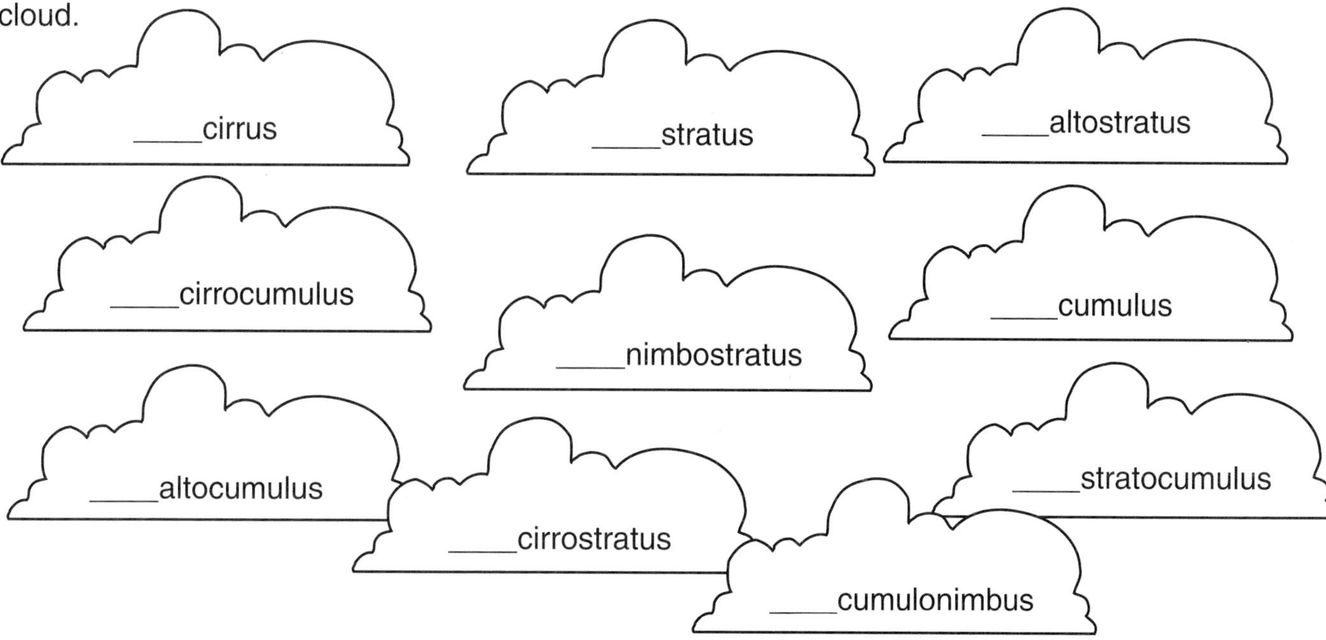

1. middle clouds which look like scattered white and gray puffs
2. a low, smooth layer of gray from which a *steady* rain or snow falls
3. a low, puffy cloud bringing heavy rain, thunder, lightning; a "thunderhead"
4. wispy, curling cloud high in the sky; signals approaching warm front
5. grayish layers of clouds found 5,000 to 20,000 feet in the sky
6. thin layer of high, cirrus clouds; forms "halo" around moon or sun
7. unbroken layers of low, gray clouds; bring *light* rain, snow, or drizzle
8. low, puffy, white cloud; can change into a cumulonimbus cloud
9. very high, thin, white clouds that look like many small pieces of cotton
10. looks like cumulus clouds pressed in layers; found low in the sky

Bonus Box: Begin a cloud journal. Staple together seven pieces of paper. Each day, identify and draw sketches of the clouds you observe in the sky at different times of the day. At the end of seven days, make a cover to staple over your journal.

Name ____________________

What's The Forecast?

Meteorologists use special symbols and codes to explain weather data on maps. Because these symbols are international, the same map can be read by an Italian or a German meteorologist. But weather maps in newspapers or on television often use simpler symbols to make them easier for everyone to understand.

clear skies	cloudy skies	partly cloudy skies	cold air, warm air cold front
cold air, warm air warm front	moderate rain	showers	snow
50°, 50° maximum temperature (all places along line)	fog	drizzle	hurricane
H high pressure system	L low pressure system	cold air, warm air stationary front	occluded front

Study the weather symbols; then use the map on page 91 to decide whether each statement below is true or false.

Write **T** or **F** in each blank.

_____ 1. A cold front is located off the coast of California.
_____ 2. The maximum temperature in the northeastern United States is 60°F.
_____ 3. The temperature is higher in South Carolina than it is in Maine.
_____ 4. There is a high pressure system in Nevada.
_____ 5. A cold front extends from western Canada into the United States.
_____ 6. It is partly cloudy in Ohio.
_____ 7. There is moderate rainfall off the coasts of Louisiana, Alabama, and Mississippi.
_____ 8. A high pressure system is located in southern California.
_____ 9. Maximum temperatures on this map range from 50° to 100°F.
_____ 10. It is drizzling in Tennessee.
_____ 11. It is foggy in southern Nebraska.

Now add the numbers of the statements you marked with a **T**. Is your total 25?

Note To Teacher: Duplicate page 91 to accompany this sheet. Have the student use a United States map in a social studies textbook to complete the activity.

Name ________________________

What's The Forecast?

Use this map to complete page 90.

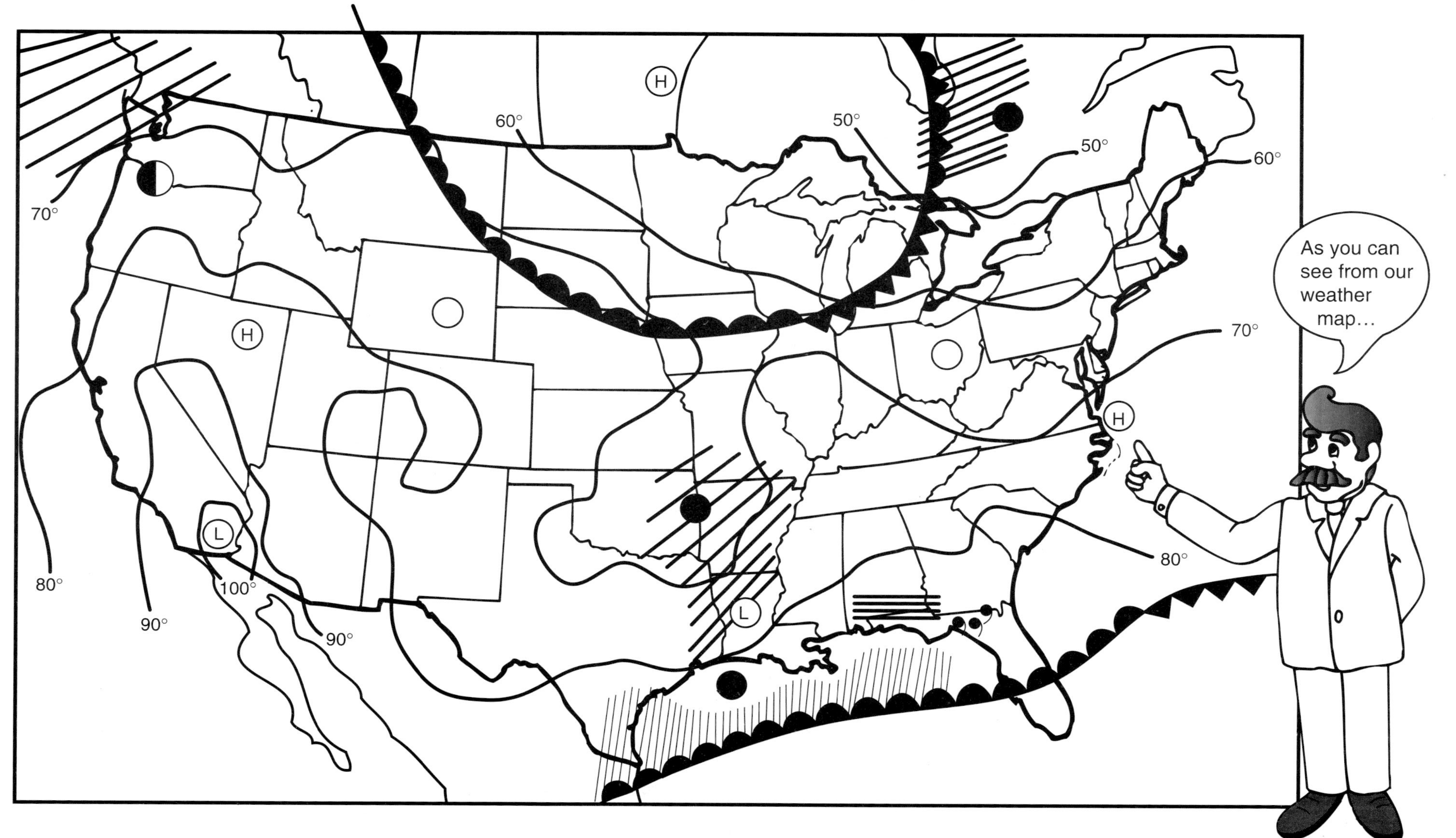

Bonus Box: Cut out a weather map from a newspaper. On another piece of paper, explain what the symbols on the map indicate about that day's weather.

You Won't Believe How Cold/Hot It Was!

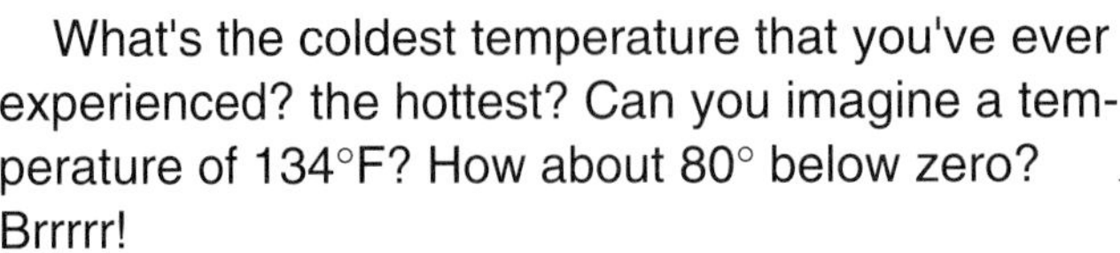

What's the coldest temperature that you've ever experienced? the hottest? Can you imagine a temperature of 134°F? How about 80° below zero? Brrrrr!

The table below shows the lowest and highest temperatures that have been recorded in ten different states. Use the information in the table to help you answer the questions below. (Show your work on a separate sheet of paper.)

Record Temperatures In Ten States

state	lowest temperature (°F)	date	highest temperature (°F)	date
Alabama	-27	Jan. 30, 1966	112	Sept. 5, 1925
Alaska	-80	Jan. 23, 1971	100	June 27, 1915
California	-45	Jan. 20, 1937	134	July 10, 1913
Delaware	-17	Jan. 17, 1893	110	July 21, 1930
Florida	-2	Feb. 13, 1899	109	June 29, 1931
Hawaii	14	Jan. 2, 1961	100	April 27, 1931
Idaho	-60	Jan. 18, 1943	118	July 28, 1934
Michigan	-51	Feb. 9, 1934	112	July 13, 1936
Montana	-70	Jan. 20, 1954	117	July 5, 1937
Nebraska	-47	Feb. 12, 1899	118	July 24, 1936

Source: National Oceanic and Atmospheric Administration

1. Which state had the lowest recorded temperature? ______________________
2. Which state had the highest recorded temperature? ______________________
3. Which state has never recorded a temperature below zero? ______________________
4. In which decade (1920s, 1930s, 1940s, etc.) were the most record highs set? ______________
5. In which month were the most record lows recorded? ______________________
6. Which state recorded its lowest and highest temperatures in the same decade? ______________
7. Which state's record low and record high were both above zero degrees? ______________
   What is the difference between this state's record low and record high? ______________
8. To find the difference between a temperature that is above zero degrees and a temperature that is below zero degrees, you can *add.* For example, the difference between Alabama's record low and record high is 139° (27 + 112 = 139).
   Find the difference between the record low and record high for these states in the table:

   AK ________ CA ________ DE ________ FL ________
   ID ________ MI ________ MT ________ NE ________
9. Which state had the greatest difference between its record low and record high? ______________
10. Which state recorded its record high in the springtime? ______________________

Bonus Box: Did the northernmost state of the United States record the lowest low? Did the southernmost state record the highest high? Use the chart and a map to find out.

Who You Gonna Call? "Stormbusters!"

These two meteorologists are going to study storms, but they need help packing the right facts in their trunks.

Write each fact below in the correct trunk. (Hint: One fact belongs in *both* trunks.)

several hundred miles in diameter
winds over 300 miles per hour
winds swirl around *eye*
develops over warm ocean water
sometimes called *cyclone* or *typhoon*
usually occurs in midwestern U.S.
several hundred yards in diameter
winds over 70 miles per hour
can cause death and destruction
usually lasts less than an hour
sometimes called *twister* or *cyclone*
produces huge waves, or *storm surge*
grows weaker as it moves over land
rotating funnel cloud

Bonus Box: The National Hurricane Center is in Miami, Florida. The National Severe Storms Forecast Center (which watches for tornadoes) is in Kansas City, Missouri. Why do you think these weather offices are located in these two cities? Write your answer on the back.

Name ______________________________

Weather-Watching Words

Weather has a language all its own. The following puzzle is filled with weather-related words. How many do you know?

Use the clues and the words in the Word Bank to help you complete the puzzle.

Clues

Across

1. arctic temperature
4. weather "eye" in the sky
7. large, tropical storm
8. fluffy, fair-weather clouds
9. rain clouds
11. edge of a moving air mass
14. ground-level cloud
15. temperature scale used in the U.S.
16. water in a solid form
18. instrument used to measure temperature
20. frozen rain
21. weight of the air
23. crystal precipitation
25. moisture that condenses on the grass
27. violent, funnel-shaped storm
28. liquid precipitation
29. weather disturbance
30. another word for *water* or *wetness*

Down

1. large mass of water droplets or ice crystals in the air
2. electrical discharge in the sky
3. weather that causes baseball games to be cancelled
5. good fortune
6. degree of heat or coldness
10. instrument used to measure air pressure
12. instrument that measures wind speed
13. what the sun does to the earth's surface
17. high clouds made of ice crystals
18. sound that follows a flash of lightning
19. species of tree
22. solid-layer cloud
24. liquid H_2O
26. not very hot

Word Bank

anemometer
barometer
cirrus
cloud
cold
cumulus
dew
elm
Fahrenheit
fog
front
heats
hurricane
ice
lightning
luck

Word Bank

moisture
nimbus
pressure
rain
rain
satellite
sleet
snow
storm
stratus
temperature
thermometer
thunder
tornado
warm
water

Things Are Really Heating Up!

STUDYING HEAT ENERGY

Heat—it can't be seen, but the work it does can! Experimenting with heat energy is an exciting way to teach students scientific procedures, energy concepts, and math skills. Include the following creative ideas and hands-on activities during National Energy Awareness Month in October.

by Bill O'Connor

Background For The Teacher

Heat can travel from one object or place to another by three methods: conduction, convection, and radiation. Heat moving through a solid object, such as the bottom of a cooking pot, travels by *conduction. Convection* is the transfer of heat by a moving gas or liquid. A hair dryer and the coolant in an automobile engine are examples of convection. *Radiation* is heat moving through space as energy waves. Heat given off by the sun or a quartz heater is an example of radiation.

Thermometer Tasks

Most of the activities and experiments in this unit require the use of thermometers. Students will enjoy experimenting with them. Use inexpensive liquid thermometers (Fahrenheit or Celsius), one for every two to four students. They can be purchased at aquarium stores or discount stores (weather thermometers), or from science supply companies. Using this scientific tool will stimulate student interest, teach valuable math skills, and encourage careful scientific procedures. Try these preliminary activities to familiarize your students with thermometers:

- Caution students not to bend or drop the thermometers, since they're definitely breakable! Tie loops of yarn or string to the thermometers and have students wear them around their necks.
- Review the thermometers' calibrations. How many degrees does each line represent? What scale is used? What are the highest and lowest temperatures shown? Try to bring several different kinds of thermometers to class for comparison.
- Have students practice using thermometers before doing any experiments. Instruct them to find and record several different temperatures around the classroom, school, and schoolyard during a ten-minute period. They'll soon discover that holding the bulb of a thermometer will cause the temperature to rise. Discuss why the groups may have recorded different temperature measures at the same site. Ask how long it took for a thermometer to register a temperature. Discuss the highest and lowest temperatures recorded and the sites where they were found.

Create plenty of sizzle in your classroom with the experiments on pages 98–102. A few easy-to-find materials and the helpful hints below will get you on your way!

Let's Mix It Up! (page 98)

Hot plus cold equals warm, right? But how warm? When mixing equal amounts of hot and cold water, the temperature of the mixture will be about halfway between the starting temperatures of the hot and cold water. Mixing two cups of hot water with one cup of cold will result in a temperature one-third of the way between the hot and cold. The results may vary if the water or the temperature is not measured carefully, or if the hot or cold water is left standing too long. The hot water should be no more than 120°F (40°C), or less if your thermometers do not measure that high.

A Convection Spinner—What A Winner! (page 99)

Students can "see" convection currents caused by an everyday item—the light bulb! Have a student hold the spinner over an unlighted bulb. Discuss what happens. (There will be very little, if any, movement.) When the convection spinner is held over a lighted bulb, the spinner rotates because the air around the light bulb is heated and expands—becoming larger but not heavier. Cooler, heavier air displaces the warm air, forcing the warm air upward. This forcing up of the warmer air causes the spinner to spin. Students often incorrectly state that "heat rises." Challenge them to explain why heat from the sun comes "down." (Energy from the sun is *radiant energy,* which can travel through space in any direction. It changes into *heat energy* when it strikes an object.)

On The Rocks (page 100)

How fast will ice cool water? During the experiment, students will discover that after an ice cube has been added to water, the water will cool rapidly for the first few minutes, and then at a decreasing rate. If students use a larger cup of water, or two ice cubes, encourage them to draw another line on the same graph for comparison. Have them label each line to show which experiment it represents. Will twice as much water cool by half as much? Will it cool more slowly? Will the ice melt faster? Encourage students to be specific in their predictions, observations, and conclusions.

The Heat's On! (page 101)

Ask students why they wear light-colored clothing in the summer and darker colors in the winter. They'll discover firsthand when performing this group activity. Divide the class into groups of three to four students each. Give each group a piece of colored construction paper or aluminum foil to cut and fit to the bottom of its container. Have students seal their containers with plastic wrap, tape, and rubber bands as securely as they can. It's okay if the tops of the thermometers protrude from the containers. Make sure that the students read the temperatures before, or immediately after, opening the containers. The black and blue containers should have the highest temperatures, while the white and the aluminum foil ones the lowest. There are many variations for this experiment. As an extension, allow motivated students to design their own experiments and share them with the class.

The Great Ice Cube Contest (page 102)

Bring out the scientific creativity in your students with ice cube contests. Who knows—you just may have a future energy whiz in your midst! Give students equal-sized cubes in plastic cups (or divide the class into groups of two to four and give each group an ice cube in a cup). Students may use body heat or sunlight to melt their ice cubes. The ice cubes melt faster if brought into contact with a warm surface, demonstrating *conduction.* Remind students that artificial sources of heat (light bulbs, heat vents, radiators, etc.) cannot be used.

Provide the suggested materials, in equal quantities, for each group to use with the ice-cube keeper activity. Suggest that students bring materials from home that they would like to use. Materials that will keep the ice from melting the longest are *insulators.* Foil will quickly conduct heat and melt the ice, but it may be useful around the outside of the cup to reflect heat.

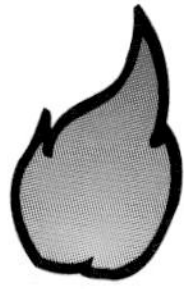

Looking for more ways to teach heat energy concepts? Energize your classroom with these activities. Use them as whole-class demonstrations, take-home assignments, center work, or experiments for small groups or individuals.

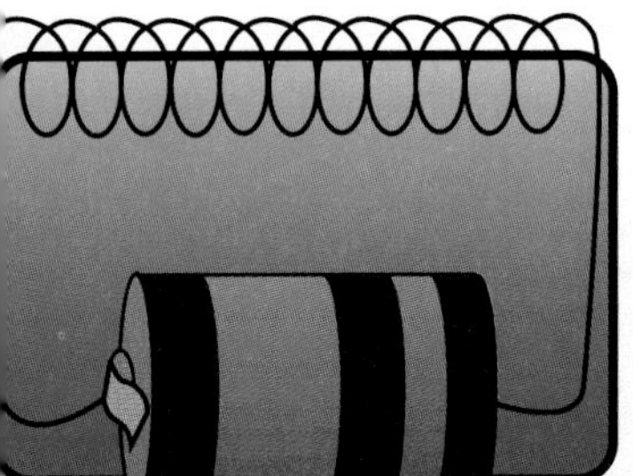

Electric energy can be converted into heat.

—Wrap a 30-centimeter piece of wire around a pencil to make a coil. Remove the pencil. Connect the two ends to a battery with electric tape. The wire will become warm. (**Do not** use a rechargeable battery.)

Heat causes expansion of solids.

—Hammer a large nail into an aluminum can. Remove the nail and heat it over a candle flame. Use pliers, a potholder, or another insulator to hold the nail. Then try to put the nail back into the hole. Heat causes the molecules in the nail to move faster and spread part. The nail is now too large to fit into its original hole.

—Stretch a wire between two solid supports. Hang a weight from the center of the wire. Measure the height of the weight. Heat the wire with a candle, moving the flame back and forth along the entire length of the wire to heat it evenly. The wire will expand, causing the weight to drop lower. Then measure the height of the weight. What is the difference between the two measures? When the wire cools, the weight will rise to its original position.

Heat causes expansion of a gas.

—Secure the opening of a balloon over the neck of a large bottle. Hold the bottle under hot running water. The balloon will inflate as the air molecules inside the bottle move faster and expand into the balloon.

—Put an inch of water into a quart or half-gallon *glass* bottle. Using clay or chewing gum, set a drinking straw into the top of the bottle so that the bottom of the straw extends into the liquid. Warm hands placed on the bottle will cause the air inside to expand, forcing the liquid up the straw.

Heat makes water molecules move faster.

—Fill two cups—one with hot and one with cold water. Allow them to stand briefly. Place a few drops of food coloring into each cup. The color will spread more quickly in the hot water because the water molecules are moving faster. The coloring in the cold water will drop to the bottom of the cup.

HOT COLD

Our senses of hot and cold are not reliable.

—In three small buckets, put cold, tepid, and warm water. Place one hand in the cold and the other hand in the warm water for one minute. Then place both hands in the tepid water. The water will feel cool to one hand and warm to the other. Thermometers are more reliable than our senses.

Name ______________________________ Experiment

Let's Mix It Up!

Can you predict the temperature you will get when you mix hot and cold water?

Materials: one large and two small cups (paper or plastic); thermometer; hot, cold, and warm water; pencil; clock or watch with a second hand

Procedure:

1. Pour the hot water into one of the small cups.
2. Pour an equal amount of cold water into the other small cup.
3. Find the temperature of the water in each cup and record it in the chart. (Leave the thermometer in the water for one minute before reading any temperature.)
4. Pour both the hot and cold water into the large cup.
5. What do you think the temperature of the mixture will be? Write your prediction in the chart.
6. Now find the actual temperature of the mixture.
7. Record the temperature in the chart. How close was your prediction?
8. Try the other combinations of hot, cold, and warm water listed in the chart. Each time, check and record the temperatures before you mix. Then record a prediction of the temperature of the mixture. Find the actual temperature to see how accurate your prediction was.

Temperatures before mixing		**Your predictions**	**Actual temperatures**
1. 1 cup hot: °	1 cup cold: °	°	°
2. 1 cup hot: °	1 cup warm: °	°	°
3. 1 cup cold: °	1 cup warm: °	°	°
4. 1 cup hot: °	2 cups cold: °	°	°
5. 2 cups hot: °	1 cup cold: °	°	°
6. 1 cup hot: °	2 cups warm: °	°	°
7. 1 cup cold: °	2 cups warm: °	°	°

Observations and conclusions:

1. How can you predict the actual temperature? ______________________________
2. Why might your predictions not always be accurate? ______________________________

 Note To Teacher: See page 96 for background information and possible results for this experiment.

Name ______________________________

A Convection Spinner—What A Winner!

What happens to air when it is heated?

Materials: spiral spinner (below), 25-cm piece of thread or lightweight string, toothpick, tape, heat source (light bulb or radiator), scissors

Procedure:

1. Cut out the spiral spinner on the **bold** line.
2. Punch a small hole through the center at the black dot.
3. Push one end of the piece of thread through the hole.
4. Tie this end of the thread to the middle of the toothpick.
5. Tape the toothpick to the back side of the spinner.
6. Hold the spinner about five centimeters above a heat source as shown. (**Do not** use a stove or an open flame for this experiment!)

Observations and conclusions:

1. What happened? ______________________________

____
2. Why did this happen? ______________________________

____

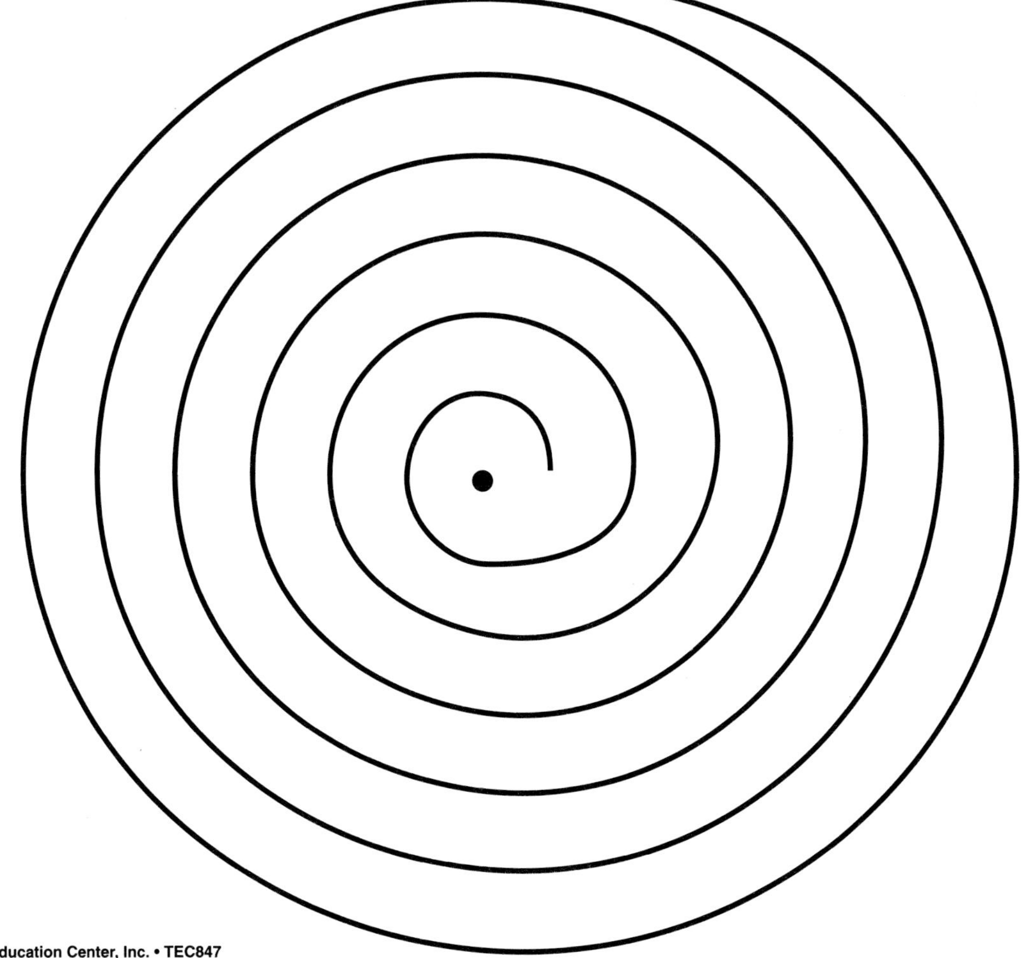

Note To Teacher: See page 96 for background information and results for this experiment.

Name____ Experiment

On The Rocks

What happens to the temperature of water when ice is added?

Materials: plastic cup, thermometer, water, ice cube, clock, pencil, ruler

Procedure:

1. Fill the cup about half full of water.
2. Record the water temperature: _____°
3. Put the ice cube into the water.
4. In the chart, record the temperature of the water every minute for 15 minutes. After the fifth minute, predict what you think the water's temperature will be after 15 minutes: _____°

Minute	Temperature
1	
2	
3	
4	
5	
6	
7	
8	
9	
10	
11	
12	
13	
14	
15	

When finished, use the information in your chart to make a line graph below:

5. Add a temperature scale on the left. If you used a Fahrenheit thermometer, number the scale 30° to 100°F, counting by tens. If you used a Celsius thermometer, label the scale 0° to 35°C, counting by fives. Begin in the bottom blank and count up.
6. To show the temperature at each minute, place a dot on the graph above the minute and even with the appropriate temperature.
7. Connect the dots, left to right, to create a line graph.

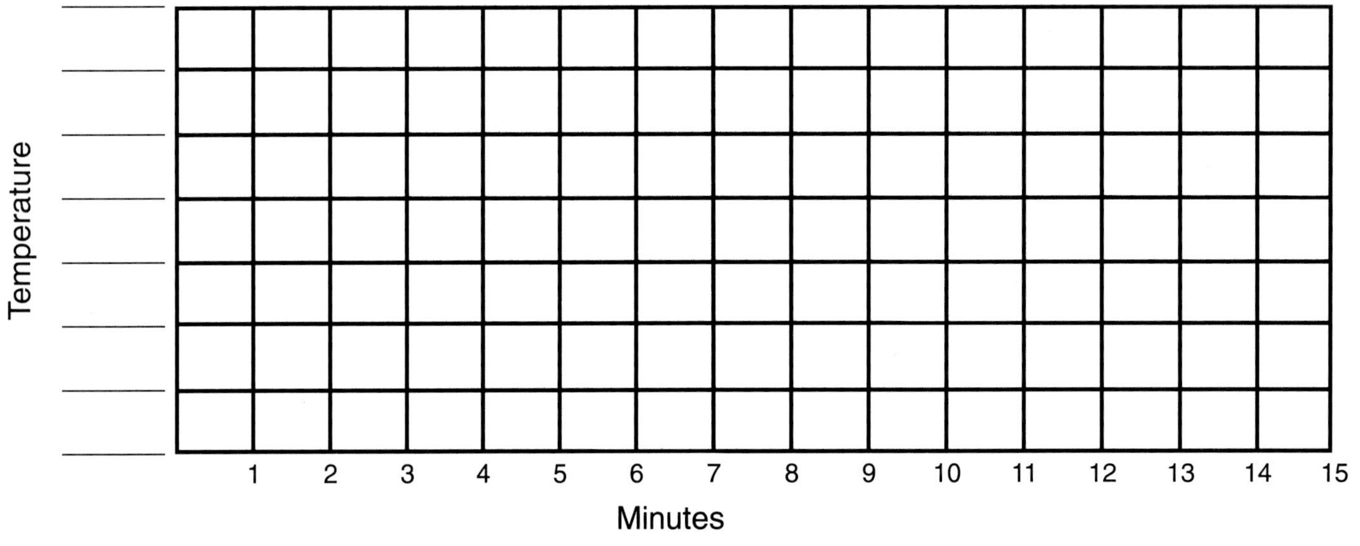

Observations and conclusions:

1. By how many degrees did the temperature of the water change? __________°
2. Did the water cool at a steady rate? _______________ Explain. ______________________________
____
3. What do you think would happen if you used a larger cup of water? ____________________
____
4. What do you think would happen if you used two ice cubes? ________________________
____

Bonus Box: Try the experiment again to answer question number 3 or 4 above. Chart and graph your information using a different-colored pen or pencil.

Note To Teacher: See page 96 for background information and results for this experiment.

Name ______________________________ Experiment

The Heat's On!

What color absorbs solar energy best?

Materials for each group: thermometer, plastic margarine tub or microwave container, clear plastic wrap, aluminum foil (for one group), construction paper (a different color for each of the other groups—see chart), scissors, tape, rubber bands, pencil

Procedure:

1. Cut the colored construction paper (or foil) to fit inside the bottom of the container.
2. Place the lower part of the thermometer in the container.
3. Use rubber bands or tape and clear plastic wrap to cover the top of the container tightly. The top of the thermometer can stick out.
4. Place the container, along with those of the other groups, in direct sunlight for 30 minutes.
5. Predict which colors will absorb the most solar energy. Record your predictions in the chart (1=hottest, etc.).
6. After 30 minutes, check the temperature of your group's container and write it in the chart.
7. Record the temperatures of the other containers in the chart also. Then complete the last column of the chart.

Color	Predicted rank (1=hottest, etc.)	Temperature (after 30 min.)	Actual rank (1=hottest, etc.)
white			
yellow			
black			
foil			
red			
blue			

Observations and conclusions:

1. Which colors absorbed the most solar energy? ______________________________

2. What ways can you think of to improve your solar energy collector? ______________________________

Note To Teacher: See page 96 for background information and results for this experiment.

Name ______________________________ Fun activity

The Great Ice Cube Contest—Part I

How fast can you make an ice cube melt?

Materials: one ice cube, plastic cup, clock or watch, pencil

Procedure:

1. Put the ice cube in the cup.
2. Note the time: ________. At a signal, try to make your ice cube melt as fast as possible. Remember:
   — You cannot break, cut, or crush the ice.
   — You cannot use any source of artificial heat (radiator, light bulb, etc.).

Observations and conclusions:

1. How long did it take your ice cube to completely melt? ___________
2. What method did you use? ______________________________
   ____
3. Did this method work well? _________ Explain. ______________________________
   ____
   ____
   ____

Name ______________________________ Fun activity

The Great Ice Cube Contest—Part II

How can you keep an ice cube *from* melting?

Materials for each group: ice cube, plastic cup, clock or watch, pencil, plastic wrap, foil, paper towels, cloth, styrofoam packing chips, and other materials provided by the teacher or students

Procedure:

1. Put your ice cube in the plastic cup. Note the time: ________.
2. Use any of the materials and invent a method that will keep your ice cube from melting.

Observations and conclusions:

1. How long did your ice cube last? ______________________________
2. Describe the method you used. ______________________________
   ____
3. On the back of this sheet, draw an illustration of your "ice-cube keeper."
4. How could you make a better ice-cube keeper? ______________________________
   ____
   ____

 Note To Teacher: See page 96 for background information and results for these two activities.

Home Sweet Home

Celebrating Earth Day

Our beautiful environment—clean water, healthy trees, fresh air. However, there is a disturbing side to our "home sweet home" as pollution, garbage, and other environmental problems continue to grow. On Earth Day—and every day—help students make a commitment to a brighter environmental future.

by Paula K. Holdren

- Get students thinking about ol' Mother Earth by using these questions as springboards for discussions: How do you and your family contribute to pollution? What do you suppose the land on which our school is built looked like 100 years ago? What will it look like 100 years from now? Why weren't people as concerned with dumps and landfills 100 years ago? What does *biodegradable* mean? Are more or fewer people using mass transit now? How would your life be different if your family didn't own a car? What is the difference between *sound* and *noise?* Why has pollution grown so much in the past century?

- "Don't throw it away—use it another way!" Spark students' imaginations with a fun art project. Have students bring in throwaway and recyclable items such as aluminum cans, bottles, paper tubes, Styrofoam® cups or containers, cartons, newspapers, etc. Challenge individuals or small groups to recycle these items into something new, useful, interesting, or decorative. Throw in some writing practice by having students write ads promoting and marketing their new creations.

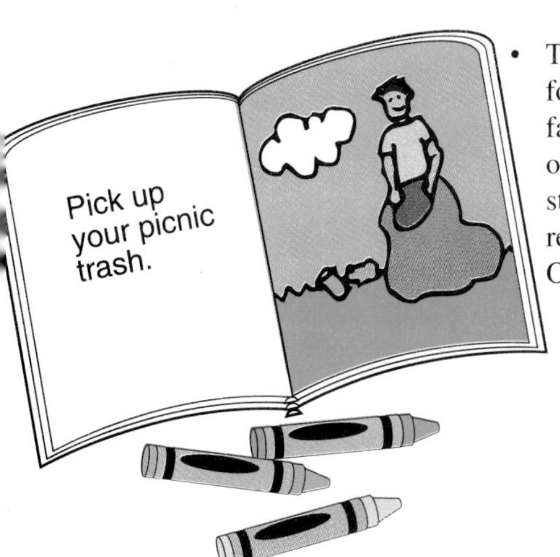

- Turn students into energy inspectors! As a class, develop an energy conservation checklist for students to take home for checking such items as water heater temperature, leaky faucets, unnecessary running of appliances, open fireplace dampers, drapes as insulators, and other energy savers or wasters. Duplicate the finished checklist; then send it home with each student. Encourage students to involve everyone in Earth Day by discussing the survey results with their families. (For another take-home survey, see "12 Ways To Save Our Ocean" on page 58 of this book.)

- Let students spread the word on good environmental practices by making coloring books to distribute to primary students. As a class, list actions which everyone can take to preserve our public forests and parks: picking up after picnics, not carving on trees, respecting wildlife, using fire wisely, etc. Have each student choose one statement and draw a simple picture to illustrate it. Make photocopies of the pictures; then have students assemble them into small booklets and add construction-paper covers.

- The first Arbor Day was held on April 10, 1872, in Nebraska. Have students research the history of Arbor Day and the importance the plains pioneers placed on tree planting. As a follow-up, contact your local Department of Natural Resources and request that a forester, conservation officer, or horticulturist visit your class. He or she can demonstrate proper tree planting and care, as well as discuss which trees grow best in your area. As a special tribute, arrange to plant an Earth Day tree in your schoolyard.

- "Only YOU can prevent forest fires." Students will easily recognize Smokey the Bear as the forest fire prevention symbol and Litter Bug as the mascot of the Anti-litter Campaign. Challenge students to design a mascot to be a spokesperson for recycling efforts. After selecting a winner from all entries, duplicate his or her picture on construction paper buttons for students to wear. Have students include your mascot on original posters to circulate throughout your school and community.

Nuts About

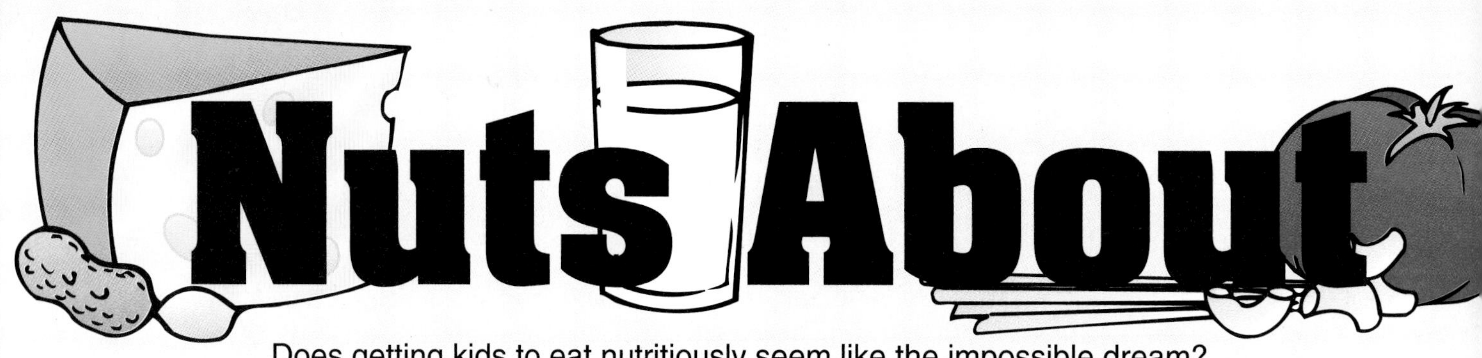

Does getting kids to eat nutritiously seem like the impossible dream? Increase students' nutrition knowledge with these appetizing activities and reproducibles.

by Mary Anne Haffner and Sue Ireland

Label Lingo

How does a consumer make wise choices when bombarded by such a huge variety of foods? One reliable tool is the food label. From it, shoppers can learn about a food's ingredients, nutritional makeup, how long it's been on a shelf, and the date by which it must be sold. Ingredients are listed in order—by weight—from the most to the least.

Have students bring in labels from their favorite packaged snack foods. Compare the ingredients. Which snacks are high in sugar? Instruct students to look for other forms of sugar, such as sucrose, maltose, lactose, dextrose, fructose, corn syrup, invert sugar, molasses, maple syrup, and honey. List snacks which give sugar as the first ingredient; then have students form conclusions as to which snacks are most nutritious. Brainstorm alternate snacks with low or no sugar. Graph the snacks according to sodium or fat content.

Nutrition News

Calcium, fiber, carbohydrates—these nutrients are making today's health headlines. Magazines and newspapers contain the latest news and research on a variety of nutrition topics. Have students clip and share information they find in current periodicals. Enlist a committee of interested students to arrange the clippings by topic in a notebook.

Nutrient Know-How

Good nutrition begins with nutrients, those nourishing food substances which help bodies function and grow. Divide your class into pairs. Assign each pair a specific nutrient such as protein, carbohydrate, fat, vitamin A, vitamin C, thiamine (B_1), riboflavin (B_2), niacin, calcium, iron, and fiber. Give each pair a file folder. Inside the folder, each pair makes a chart explaining the food sources and functions of the nutrient. Have children include magazine pictures and drawings in the folders. After decorating the covers, students place their folders at your science center.

Dynamic Dietary Duos

Most nutritionists recommend 3–5 servings from the vegetable group, 2–4 servings from the fruit group, 2–3 servings from both the milk and meat groups, and 6–11 servings from the bread group per day.

Let students become diet counselors by forming Dynamic Dietary Duos. Have students in each pair interview each other about food likes and dislikes. Using this information, each child designs a one-day food plan for his partner. The plan should include three meals and snacks, and fulfill the daily food group requirements. After partners present their personalized plans to each other, challenge students to follow them for one day. Discuss reactions to the plan later.

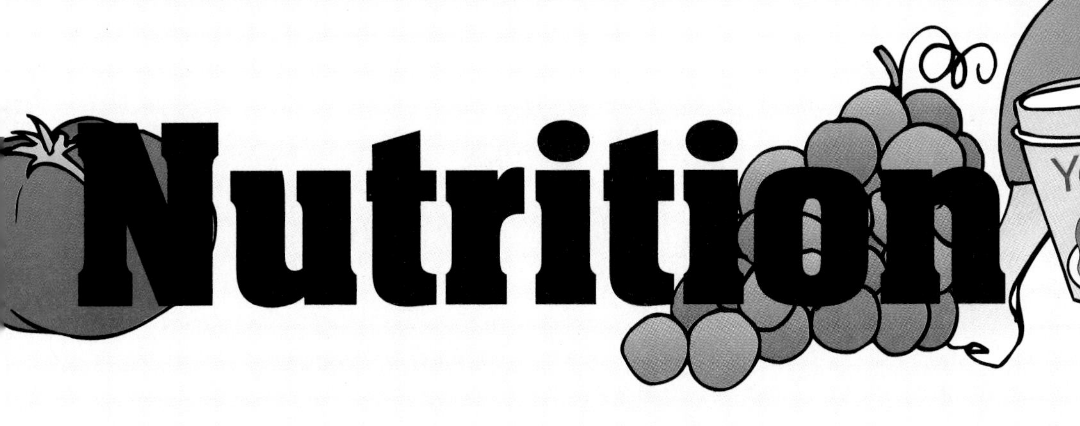

Menu Magic

Enjoy a smorgasbord of activities using menus from local restaurants. Duplicate the menus so students can feast on the following:

- Select two menus. Compare methods of food preparation, such as deep-fat frying, baking, boiling, roasting, stewing, broiling, or grilling. Which restaurant uses healthy methods more frequently? Write a paragraph giving your comparison and recommendation.
- You have been given $20 to take yourself and a friend to dinner. Choose a menu. Order two meals (one for you and one for your friend) which each include one item from each food group. Calculate your cost, including tax and tip. How much change will you receive?
- After reading through the menus, pretend that you are a restaurant manager. Prepare a short presentation to give to the class on "The Nutritious Guide To Eating Out."

The Food Guide Pyramid

The U.S. Department of Agriculture (USDA) and the Department of Health and Human Services (DHHS) have developed guidelines to teach people how they can improve their diets and their health at the same time.

The Food Guide Pyramid calls for eating a variety of foods to get the nutrients we need and, at the same time, the right amount of calories to maintain healthy weight. The pyramid emphasizes foods from the five major groups in the three lower levels; however, no group is more important than any other. For good health, we need them all!

Have students use the illustration as a guide in developing their own bulletin-board display of the Food Guide Pyramid.

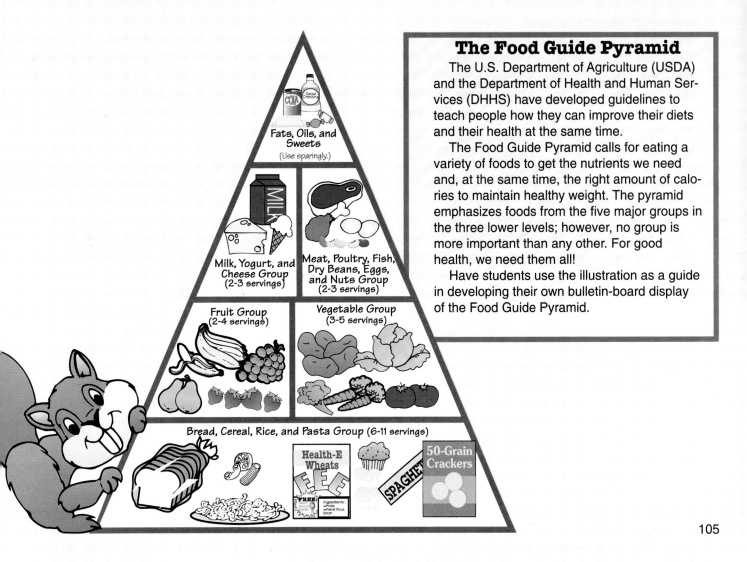

Fats, Oils, and Sweets (Use sparingly.)

Milk, Yogurt, and Cheese Group (2-3 servings)

Meat, Poultry, Fish, Dry Beans, Eggs, and Nuts Group (2-3 servings)

Fruit Group (2-4 servings)

Vegetable Group (3-5 servings)

Bread, Cereal, Rice, and Pasta Group (6-11 servings)

Bag It!

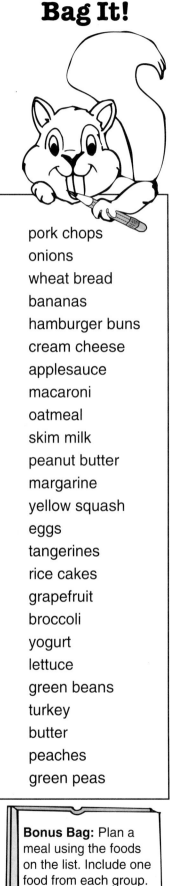

Nutritionists divide foods into six groups. Write each food on the shopping list on the correct bag.

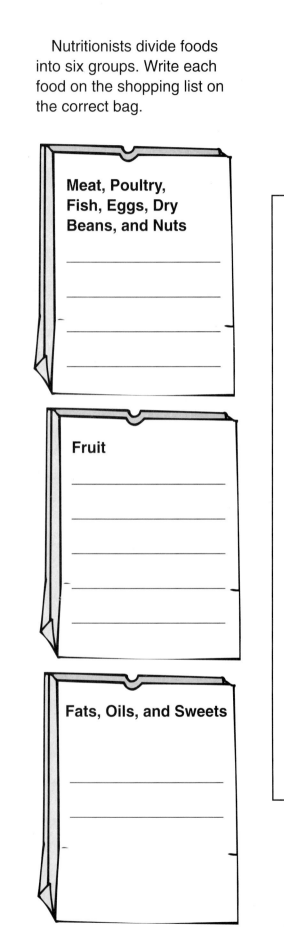

Meat, Poultry, Fish, Eggs, Dry Beans, and Nuts

____

____

____

____

Fruit

____

____

____

____

____

Fats, Oils, and Sweets

____

____

pork chops
onions
wheat bread
bananas
hamburger buns
cream cheese
applesauce
macaroni
oatmeal
skim milk
peanut butter
margarine
yellow squash
eggs
tangerines
rice cakes
grapefruit
broccoli
yogurt
lettuce
green beans
turkey
butter
peaches
green peas

Bonus Bag: Plan a meal using the foods on the list. Include one food from each group. Write your meal on the back of this sheet.

Vegetable

____

____

____

____

____

____

Bread, Cereal, Rice, and Pasta

____

____

____

____

____

Milk, Yogurt, and Cheese

____

____

____

Name ______________________________

The Nutrient College Of Knowledge

Whet your appetite for nutrient information! Use the chart to answer the questions. Write your answers on the back of this sheet.

Nutrient and Food Sources	Nutrient's Jobs
Carbohydrate: whole grains, breads, cereals, legumes, pasta, rice, fruits, vegetables	• Supplies best source of energy • Adds fiber to diet
Calcium: milk, cheese, yogurt, salmon, sardines, spinach, broccoli	• Builds and maintains strong bones and teeth • Helps nerves to function and blood to clot normally
Iron: lean meat, poultry, shrimp, liver, tofu, eggs, legumes, spinach, lima beans, dried fruit	• Helps build red blood cells • Helps cells turn food to energy • Increases resistance to infection
Protein: fish, poultry, lean meat, eggs, cheese, milk, legumes, peanut butter	• Helps build and repair body tissue • Helps form antibodies that fight infection • Supplies energy
Fat: vegetable oils, margarine, mayonnaise	• Supplies important fatty acids • Supplies energy

1. Which nutrients supply energy to your body?
2. Which foods are sources of both protein and calcium?
3. Dried fruit and tofu contain what nutrient?
4. What foods are sources of fat?
5. For lunch you ate a hamburger on a bun with lettuce, tomato, onion, and mayonnaise, plus drank a carton of milk. Which nutrients made up your meal?
6. Name a snack that includes at least two of the nutrients above. Identify the nutrients.
7. Athletes eat lots of carbohydrates before sporting events. This is called "carbohydrate loading." Why do you think athletes do this?
8. Design a meal that would help an athlete "carbohydrate load."
9. Name four foods which supply fiber to your diet.
10. Use the chart's information to write your own definition of *nutrient.*
11. What foods would your dentist recommend that you eat regularly?
12. What nutrient aids blood clotting?

Bonus Box: Vitamins A, C, D, B_1, B_2, and B_{12} are missing from the chart. Do research on one of the vitamins to find out its jobs and food sources. Circle any foods on the chart that contain the vitamin.

Name ____

Food For Thought

Use the words in the Word Bank to complete the puzzle.

Word Bank

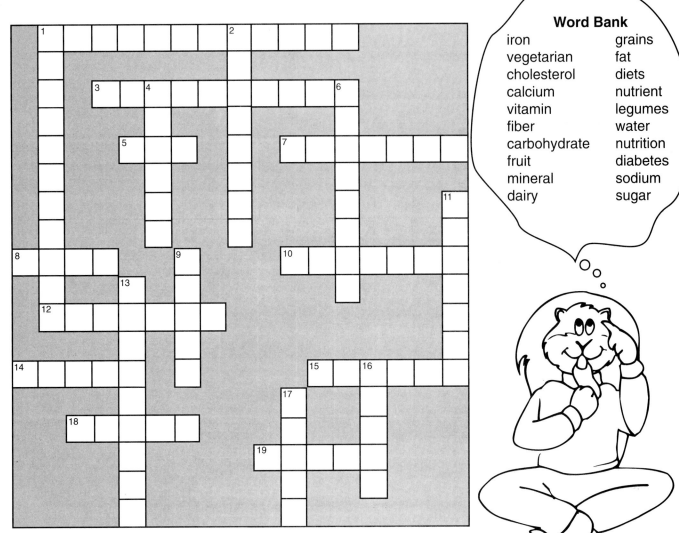

iron	grains
vegetarian	fat
cholesterol	diets
calcium	nutrient
vitamin	legumes
fiber	water
carbohydrate	nutrition
fruit	diabetes
mineral	sodium
dairy	sugar

Across:

1. nutrient that provides fuel for body
3. person who eats no meat
5. nutrient that provides fatty acids
7. nutrient needed by body in small amounts
8. nutrient that helps build red blood cells
10. Iron is an example of this nutrient.
12. dried peas and beans
14. also known as "roughage"
15. a mineral in salt
18. the most important nutrient
19. sweet substance

Down:

1. Too much can lead to heart disease.
2. disease in which body can't absorb normal amounts of sugar
4. wheat, rice, oats
6. substance needed by body to grow and function
9. A dietitian plans meals or __________.
11. builds strong bones and teeth
13. study of nutrients
16. another name for milk products
17. apples, grapes, bananas

Bonus Box: Make a list of appliances that help in food storage and preparation. Can you list 12 or more?

Name ____ Nutrition: reading a graph, math word problems

Walk It Off!

Exercise can "burn off" extra calories from snacking. An easy way to exercise is walking. It requires no special training or equipment, just the right type of shoes. The graph below will show you how long it takes to burn extra calories if you walk three miles per hour.

Pizza—1 slice (185 calories)												
Apple—1 medium (80 calories)												
Doughnut (150 calories)												
Peanuts—20 nuts (120 calories)												
Popcorn—1 cup plain (25 calories)												
Potato chips—15 chips (172 calories)												
Ice cream—1 cup (270 calories)												

0 5 10 15 20 25 30 35 40 45 50 55 60

Number of Minutes of Walking To Burn Off Calories

1. Color the graph to show the number of minutes of walking needed to burn off the calories: pizza = 36, apple = 16, doughnut = 29, peanuts = 23, popcorn = 5, potato chips = 34, ice cream = 54.

Answer these questions on the back.

2. Which foods take less than a half hour to burn off?
3. Which would take longer to burn off, two slices of pizza or one cup of ice cream with 20 peanuts on top? How much longer?
4. Using the number of minutes for one doughnut, about how many calories does walking burn off in one hour?
5. You walked for one hour. What snacks above could you have eaten that would be burned off in that amount of time?
6. How many minutes would you have to walk to burn off five cups of popcorn?
7. How many calories are in 60 peanuts? How long must you walk to burn off those calories?
8. You ate three cups of popcorn with one tablespoon of margarine (100 calories). How many calories in all?
9. Approximately how many minutes would you walk to burn off 30 potato chips?
10. Why do you think biking burns more calories than walking?

Bonus Box: On the back of this sheet, write directions that describe how to keep your body in shape.

Name ______________________________

Nutrition Mission

Color each flight plan as you complete the activity.

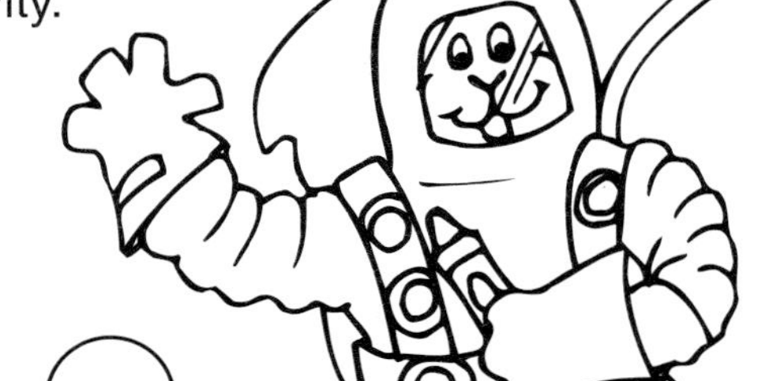

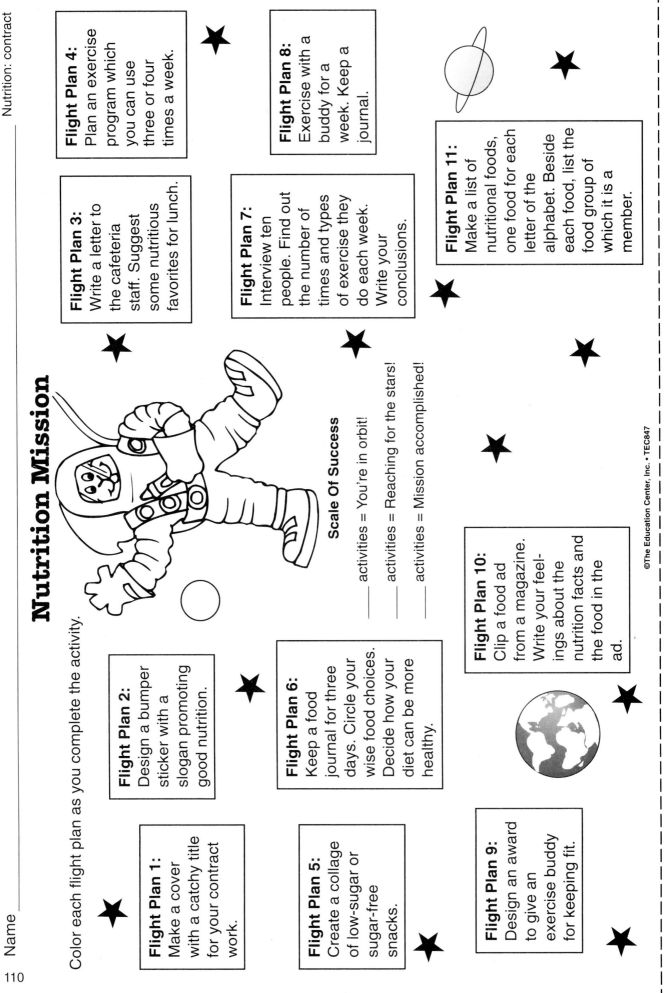

Flight Plan 1:
Make a cover with a catchy title for your contract work.

Flight Plan 2:
Design a bumper sticker with a slogan promoting good nutrition.

Flight Plan 3:
Write a letter to the cafeteria staff. Suggest some nutritious favorites for lunch.

Flight Plan 4:
Plan an exercise program which you can use three or four times a week.

Flight Plan 5:
Create a collage of low-sugar or sugar-free snacks.

Flight Plan 6:
Keep a food journal for three days. Circle your wise food choices. Decide how your diet can be more healthy.

Scale Of Success

____ activities = You're in orbit!

____ activities = Reaching for the stars!

____ activities = Mission accomplished!

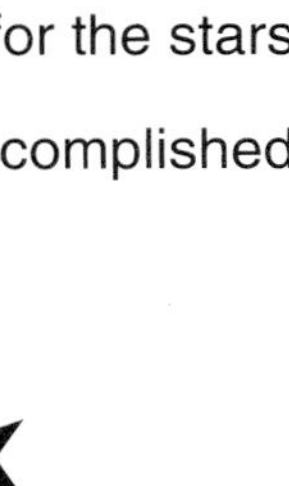

Flight Plan 7:
Interview ten people. Find out the number of times and types of exercise they do each week. Write your conclusions.

Flight Plan 8:
Exercise with a buddy for a week. Keep a journal.

Flight Plan 9:
Design an award to give an exercise buddy for keeping fit.

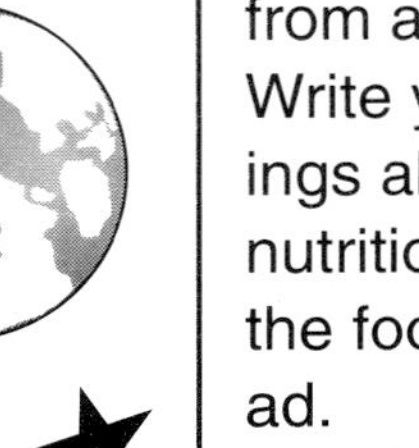

Flight Plan 10:
Clip a food ad from a magazine. Write your feelings about the nutrition facts and the food in the ad.

Flight Plan 11:
Make a list of nutritional foods, one food for each letter of the alphabet. Beside each food, list the food group of which it is a member.

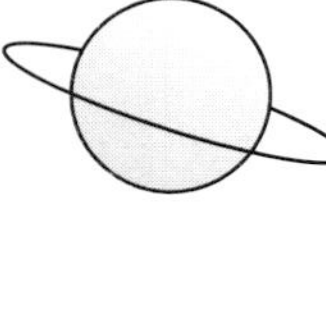

Note To Teacher: Before duplication, fill in the required number of activities for each level of achievement.

...5...4...3...2...1...

Blast Off!

Hands-On Activities For Junior Astronauts

"How does a rocket get into space? What do I have to do to become an astronaut?" Kids of the space shuttle era have a natural curiosity about space travel. Use the following activities and reproducibles to turn your classroom into a miniature space camp—all ready for its first batch of recruits!

by Bill O'Connor

Background For The Teacher

What could be more fun than flying space vehicles, piloting a shuttle, or drifting weightless in orbit? An astronaut's career is exciting, but it's much harder work than it sounds. Becoming an astronaut means many hours of special training. Educational requirements are high, but they are not the only important qualification. The abilities to do well at new tasks, get along with others, and work well as part of a team are equally important. All of these qualities are considered when men and women apply to become astronauts.

Setting Up Space Camp

Teamwork, new science concepts, simulations, and fun are components of this miniature space camp. These exciting, hands-on experiences are designed for easy classroom setup. Enlist the help of student and parent volunteers to gather materials for the stations. Divide your class into teams of three to five "astronaut trainees" each to rotate through the stations. Duplicate the checklist on page 113 for each student to record his results. Reproduce the Certificate of Graduation, also on page 113, to award students for participation in the Space Camp.

Balloon Me To The Moon

It'll never get off the ground! Just how *does* a rocket, loaded with 30 tons of cargo, get up into space? To observe the simple principle of *thrust* (see below), thread one-half of a plastic drinking straw onto a 15-foot, lightweight string. Tie each end of the string to the back of a chair. Move the chairs apart until the string is taut. Slide the straw to one end. Give each student an identical balloon. In turn, each team member blows up his balloon, keeping the opening securely pinched. The student holds the balloon under the midpoint of the straw, so that its opening faces the nearest chair. A teammate then drapes a five-inch piece of tape over the middle of the straw, so that the balloon is secured to the straw. When ready, the student releases the balloon. Teammates measure how far the balloon and straw travel down the string, and the student records the distance on his checklist.

(Overcoming gravity is the biggest obstacle in getting into space. A rocket produces a pushing force, called thrust, *to overcome gravity. Fuel burns in a combustion chamber and creates rapidly expanding gas that presses out in all directions inside the rocket. The pressure of the gas against opposite sides of the rocket is balanced. The gas flowing to the rear of the rocket escapes through a nozzle. Since this exhaust gas does not balance the pressure of gas against the front of the rocket, the uneven pressure drives the rocket forward.)*

Station 2

Coordination Station

What does a gigantic water tank have to do with astronaut training? Future astronauts carry out operations they expect to perform in space in such a tank, simulating weightlessness. Use a plastic tub filled with water (over half full) to simulate these conditions. Into the tub, place five various sizes of nut-and-bolt pairs, spreading them on the bottom. Each team member takes turns and tries to match each bolt with its corresponding nut, using *one* hand only. The student should screw the nut onto the bolt far enough so that the two are even, ensuring a correct match. Each student is timed by a teammate.

Station 3

"Lite" Food

Have you ever seen astronauts trying to eat their food as it floats around due to weightlessness? Students will enjoy trying to eat miniature marshmallows in free-fall! At this station, provide each student with ten marshmallows. A team member tosses his marshmallows in the air above his head, one at a time, and tries to catch them in his mouth. The student then tallies his score, earning one point for each on-target marshmallow.

(Food on any space flight must be nutritious, easy to eat, and easily stored. The space shuttle orbiter has a galley attached to the wall of the mid-deck alongside the main hatch. It is a combination kitchen, food storage area, water dispenser, and pantry. One crew member prepares food for all the crew. The crews even use dishes and silverware!)

Station 4

A Docking In Space

Astronauts must rendezvous with satellites moving at high speeds in orbit. How well can your students pilot their spacecraft to dock with a moving satellite? Use a coat hanger to make a loop to represent a satellite. Hang it from the ceiling with a piece of string. Pull it far to one side and let it make a complete swing (or "orbit"). Each student tries to toss a tennis ball or beanbag underhand through the moving hoop, as it swings back. Allow three opportunities.

Station 5

Emergency!

Astronauts are trained to respond quickly to any emergency. Suppose there was a power failure on board or the spacecraft began to spin out of control. Both of these emergencies have happened during spaceflights! Make a simple "control panel" out of oaktag. Draw five circles (two red, two black, and one green) having a diameter of five centimeters each. The circles should be ten centimeters apart and labeled as shown to represent buttons. Tape the control panel to a wall, at student eye level. Explain to the astronaut trainee that his spacecraft is spinning out of control and power is failing. He or she must press the "altitude control" button in order to stabilize the craft. The student's teammates then spin the trainee around (not too fast) about ten times, and stop when he or she is facing the control panel. A teammate places a piece of black paper in front of the trainee's eyes and shouts, "Blackout!" Can the trainee hit the right button without looking? The green button scores ten points, black five, and red zero.

(This activity simulates the disorientation that astronauts can experience in weightlessness. It may be a good idea for the teacher or another adult to supervise this station. Make sure that teammates offer support if the trainee becomes dizzy. And don't try the activity immediately following lunch!)

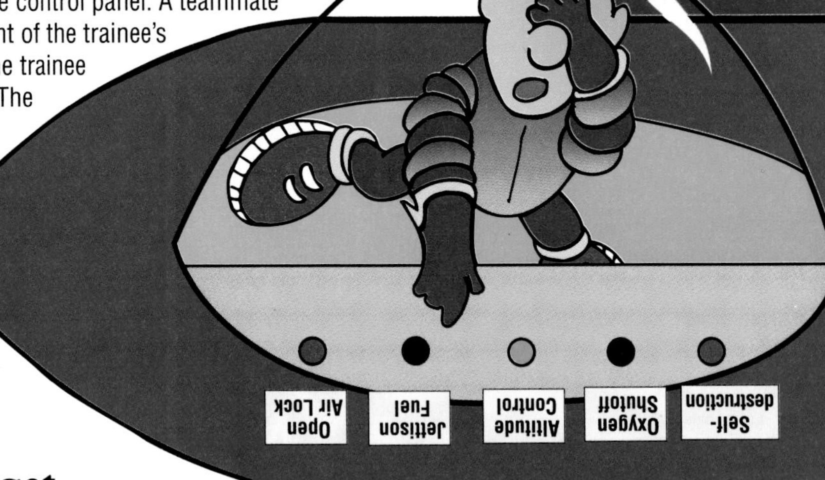

Station 6

On Target

The space shuttle lands with no engine power, much like a glider. Use masking tape to mark a 1 m X 2 m rectangle on the classroom floor to represent the landing strip. About five meters from one of the narrow ends, mark a starting line. Each team member makes a paper airplane. He then stands behind the starting line and tries to glide the airplane for a landing within the rectangle. Award ten points for a landing entirely within the rectangle and five points if the plane hits any part of the rectangle. Allow three opportunities for each trainee.

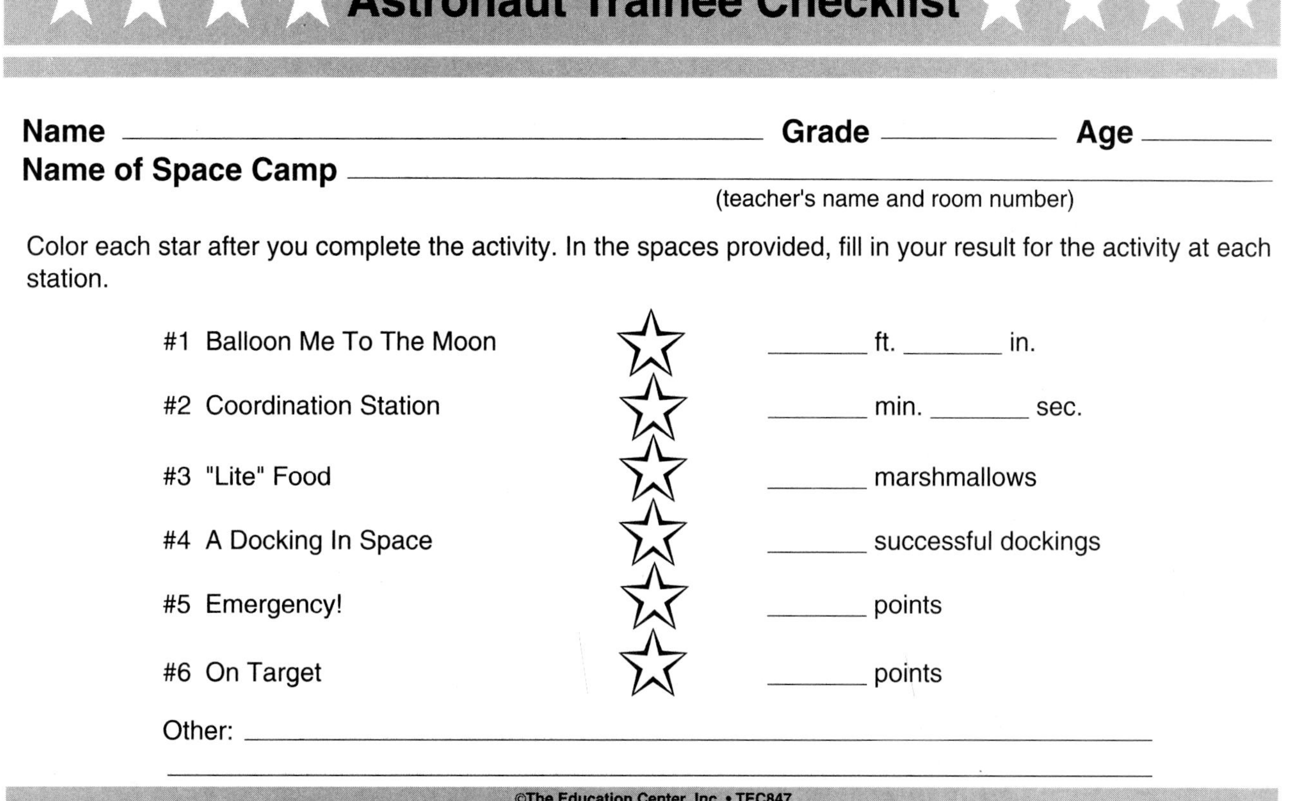

Astronaut Trainee Checklist

Name ______________________ **Grade** __________ **Age** ________

Name of Space Camp ______________________________

(teacher's name and room number)

Color each star after you complete the activity. In the spaces provided, fill in your result for the activity at each station.

#1 Balloon Me To The Moon	☆	_______ ft. _______ in.
#2 Coordination Station	☆	_______ min. _______ sec.
#3 "Lite" Food	☆	_______ marshmallows
#4 A Docking In Space	☆	_______ successful dockings
#5 Emergency!	☆	_______ points
#6 On Target	☆	_______ points

Other: ______________________________

Certificate of Graduation

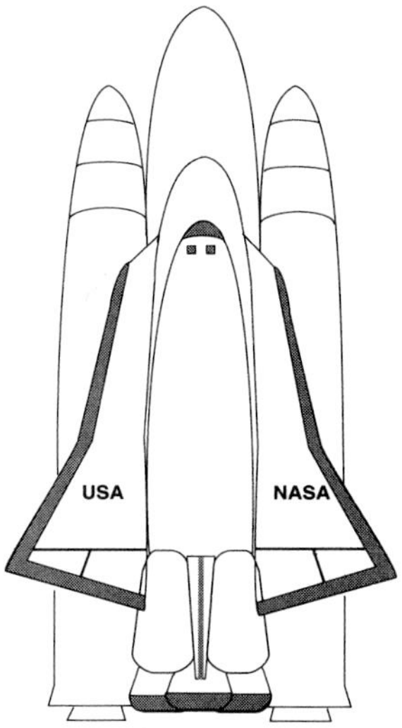

awarded to

____

for completion of all requirements to become a Junior Astronaut.

Astronaut Space Camp

USA NASA

____

Space Camp Director

____

Date

Note To Teacher: Duplicate the Astronaut Trainee Checklist to use with the activities on pages 111–112. Use the Certificate of Graduation to award students for participation in the Space Camp.

Name ______________________________

✯ Your Mission: *Research!* ✯

Congratulations! You have been selected to travel on an expedition to

______________________ .
(planet or moon)

To prepare for your expedition, you must find out as much as possible about this destination, so that you'll know what to expect when you land. Use current resources to find information about your planet or moon.

1. Distance from the sun (include units): ______________________
2. Diameter (include units): ______________________
3. Orbital period (length of a year in earth-days): ______________________
4. Describe the atmosphere: ______________________
5. Average temperatures (include scale used): ______________________
6. How many moons or rings (if any) are in this planetary system? ______________________
7. How and when was your destination discovered? ______________________
8. How did it get its name? ______________________
9. Has a spacecraft ever visited this planet or moon? If so, which spacecraft, and in what year? ______________________
10. List three interesting facts about your planet or moon. ______________________
11. Do you think a human colony could survive on this world? Explain. ______________________

Note To Teacher: For cooperative learning, assign each team of astronaut trainees a planet or moon in the solar system to research. Or, if preferred, allow each child to choose a planet or moon to study independently.

Name ______________________

Rocket Science (In One Easy Lesson!)

A rocket is the simplest and most powerful kind of heat engine. But how does it escape the earth's gravity? Read the following information about rockets; then answer the questions below.

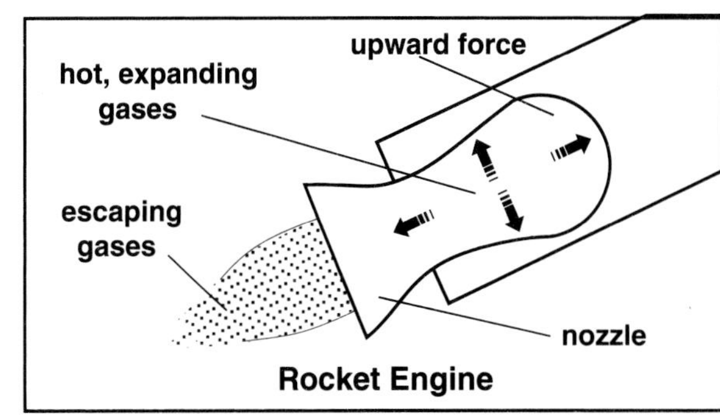

Rocket Engine

A rocket is very different from an airplane. Air passing under its wings lifts an airplane. Engine *thrust* is what lifts a rocket. An airplane engine uses oxygen from the air in burning its fuel. A rocket carries a chemical called an *oxidizer* to do the job. That is why a rocket can fly in space where there is no air.

When a rocket engine ignites, the fuel and oxidizer burn to create hot gases. The gases expand inside the engine and push in all directions. The gases push on the upper part of the rocket motor. This causes an upward force, or push, on the rocket. But the hot gases escape through the bottom, so there is no downward force on the rocket. If the upward force is strong enough, the rocket lifts off.

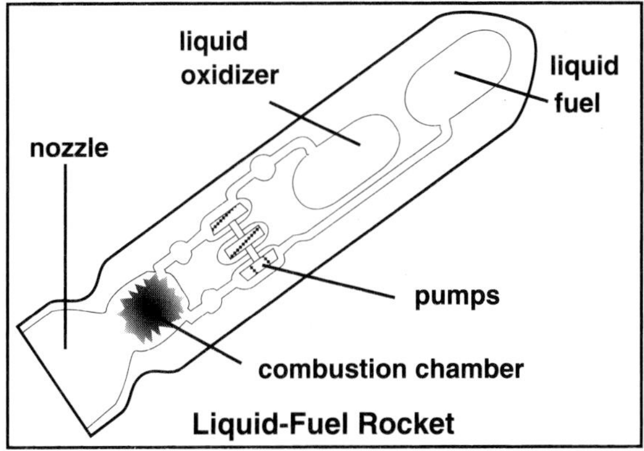

Liquid-Fuel Rocket

Some rockets use liquid fuel and liquid oxidizer. These are kept in separate tanks and pumped into the rocket engine. The space shuttle's main engines use liquid hydrogen as fuel and liquid oxygen as the oxidizer. These liquids are very cold and must be put into the tank just before lift-off. Liquid-fuel rockets can be controlled, stopped, or restarted. But liquid fuels may also explode.

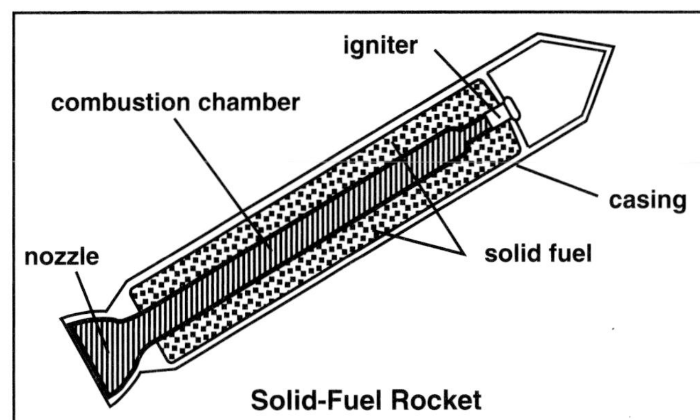

Solid-Fuel Rocket

Some rockets use solid fuel. The fuel and oxidizer are mixed together into a rubbery substance. The solid fuel can be put into the rocket months in advance. This mixture burns up inside the rocket. Solid-fuel rockets are very powerful but cannot be turned off or controlled once they are ignited. The space shuttle boosters are solid-fuel rockets.

1. What two substances does a rocket need to work? ______________________
2. Why does an airplane need air to fly? ______________________
3. What are the advantages of a liquid-fuel rocket? ______________________
4. What are the advantages of a solid-fuel rocket? ______________________
5. What makes the force of a rocket engine? ______________________
6. What is one disadvantage of liquid fuel? ______________________

Name ______________________________

Space Math

Gravity is the force that attracts an object in space to another object. Your weight on Earth is an effect of the Earth's gravity on your body. Did you know that the force of gravity is different on other planets, the sun, and the moon?

Multiply your weight by each gravity factor listed in the chart below. You may multiply by the decimal or the fraction. Round the product to the nearest whole number. Your answer tells how much you would weigh on that particular world. Write your answers in the last column.

My weight on Earth is ________________ pounds.

Place	Gravity Factor	My Weight
1. Mercury	0.38 or 3/8	
2. Venus	0.91 or 9/10	
3. Mars	0.38 or 3/8	
4. Jupiter	2.5 or 2 1/2	
5. Saturn	1.07 or 1 1/14	
6. Uranus	0.93 or 14/15	
7. Neptune	1.2 or 1 1/5	
8. Pluto	0.03 or 1/33	
9. Earth's moon	0.16 or 1/6	
10. Sun	27.8 or about 28 times	

After completing the chart, answer the following questions:

1. Which planets have about the same surface gravity as the Earth? ________________

2. What can you tell about Pluto from its gravity? ________________

3. How do you think the gravity of Jupiter would affect any astronauts who might land there?

Bonus Box: To change pounds to kilograms, you multiply by 0.45. Change all the weights above to kilograms.

Name ______________________________ Experiment

A Spacelab Experiment: Which Way Is Up?

Space Seeds
Day 1
Day 2
Day 3
Day 4
Day 5

On earth, the roots of plants grow down and the stems grow up. What would happen in space, where there is no "up" or "down"? Try the following experiment to find out.

Materials:

two 10 cm X 10 cm cardboard squares
paper towels
plastic wrap
radish seeds that have been soaked overnight
dish or plastic tray
water
pencil
marker

Procedure:

1. Fold two paper towels so that they will fit onto the cardboard squares.
2. Wet each towel and place it on a square.
3. Place five radish seeds on each towel, spacing them out evenly.
4. Wrap the squares with plastic wrap. Fold the wrap securely on the back side, so that you can see the seeds on the front.
5. With a marker, label one square "gravity." Label the other "space."
6. Stand the squares up in a dish or plastic tray. Answer questions 1 and 2 below.
7. Each day, give the square labeled space a 90-degree turn. (By doing this, gravity will act evenly on the seeds in four directions.)
8. Make drawings of the squares each day, showing how the seeds are sprouting.
9. After the fifth day, answer question 3.

Questions:

1. Each day, the space seeds' square will be turned 90 degrees. What do you think will happen to these seeds? ______________________________
____
____
____
2. What do you think will happen to the seeds labeled gravity, which will not be turned? ______________________________
____
____
3. After five days, what is the difference between the gravity seeds and the space seeds? ______________________________
____
____

Gravity Seeds
Day 1
Day 2
Day 3
Day 4
Day 5

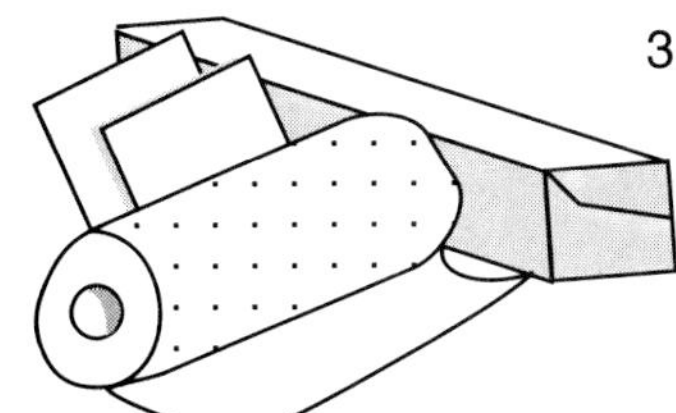

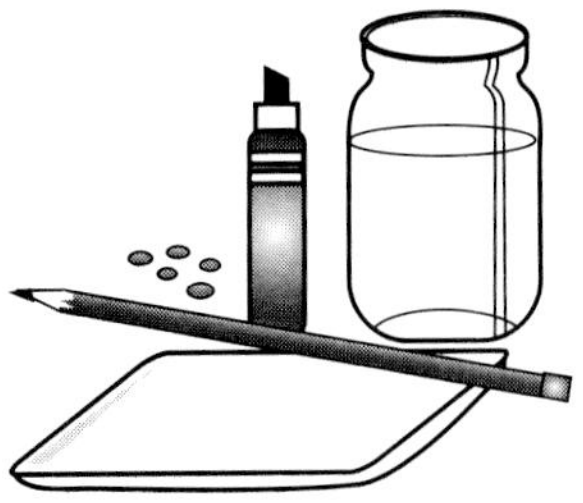

Note To Teacher: If possible, soak the radish seeds on Sunday and begin the experiment on Monday. In step 7, demonstrate for students how to turn their squares clockwise 90°.

Saying No To Drugs and Alcohol

by Melissa Matusevich and Becky Andrews

It's a harsh reality, but the fact is that pressure to experiment with drugs and alcohol is reaching young people at earlier ages than ever before. Here are some facts from the American Council for Drug Education:

- America's youth are concerned about drugs. The highest concern is among fifth and sixth graders: 61.4%.
- By the time children are in the fourth grade, 40% feel pressured by their friends to smoke cigarettes, 34% feel pressured to drink wine coolers, and 24% say that they have been encouraged by their friends to try cocaine or crack.
- Most students (93%) in grades 4–6 know that cocaine or crack is a drug. But less than half of these students call beer, wine, or liquor a drug.
- One out of three sixth graders say they feel pressured by their peers to use marijuana.

Elementary students are at an age when they can understand many adult topics yet will still accept guidance from teachers and parents. Teachers have an exciting opportunity to prepare students to battle the powerful, sometimes negative peer pressure they face every day.

And that means more than just dispensing facts about drugs and alcohol and the legal consequences of abusing them. Recent studies have shown that self-esteem plays a major role in preventing drug abuse. The following activities are designed to not only make students aware of the dangers of drug abuse but also build the self-respect that makes saying no possible.

What Is Drug Abuse?

Begin your unit by writing the following questions on the board:

Do you know what a drug is?
Do you know what drug abuse is?
Do you know anyone who abuses drugs?
Have you ever abused a drug?

After students have had a chance to ponder the questions, discuss their definitions of "drug." Explain that a drug can be any substance which affects the brain and body. Brainstorm a list of substances students would classify as drugs. Can a drug be good for one person, yet bad for another? Elicit the response that not all drugs are bad, but all drugs can be abused. (Experts define *drug abuse* as the nonmedical, harmful use of a mind-altering substance, which explains why alcohol is considered a drug.) At the end of the discussion, ask students if their answers to the questions have changed and how.

We're learning about drugs and drug abuse prevention.

Media Messages

Americans are bombarded with advertising which depicts glamorous people enjoying alcoholic beverages or finding relief with a variety of drugs. For a few days, have students list all the drug ads they see or hear and the locations of the ads (television, radio, billboards, city buses, newspapers, magazines). Be sure they include common drugs like aspirin, nasal spray, and cough medicine, and that they also keep track of antidrug messages. Discuss which occurred more frequently, anti- or pro-drug messages. Make a class graph of their findings.

Discuss the purpose behind most ads. Lead students to see that many ads appeal not to their good sense, but to their emotions and desires to be accepted or admired. Discuss how ads are different from public service announcements which give information.

I've Got A Question!

Accurate information can help children understand the good reasons not to start experimenting with drugs. Place a box on your desk in which students can deposit written questions they have about drugs, alcohol, or personal problems related to drug abuse. You can answer questions of a nonpersonal nature in class but will probably want to respond privately to more personal questions. If you encounter a serious problem, seek the help of your school nurse or guidance counselor, community drug hot line, or other area resources.

Having Fun Without Drugs

Kids often turn to drugs out of boredom or because they don't have any positive activities with which to fill the hours. As a class, brainstorm ways students can have fun without drinking or using drugs. Point out that one way to say no to a friend who wants you to try drugs is to suggest an alternate activity.

Divide the class into groups of three or four. Have each group make a mural showing its favorite fun activities. Be sure to share with students ways in which you spend your free time, too. Make this a year-round project by choosing one student a week to decorate a "Kids Just Want To Have Fun" bulletin board with photos and drawings of his favorite hobbies and fun activities.

There's More Than One Way To Say No!

Saying no isn't always simple, especially for the student who doesn't know how to refuse, longs to fit in with friends, or wants to feel smarter or funnier. Your students need help finding positive ways to say no. Discuss whether doing drugs or drinking really helps someone become more popular, smarter, or funnier. Does a "real" friend accept no for an answer? Cut out several speech bubbles from construction paper and program them as shown. Attach the bubbles to a small bulletin board entitled "There's More Than One Way To Say No!" After reading the serious and not-so-serious ways to say no, have each student cut out a speech bubble from white paper. The child labels it with his own "thanks, but no thanks" reply. Encourage creativity and originality. Display the replies on the board.

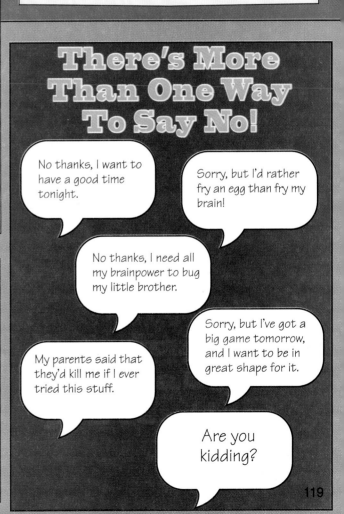

There's More Than One Way To Say No!

No thanks, I want to have a good time tonight.

Sorry, but I'd rather fry an egg than fry my brain!

No thanks, I need all my brainpower to bug my little brother.

Sorry, but I've got a big game tomorrow, and I want to be in great shape for it.

My parents said that they'd kill me if I ever tried this stuff.

Are you kidding?

They Reached For The Stars!

Building Self-Esteem

Wanting to say no may be more important than learning how to say no. According to recent research, a healthy self-respect appears to be a major reason why some kids decide to avoid drugs. Use these activities to foster self-esteem in your classroom:

- Let your students become their own publicity agents by creating "publicity packets." Give each student a large, manila envelope. The child fills his envelope with a self-portrait, biographical sketch, fact sheet telling about his favorite things, photographs of himself and his family, and any other information. After students decorate their envelopes, place the packets at a center for sharing.
- Cover a bulletin board with dark blue or black background paper. Add several poster-board stars covered with aluminum foil. Have students bring in magazine or newspaper articles about people who have met personal goals or overcome problems. Display these on the board with the title "They Reached For The Stars."

Involving Parents

Involve parents in your class's study of drug abuse. Duplicate the "Dear Parents" letter on page 121 to send home at the start of your unit. Parents in the health, legal, or volunteer services professions can also serve as valuable resource persons. Invite several resource persons from your community to speak to parents in your classroom after school. Try contacting local chapters of the American Bar Association, American Academy of Pediatrics, American Academy of Family Physicians, 4-H Clubs, and other community organizations. Parents will appreciate your efforts to help their children become responsible decision-makers.

What's The Smart Thing To Do?

Creative dramatics is a great way to help kids learn the skills of wise decision making. Have students role-play these situations:

- You're visiting a friend. His parents have gone to the store. He takes a beer from the refrigerator, begins to drink it, and asks you to have one, too. What do you do?
- You've just found out that your older sister has been to a party where some people were doing drugs. You think she tried the drugs, and you want to talk with her about it. What do you say?
- Your friend is having a lot of problems at home. Lately he is getting behind in school and seems to be avoiding his good friends. You suspect that he is using drugs to "help" with his problems. What do you do?
- You've finally been invited to a party given by the "coolest" kids in school. But now you hear that there's going to be drinking and drugs at the party. You really want these kids to like you, but you don't want to mess around with drugs or alcohol. What do you do?

Say NO To Drugs.

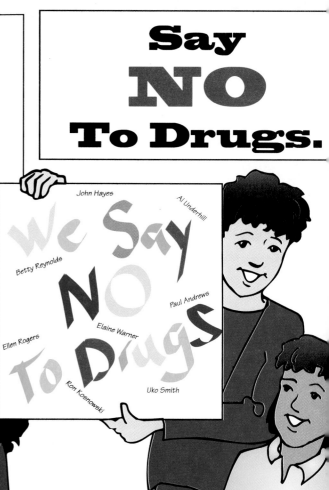

We Say NO To Drugs
John Hayes
Al Underhill
Betty Reynolds
Paul Andrews
Elaine Warner
Ellen Rogers
Ron Kosnowski
Uko Smith

Dear Parents,

Our class will soon begin a study of drug and alcohol abuse. Elementary children are at an age when they can understand adult topics yet are still willing to accept the guidance of parents and teachers. Providing accurate information, encouraging wise decision making, and exploring the reasons and ways to say no can help a child prepare to face the powerful force of peer pressure.

Recent studies have shown that self-esteem plays a major role in preventing drug abuse. Children who *want* to say no because they have a healthy sense of self-respect find it easier to face the inevitable peer pressure that comes with adolescence. Below is a list of things you can do to build self-esteem and help your child say no to drugs and alcohol.

- Praise your child often. And don't just praise achievements. Let your child know you are proud of her efforts as well as her accomplishments.

- Show your child that you love him. A hug, a touch on the shoulder, and saying, "I love you" help your child, no matter what age, feel good about himself.

- Give your child responsibilities at home. His self-esteem will grow as he sees himself accomplishing the tasks for which he's responsible. And feeling like part of a family team will help your child see himself as a valuable contributor.

- Give your child room to make mistakes. Offer guidance and help your child correct her error. Admitting that *you* make mistakes too will help her realize that nobody's perfect.

- When pointing out mistakes, criticize the action, not the child. Avoid saying, "I can't believe you don't have the sense to stay away from the road!" Instead say, "You could have been hurt playing so close to the road. I don't want you to do that again."

- Children with a strong sense of family usually have a good sense of self-confidence. With your child, plan activities to do together.

- And don't forget to talk with your child and listen to what she has to say. Don't make any topic off-limits. Your child needs to know that she can talk with you about whatever is on her mind. Communication is hard work, but the benefits can help ensure that your child will come to you with her problems.

Building your child's self-confidence isn't always easy. But you can make a difference in how your child will handle the peer pressure to experiment with drugs and alcohol. I hope these suggestions will be helpful.

Sincerely,

Name____

What Would You Do If…?

Directions:

1. Choose a situation slip below.
2. Cut out the slip and glue it to the top of a 12" x 18" piece of construction paper (see the example).
3. Write your decision on a large index card. Glue it under the situation slip.
4. On a white piece of art paper, draw a picture to illustrate your decision.
5. Glue your picture under the index card to complete your decision poster.

Example

Situation Slips: What would you do if…?

• you are having an allergy attack. Your parents aren't home, but you need your medication.
• on your way home from school, you find a small bag with marijuana in it.
• your uncle has been drinking beer and wants to drive you to baseball practice.
• you're at a party with your friends and someone offers you a wine cooler.
• your best friend tells you that he/she is having problems and thinks that getting high would help him/her feel better.
• you find an unopened can of beer, and you've always wondered what beer tastes like.
• at a friend's party, his/her father offers all of the kids some beer.
• your new friend tells you that if you don't try drugs like the rest of the gang, he/she won't be your friend anymore.
• while snooping in your sister's room, you find a half-empty bottle of liquor in a dresser drawer.

Note To Teacher: Provide each student with scissors, glue, a 4" x 6" index card, an 8 1/2" x 11" piece of white art paper, and a 12" x 18" piece of construction paper. After sharing their posters, have children hang them in a school hallway for other students to read.

Name ____

Know The Facts

Circle each number in the correct column. When you finish, add the circled numbers. Is the total 60?

When you're done, color the pencil topper. Cut it out on the dotted lines and slip it on your pencil.

		True	False
1.	All drugs can be harmful.	1	3
2.	Harmful effects of drugs can remain in your body long after you've stopped using drugs.	5	2
3.	Since alcohol is legal for adults, it is not dangerous.	7	1
4.	Drug abuse could lead to a jail term.	4	6
5.	Children's bodies can handle the effects of alcohol better than adults.	2	0
6.	Cocaine in any form (like "crack") can cause a heart attack and death.	8	3
7.	Sometimes people take drugs because they think it will help them deal with their problems.	1	5
8.	It is okay to refuse to ride with someone who is drunk.	9	6
9.	Beer is safer than wine or liquor.	8	3
10.	A wine cooler is just like fruit juice.	6	2
11.	Cigarette smoke has more cancer-causing elements than marijuana smoke.	8	1
12.	Even small amounts of alcohol can harm the brain and liver.	7	3
13.	Even one dose of some illegal drugs can cause brain damage.	4	5
14.	People who use drugs can endanger the lives of others.	6	0
15.	Alcohol doesn't have many calories and is not fattening.	2	8

Bonus Box: Many items sold at stores have warning labels to protect buyers from the dangers of misusing them. Design a warning label to go on the bottle of an alcoholic beverage or on an illegal drug.

 Key p. 175

A Real Friend Takes No For An Answer

Carl hurried down the sidewalk.

"Great! My little sister hides Dad's car keys and now *I'm* late for the biggest party of the year! I hope the gang won't be mad."

When he opened the door to Andrew's house, Carl could see that the party had already started. There was loud music coming from the stereo. Lots of kids were dancing or just sitting around. No adults were anywhere to be seen. Carl could also see that some of the kids were drinking beer and acting kind of goofy. Andrew walked up to him.

"Hey, buddy, where have you been? We got this party rolling a long time ago. Here, have a beer."

Carl hesitated. He was confused. He'd never been to a party like this one. All of a sudden he realized that some of his friends weren't there.

"Where are Mickey and Lisa and Carmine and Louis?" Carl asked.

"Oh, they left when they saw some of us drinking. Who needs those big babies anyway?" said Andrew. "Come on. Have a beer."

Carl thought for a few seconds. "No. I don't want any. And I don't think I want to be at this party either. I think I'll call my dad and ask him to come pick me up."

"Come on, Carl, drinking's not that big a deal. Everyone does it," said Andrew.

Carl replied, "Not everyone. And even if they did, that doesn't mean I have to. I've got better things to do with my time! Now, where's your phone?"

Answer these questions on the back of this sheet.

1. Do you think Carl did the smart thing? Why or why not?
2. How did Carl feel when he saw some of the other kids drinking? How would you have felt if you had been Carl?
3. Why do you think Andrew wanted Carl to have a beer?
4. Was Andrew being a good friend to Carl? Why or why not?
5. Was Carl being a good friend to Andrew? Why or why not?
6. Have you ever been in a situation like this? If so, how did you handle it?
7. A real friend will respect your decision to say no to drugs and alcohol. What are some other characteristics of a real friend?

Bonus Box: On another sheet of paper, write an ending to the story about Carl and Andrew.

Name ____

The Best Me I Can Be

There's no one quite like you! You're unique and special. But drugs and alcohol can keep you from being the best you can be.

Think of some things you would like to accomplish—either in the next year or when you are older. In each box, list the goal and one step you could take to reach it. On the lines below, explain how using drugs or alcohol would keep you from reaching each goal.

1. This year I'd like to ____.

I can work on this goal by ____.

2. This year I'd like to ____.

I can work on this goal by ____.

3. In the future, I'd like to ____.

I can work on this goal by ____.

4. In the future, I'd like to ____.

I can work on this goal by ____.

1. ____

2. ____

3. ____

4. ____

Note To Teacher: Help your students set realistic goals. Emphasize that the effort extended towards reaching a goal is just as important as achieving it.

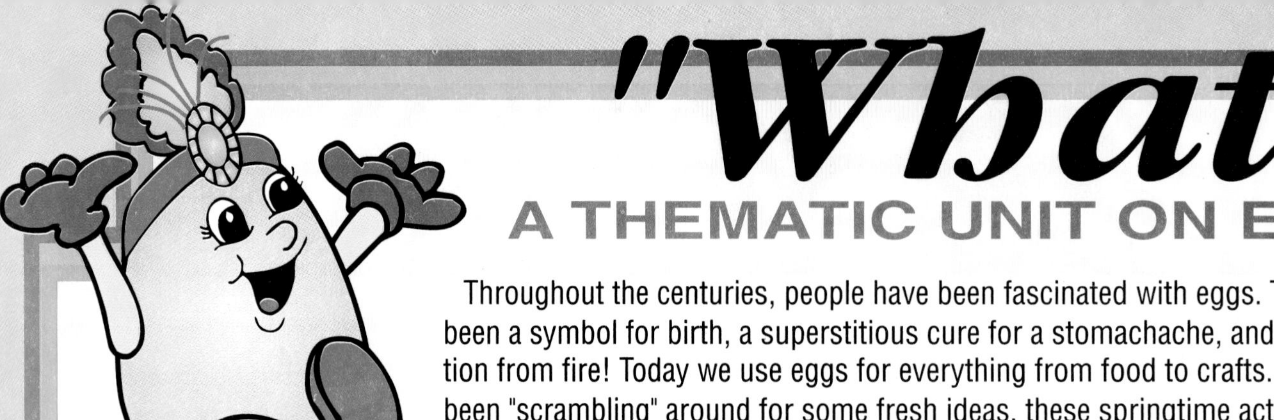

"What's

A THEMATIC UNIT ON EGGS

Throughout the centuries, people have been fascinated with eggs. The egg has been a symbol for birth, a superstitious cure for a stomachache, and even protection from fire! Today we use eggs for everything from food to crafts. If you've been "scrambling" around for some fresh ideas, these springtime activities might be "egg-zactly" what you're looking for!

by Janice Torrence

"Egg-spressions"

There are lots of sayings that incorporate the word *egg.* Brainstorm with students as many sayings as possible and discuss their meanings. List the sayings on a chalkboard. Then have each student choose one to illustrate, using eggs as the main characters. Don't forget these:

- He's a good egg.
- Don't put all your eggs in one basket.
- Last one in is a rotten egg!
- You're a real egghead!
- He has egg on his face.
- She's really walking on eggshells.

"Egg-splain" This!

Students will be amazed when an eggshell seems to disappear before their very eyes! Place a raw egg in a clear glass and weigh it down with a spoon. Cover the egg completely with vinegar. (Carbon dioxide bubbles will form, which means that the eggshell is beginning to dissolve.) Have students observe the egg for a day. The next day, gently lift the egg from the glass and let students touch it. The shell will be gone, leaving a soft, rubbery texture. The "egg-splanation" is simple: vinegar, which is a mild acid, dissolves the calcium carbonate shell.

"Eggs-amine" An Egg

A bird's egg has five main parts: the *shell*, the *shell membranes* (two thin white skins inside the shell), the *white*, the *yolk*, and the *germ*. The germ is a pinhead-sized spot on the upper surface of the yolk that is a little paler in color. Each part of an egg has a function. The germ is the part that is able to develop into an embryo, while the other parts provide food and protection for it. Crack an egg and identify the parts with your class. Although they have all seen an egg, your students probably haven't thought about it as a "package for life."

Bird Boutique

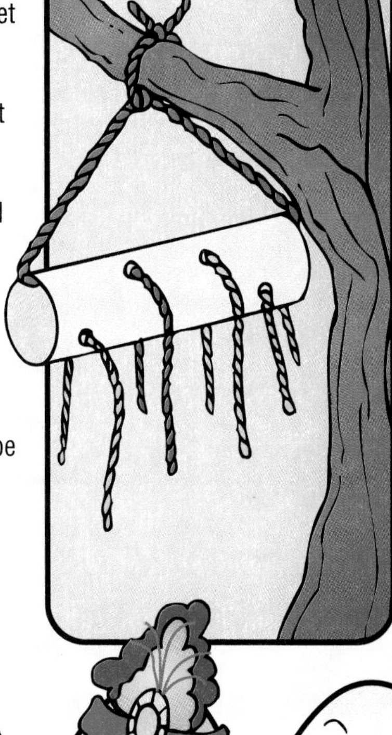

It's not only the season that kids get spring fever. Birds are also becoming restless to build their nests for laying eggs. You can encourage birds to nest nearby by making simple building supplies available. Have students use empty toilet paper tubes to make "Bird Boutiques." Instruct students to use scissors and carefully poke holes in their tubes. Then each student sticks pieces of yarn (about four inches long), cotton, string, and cloth scraps into the holes. He then loops a long piece of yarn or string through the tube and ties it to a tree branch. Birds will check out these "boutiques" to see what building materials they can use. Maybe they'll even thank you with a spring song!

Hatching?"

All Cracked Up?

Although the dome shape is basically strong, an eggshell itself is fragile. Cracked eggs cost farmers millions of dollars in lost sales. How can eggs be packaged so that there is little breakage during shipping? Try a cooperative project that puts students' inventiveness to the test. Divide the class into pairs. Then challenge each pair of students to design a container that will best protect an egg when dropped from a predetermined height. To culminate the project, hold an Egg Drop Day when students show off their completed containers. Have each student pair place an egg in its container, drop the container from the predetermined height, and check inside to see if the egg survived. Compare the different types of packaging used and the ones that worked best.

"Egg-straordinary" Strength

Just "eggs-actly" how fragile are eggshells? Two factors make an eggshell stronger than you might think: calcium carbonate and its dome shape. Have students predict the number of same-sized books that they think eggshells might support before breaking. Then, to find out, use a knife to crack two eggs into four equal-as-possible halves. Place the halves on a table in a square formation (see illustration). Then begin stacking books onto the shells.

The seemingly fragile shells can support a surprising amount of weight because the weight doesn't press down on one point. It travels from the curved sides of the eggshell down to the widest part of the dome. Thus the weight is shared by all points around each dome. The dome is one of our strongest shapes and is evident in many architectural designs.

The Amazing Egg

WINDOW INTO AN EGG

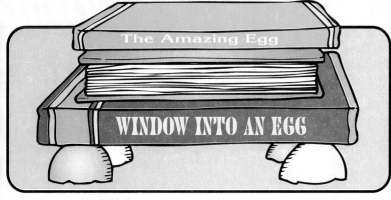

An "Egg-citing" Contest

Challenge students to perform an impossible feat: to roll an egg in a straight line! Students should experiment with hard-boiled chicken eggs. Because an egg is oval and narrower at one end, it tends to roll in a circle. (This shape is an advantage to birds. Several eggs fit neatly in a nest with their narrower ends pointing toward the center.)

How About An Egg Float?

Try a simple demonstration that explains why it's easier to swim in the ocean than in fresh water. Place a raw egg (in its shell) in a half-full glass of water. Have the class observe it. (The egg will sink.) Next slowly add table salt to the water and stir gently. You may need to add about 10–12 tablespoons of salt before the egg floats to the surface of the mixture. Why? Salt increases the density of water; the higher the density, the more buoyant the water becomes. Thus objects float on it more readily.

Grade-A Reading

Head to the library to check out these "egg-cellent" books:

Window Into An Egg by Geraldine Flanagan
Hatch! by Karyn Henley
Inside An Egg by Sylvia A. Johnson
The Amazing Egg by Robert M. McClung
The Enormous Egg by Oliver Butterworth
Rechenka's Eggs by Patricia Polacco
Chickens Aren't The Only Ones by Ruth Heller
Egg-drop Day by Harriet Ziefert
The Baby Uggs Are Hatching by Jack Prelutsky

Digging Into Rocks And Minerals

Time to round up your rock hounds and dig into the earth's story found in rocks. The resources in this unit and the reproducibles on pages 131–135 will provide your class with a hands-on approach to rocks. Dig in!

by Louise Welder and Linda D. Rourke

Step Into My Rock Laboratory

What better way to learn about rocks and minerals than with some hands-on experiences? Set up a variety of rock lab stations around your room. Use the reproducibles on pages 132 and 133 to help. Divide your class into groups of three or four students each, and have them circulate through each of the following stations:

- **Try The Acid Test** (page 132)—This is a simple experiment to test for the presence of limestone.
- **Examine A Crystal** (page 132)—Here is a striking way to visualize the differences in crystal shapes.
- **Create A Conglomeration!** (page 133)—What a way to have fun and learn about sedimentary rocks!
- **Try The Scratch Test** (page 133)—This is a practical way of introducing the concept of hardness and its use as a mineral identification tool. Post a copy of Moh's Hardness Scale, found in a rock and mineral field guide, to encourage students to explore the hardness value of other minerals.
- **Be A "Rock Groupie"**—Here is an exercise which will assess your students' understanding of the three rock forms. Put a selection of 12 rocks in an egg carton. Number each rock. Ask students to identify these rocks as *igneous, sedimentary, or metamorphic* using only a hand lens and a rock and mineral field guide.
- **Be A Rock Hound**—This experiment will give your class practice in the identification of rocks. Put 12 different rocks in an egg carton. Number the rocks. Ask students to identify the name of each rock. Include a rock and mineral field guide for use as a reference.
- **Streak Test**—Another way of identifying an unknown mineral is by the mark or streak it makes when rubbed against a piece of unglazed porcelain tile. Borrow a streak test kit from a local high school, or make your own using a variety of rocks and unglazed tiles. Use a rock and mineral field guide to make a streak chart as a reference for the class. Generally, nonmetallic minerals make colorless to light grey streaks when rubbed on an unglazed tile, while metallic minerals make dark grey to black streaks. Have students take rock samples and make streaks on a tile. Have them compare the streaks to the chart for identification purposes.

Fun With Puns

A *pun* is a funny way of using a word so that it suggests two or more of its meanings or the meaning of another word that sounds like it. Your students will be rocking and rolling in the aisles when they make up their own rock and mineral puns. Have students print their puns on stone-shaped pieces of construction paper. Attach the work to a bulletin board for all to enjoy. To get students thinking in the right direction, give some examples like:

Don't *sulphur* with sunburn; use a good sunscreen.
He graduated *magma* cum laude.
Don't play with your dessert—eat your *pyrite!*

Glow, Rock, Glow

Ask students to define the word *fluorescence;* then discuss its meaning (a glowing that occurs when an object absorbs radiation from another source). Relate it to fluorescent paints used on some T-shirts and posters. Certain rocks like *franklinite* and *willemite* become fluorescent when exposed to an ultraviolet or black light. See if a local rock collector has an ultraviolet light and fluorescent rock specimens which could be shared with your class. Your students will long remember the transformation of an ordinary-looking rock under normal light to a brilliant orange or green sensation under a black light.

Rock Collage

Get the entire class involved by making a bulletin board-sized collage. Ask each student to bring in three pictures from a newspaper or magazine showing examples of uses for rocks and minerals. For example, the class could look for pictures of a marble floor, stone building, salt shaker, diamond ring, or laundry detergent. To complete your bulletin board, add the title "The Role Of Rocks."

Rockin' Vocabulary

Minerals can be identified by their distinctive color and shine. Your students can train their eyes to observe certain features of a rock.

Introduce the terms *transparent, translucent,* and *opaque.* A mineral is transparent if an object can be seen through it. A mineral is translucent if light can pass through it. A mineral is opaque if nothing can be seen through it.

Give students practice identifying certain rock samples to determine if they are transparent, translucent, or opaque.

Next describe the *luster* of a mineral as the way a mineral shines when light strikes it and is reflected from it. Some minerals have a metallic luster while others have a nonmetallic luster. Such adjectives as *sparkly, waxy, glassy, greasy, silky, earthy,* or *dull* may be used to describe the luster of minerals. Have each student use some of these descriptive words in a story entitled "The Rock Who Hated The Outdoors" or "Starring Rock 'n' Roll Sensation ___________."

Pet Rock Contest

Have each student bring in a rock of his choice. Transform these rocks into "Pet Rocks" with some imagination and art supplies. Have students glue pieces of felt to their rocks, adding features with permanent markers. Encourage students to create appropriate names for their pets. Display finished projects on a windowsill; then hold a pet rock contest. Give out such honors as the "Heavy Metal Award," "Most Glassy," "Down-To-Earth Distinction," or the "Crystal Light Award."

Rocks, Rocks Everywhere

Get the most out of your rock and mineral unit by using the great outdoors. Here are a few fun ways to provide some earthy activities:

- Show your students how easy it is to start collecting rocks by exploring the schoolyard to find rock samples.
- Take a shovel and dig a hole. Give each group a cup of dirt to examine closely. Encourage students to identify rock samples and give a scenario telling how they think these rocks were formed.
- Take a walk around the school block and make a list of all things that are made with rocks (buildings, monuments, foundations, walls, gravestones, etc.).
- Take a field trip to a nearby park, quarry, mine dump, cave, gravel pit, science center, or museum.

Put Your Hand In The Sand

Help students see that sedimentary rocks are made up of bits and pieces of other minerals. Have students take a closer look at sand under a microscope or hand lens. They should be able to note the color, shape, and size of each mineral grain. The glassy, colorless crystals are *quartz.* Red crystals are usually *garnet.* Thin, flaky, black crystals may be *mica,* while rectangular black crystals may be *hornblende.* If black crystals are attracted to a magnet, they are probably *magnetite.* Purple crystals may be *amethyst,* and green crystals may be *olivine.* Be sure the rock and mineral field guide is available for reference.

Three Ways To Grow A Crystal Garden

To create mineral crystals which mirror those found in the earth, follow any of these methods:

1. A supersaturated solution of either salt or sugar will form crystals over a week or two. Begin with very hot (but not boiling) water in a disposable, clear, clean jar. Slowly stir in salt or sugar until it will no longer dissolve. Tie a pencil to one end of a string and a button to the other end. Lower the string into the solution until the pencil rests on the top of the jar. Place the jar in a draft-free, quiet location. To promote evaporation, occasionally clear away the scum which may collect on the water's surface. Crystals will form on the string.

2. Within a day, this method produces lovely crystals which will continue to grow for about a week. Place pieces of charcoal briquettes, porous bricks, or sponge in a foam meat tray. In a clean, clear glass jar, combine four tablespoons each of noniodized salt, water, and liquid bluing (found in the laundry supplies aisle of a grocery store). Pour the mixture over the pieces in the meat tray. Drizzle one tablespoon of ammonia over the mixture. Add food coloring to create crystals of different colors. The crystals need to be placed in a well-ventilated area.
3. Obtain a chemical called *copper sulfate* from a high school chemistry teacher or a garden or pool supply store. Copper sulfate is a poisonous algaecide that must be handled with care. It is used to keep decorative pools free of algae. Begin with very hot (but not boiling) water in a disposable, clear, clean glass jar. Slowly stir in copper sulfate until it will no longer dissolve. Tie a pencil to one end of a string and a button to the other end. Lower the string into the solution until the pencil rests on the top of the jar. Place the jar in a draft-free, quiet location.

Name ________________________________

The Rock Cycle

Look at the diagram of the rock cycle. It shows how forces deep within the earth and on the surface can change the form of rocks.

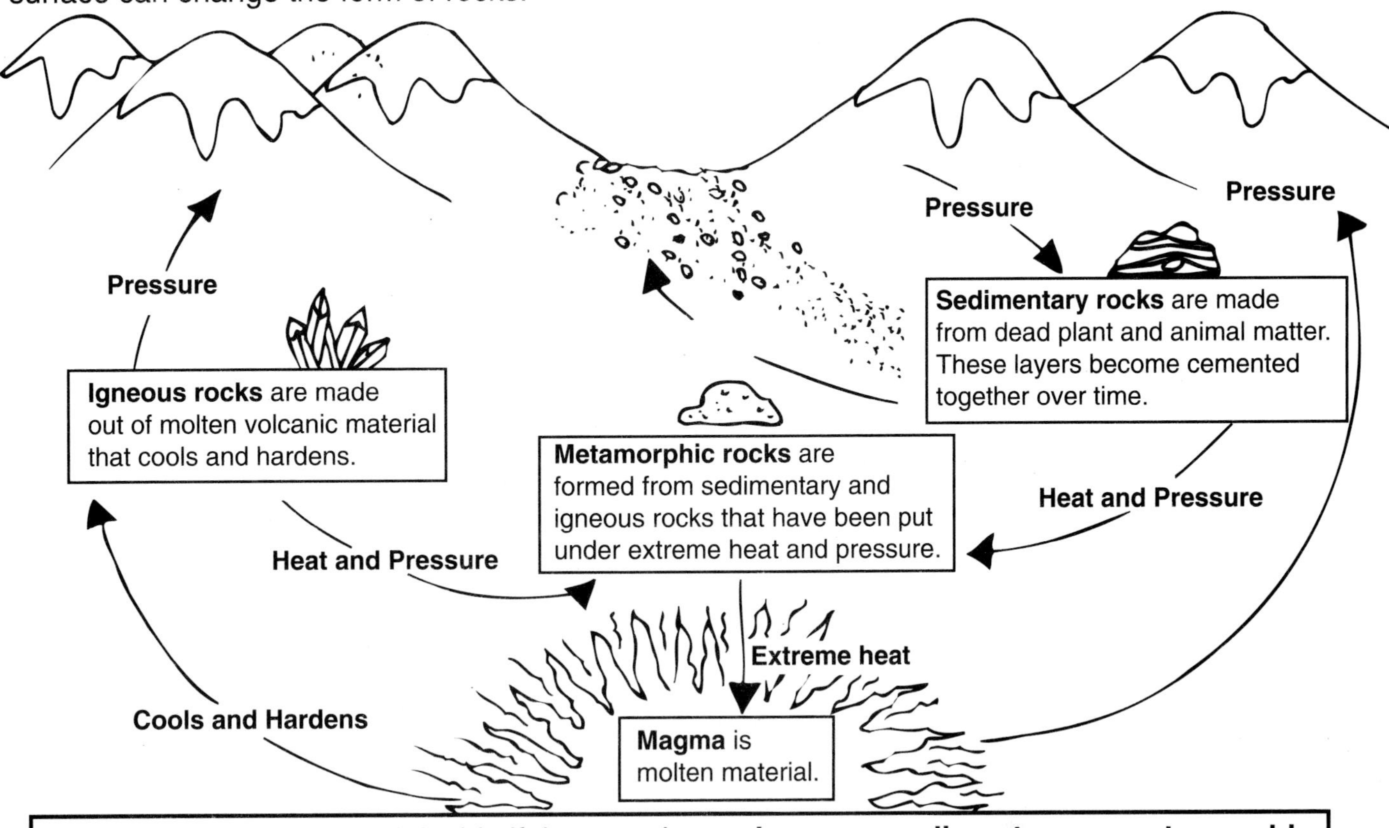

Pressure
Pressure
Pressure
Sedimentary rocks are made from dead plant and animal matter. These layers become cemented together over time.
Igneous rocks are made out of molten volcanic material that cools and hardens.
Metamorphic rocks are formed from sedimentary and igneous rocks that have been put under extreme heat and pressure.
Heat and Pressure
Heat and Pressure
Extreme heat
Cools and Hardens
Magma is molten material.

Read the clues below and decide if these rocks are **igneous, sedimentary,** or **metamorphic.** Write the correct rock type on the line.

1. Wind breaks small bits from large rocks. Rain takes the particles to a creek. They drop to the bottom and harden over time into limestone. ____________
2. A volcano sends lava out of its cone. The lava cools as it falls and makes basalt. ____________
3. A slow river puts soft, wet clay on a dead fish. The piled clay lies in place for years. The fish body is replaced with stone. ____________
4. Melted rock moves in the earth. It cools as it nears the earth's surface. ____________
5. The weight and pressure of a mountain over time turn shale into slate. ____________
6. Space in packed sand on the sea floor fills with minerals in the water. These minerals over time become cemented and turn into sandstone. ____________
7. Magma presses against limestone. Over time it forms into marble. ____________
8. The continental plates move and make folds in the rock. This pressure can cause granite to form into gneiss. ____________
9. The ocean waves blast coral into bits which settle on old shells. The coral and shell particles build up. Over the years they harden together to form coquina. ____________
10. Lava flows in huge sheets on the earth. It cools quickly into obsidian. ____________

Bonus Box: Make up two more rock clues that your teacher could add to this page.

Name ______________________________ Experiment

Try The Acid Test

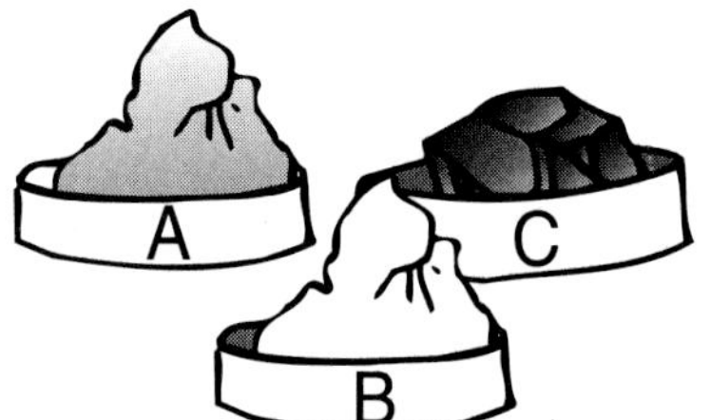

Find out if the following rocks contain limestone. Limestone is a sedimentary rock that usually forms from tiny particles of weathered seashells. Use a dropper filled with a weak acid like vinegar. Test for the presence of limestone by dropping vinegar onto the rock's surface. If the rock contains limestone, it will bubble (effervesce) where the acid touches the limestone. Try it!

1. Do the following rocks bubble (effervesce) when vinegar is placed on them? Answer yes or no.

   Rock A ____________ **Rock C** ____________ **Rock E** ____________

   Rock B ____________ **Rock D** ____________ **Rock F** ____________

2. What do you think causes the bubbles? ______________________________

   ____

   ____

Note To Teacher: Gather six different rocks. Three rocks should contain types of limestone (chalk, coquina, gray limestone, travertine, for example). Place rocks in six plastic lids labeled A–F. Provide a cup of vinegar and droppers.

Name ______________________________ Experiment

Examine A Crystal

Crystals form in rocks from melted (molten) material in the earth. They need room to grow and must grow slowly. Crystals form in one of six distinct shapes. Examine the crystal shapes of salt and sugar by following these directions:

1. Sprinkle some sugar granules on a blank slide.
2. Drop water from an eyedropper onto the sugar to make a sugar solution.
3. Place the slide under a hand lens or microscope to examine the crystal structure.
4. Draw a sketch of a sugar crystal.

Sugar Crystal

Salt Crystal

5. Repeat steps 1–4 using salt instead of sugar.
6. What are the differences between the sugar and salt crystals? ______________________________

   ____

   ____

Note To Teacher: Provide salt, sugar, water in cups, droppers, slides, and hand lenses or a microscope.

Name ______________________________ Experiment

Create A Conglomeration!

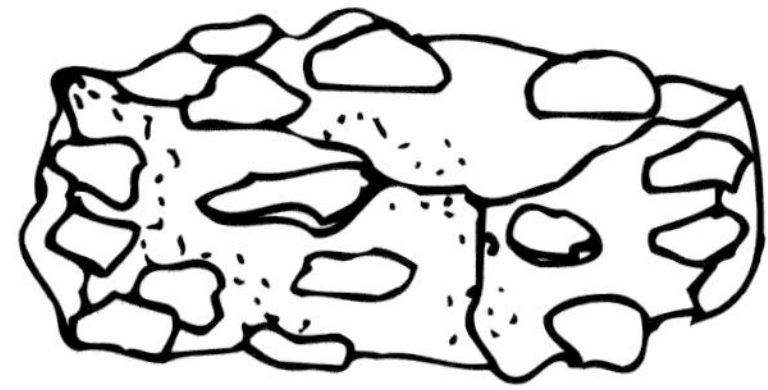

Sedimentary rocks are made over time from bits and pieces of rocks that have been deposited by wind, water, or glaciers. Make a "quickie" sedimentary rock following these instructions:

1. Gather a cup full of small rocks and pebbles.
2. Cut off the bottom of a one-gallon milk jug and put 1/2 cup of plaster of paris in the bottom.
3. With a spoon, stir in about 1/4 cup of water (should be consistency of pancake batter).
4. Shape the mixture into a ball and place on waxed paper. Push the remaining rocks into the mixture.
5. Let the mixture dry overnight. You've created a rock similar to conglomerate, or pudding stone.
6. In nature, how do pieces of rock bind together to make a new rock? ______________________________

____

____

Note To Teacher: You will need a measuring cup, small rocks, pebbles, a milk jug, plaster of paris, water, a spoon, waxed paper, and scissors.

Name ______________________________ Experiment

Try The Scratch Test

One way to identify an unknown mineral is to check its hardness. Scientists have given every mineral a hardness value that can be identified with a scratch test. Talc is the softest mineral with a hardness value of 1, and diamond is the hardest with a hardness value of 10. A mineral will scratch anything softer than itself and be scratched by anything harder.

Try to discover the hardness of a penny. Use the following chart as a guide:

Test Sample	Hardness Value
coarse sandpaper	9.0
tempered steel file	7.0
your fingernail	2.5
No. 2 pencil	1.0

1. Take the penny and scratch a No. 2 pencil, your fingernail, and the sandpaper. You can determine the penny's hardness value by seeing which of these items will scratch and which of these items will scratch the penny.
2. What items will the penny scratch? ______________________________
3. What items scratch the penny? ______________________________
4. Between which samples would the penny fit on the chart? ______________________________

   ______________________________ ______________________________
5. What hardness value would you give the penny? ______________________________
6. Repeat the experiment using a glass microscope slide instead of a penny. Include the penny as one of your test samples.

Note To Teacher: You will need coarse sandpaper, pennies, No. 2 pencils, steel files, and glass microscope slides.

Name ____________________

Master The Mineral Maze

Help Rocky find his way through the mine. Read each car's description. Write a matching word from the mine entrance in the blank.

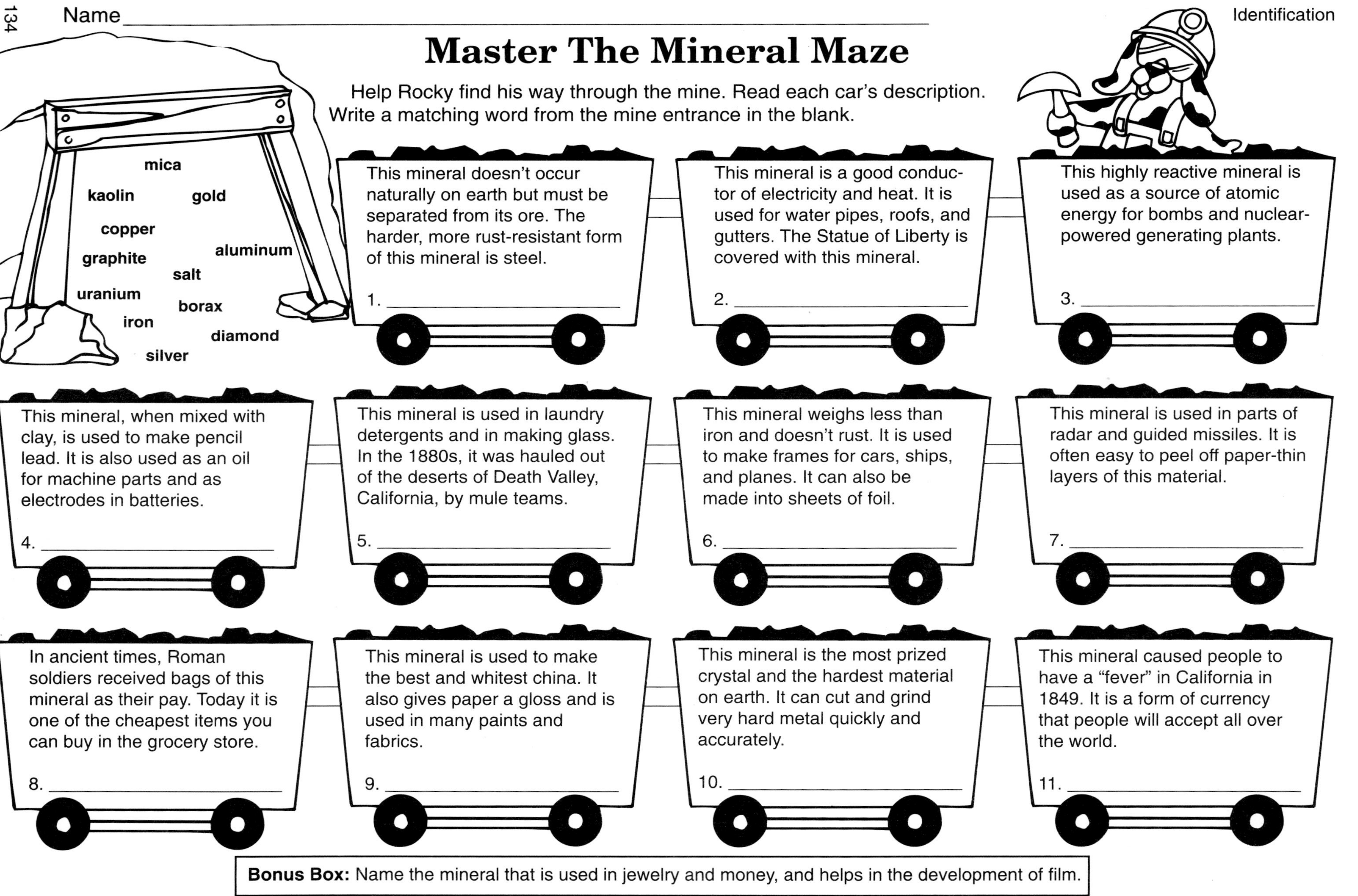

This mineral doesn't occur naturally on earth but must be separated from its ore. The harder, more rust-resistant form of this mineral is steel.

1. ____________________

This mineral is a good conductor of electricity and heat. It is used for water pipes, roofs, and gutters. The Statue of Liberty is covered with this mineral.

2. ____________________

This highly reactive mineral is used as a source of atomic energy for bombs and nuclear-powered generating plants.

3. ____________________

This mineral, when mixed with clay, is used to make pencil lead. It is also used as an oil for machine parts and as electrodes in batteries.

4. ____________________

This mineral is used in laundry detergents and in making glass. In the 1880s, it was hauled out of the deserts of Death Valley, California, by mule teams.

5. ____________________

This mineral weighs less than iron and doesn't rust. It is used to make frames for cars, ships, and planes. It can also be made into sheets of foil.

6. ____________________

This mineral is used in parts of radar and guided missiles. It is often easy to peel off paper-thin layers of this material.

7. ____________________

In ancient times, Roman soldiers received bags of this mineral as their pay. Today it is one of the cheapest items you can buy in the grocery store.

8. ____________________

This mineral is used to make the best and whitest china. It also gives paper a gloss and is used in many paints and fabrics.

9. ____________________

This mineral is the most prized crystal and the hardest material on earth. It can cut and grind very hard metal quickly and accurately.

10. ____________________

This mineral caused people to have a "fever" in California in 1849. It is a form of currency that people will accept all over the world.

11. ____________________

Bonus Box: Name the mineral that is used in jewelry and money, and helps in the development of film.

Name ______________________________

Pointers For A Rock Hound

Rock Collecting
by Cary Granite

Starting your own rock collection can be fun. By studying rocks, you can learn a lot about the earth. With an observant eye and a few simple supplies, you can begin collecting rocks. The following items can help you when you go rock hunting:

— a backpack for carrying rock samples and supplies
— zippered plastic bags to hold rocks and prevent chips and scratches
— a small notebook to write down the date when the rock was found, the location where the rock was found, and an identification number which you give the rock
— white-out correction fluid to dab on the rock for identification purposes
— a permanent marker or pen to number the rock and write information in the notebook

Where are the best places to look for rocks?

Rocks can be found everywhere. However, different kinds of rocks are found in different geographical areas. Where you live will determine the kinds of rocks you will find. Here are some good places to look for rocks:

— along a stream
— along a riverbank
— in a roadcut (where a new road is made)
— on a stone driveway
— along a mountain trail
— on a playground
— along an outcrop (an area of exposed bedrock)

Be safe! Never go rockhounding alone. Always let someone know where you're going. Stay out of caves and mine shafts. Wear boots or sturdy shoes.

How do you identify rocks?

You need to train the eye to see the different features of rocks. These features will help you to identify rocks. Here are some pointers:

— Use an old toothbrush to brush off the dirt and mud so that you can view the rock better.
— Use a spray bottle of water to wet the rock. This cleans the rock and allows the color and grains to be seen better.
— Notice whether the rock is heavy or light. Does the rock have layers or is it solid and smooth?
— Use a hand lens (a pocket magnifier with 6-power or 10-power is best) to identify the speckles or mineral grains.
— Use a rock and mineral field guide to help you identify the name of the rock and rock type.
— Write the information about each rock in a notebook or on index cards.
— Display rocks in egg cartons or box lids.

Checklist

_____ 1. I have ______________ rocks in my rock collection.
(number)

_____ 2. I have identified the date when each rock was found and the location where each rock was found.

_____ 3. I have identified the name of each rock in my collection.

_____ 4. I have identified each rock as igneous, metamorphic, or sedimentary.

_____ 5. I will bring my rock collection and notebook to school on ______________________.
(date)

____
student's signature

Get A Charge Out Of Magnetism And Electricity

Turn on to a field bound to enlighten any classroom. Use any of the following activities and experiments to help your students get a "charge" out of magnets and electricity.

by Chris Christensen

Magnetism is a property of some substances which have the ability to attract other substances. Magnets are usually made of iron or steel, and they attract certain objects made of iron, steel, nickel, or cobalt. Every magnet has a north and a south pole where its strength is concentrated. The law of magnetic attraction states that like poles repel and unlike poles attract. Natural magnets are called *permanent magnets,* as opposed to *electromagnets* that work only as long as electricity flows through their inner coils of wire. Electromagnets are commonly found in telephones, televisions, radios, telegraphs, electrical appliances, and motors. Here are some hands-on activities to try with magnets.

- **North And South Poles**—Demonstrate the invisible lines of force within magnetic fields in a simple and clean manner. Put iron filings into a plastic zippered bag. Place the bag on top of a magnet. The iron filings will form a pattern to show the location of the north and south poles of the magnet. The largest clusters of filings will be around both poles.

- **3-D Magnetic Field**—You will need a baby food jar, iron filings, salad oil, and magnets. Place some iron filings in the jar and add enough salad oil to almost fill it. Close the container tightly and shake well. Hold one pole of the magnet near one side of the jar and observe. Then add a second magnet with the opposite pole against the other side of the jar and observe. The iron filings will cluster around the poles.

- **Erase-A-Tape**—Take an *old* audiocassette tape and see how you can erase the tape with a magnet. Have students manually wind the tape and hypothesize what happened. A magnet, when held close to the tape at the head opening, will disturb the arrangement of particles on the cassette tape and erase what was recorded on the tape.

- **Magnetic Treasure Hunt**—Hide metallic objects like paper clips, nuts, screws, nails, tacks, etc., in a box of sand. See how many objects your students can find with a magnet.

- **Attraction-Repulsion Test**—Take two small medication cups (the type that comes with children's cold medicine) and tape a magnet securely to the inside bottom of each cup. Use refrigerator-type magnets. Have your students place one cup inside the other and observe what happens. The children should observe that when the poles are lined up, with north to north and south to south, the inner cup will be suspended as it is being repelled. When north pole is against south pole, the cups are attracted and fit snugly inside one another.

- **Make An Electromagnet**—Wrap a large nail (three inches or more in size) with about ten feet of insulated copper wire. Scrape off the insulation from both ends of the wire and attach the wire ends to the terminals of a nine-volt battery. Put the tip of the nail near some metallic objects like pins, tacks, staples, paper clips, etc., and observe. Your students should observe that the nail acts like a magnet, attracting the metallic objects. It works only as long as the current is running through the wire.

- **Let The Force Be With You**—Have a child hold up his index and middle fingers. They should be pointing toward the ceiling. Place one bar magnet on the palm side of the fingers and another bar magnet on the nail side of the fingers. Try to get the second magnet just below the first one. The magnets will stay in place. The child cannot see the force, but he will be able to feel it.

Here are some basics on electricity that go along with the experiments below. Most substances have a neutral electrical charge, which means that there is neither a surplus of electrons nor a shortage of electrons. Electricity occurs when there is movement in the electrons in which an object might gain electrons, causing a negative charge; or lose electrons, causing a positive charge.

When two different substances (especially nonmetals) are rubbed together, electrons may jump from one material to the other. This type of electricity does not flow and is called *static electricity.* Certain materials (especially metals) are considered to be good conductors of electricity as they allow the electrons to move through them easily. When the electrons flow freely from one object to another, it is called *current electricity.* To get the electrons moving, a "push" is needed to get one electron moving toward another. This push can come from a wet cell, a dry cell, a storage battery, a generator, or a solar cell.

- **The Electric Comb**—The best time to try this experiment is on a day with low humidity. Have each student bring in a comb from home. Put some puffed rice cereal or tiny bits of paper on paper plates in front of your students. Show static electricity by directing students to comb their hair vigorously and then to place the combs close to the cereal or paper. Students will love seeing what happens when the negatively charged combs attract and pick up the positively charged cereal or paper.

- **Balloon Test**—Try these fun static-electricity experiments. Rub a balloon vigorously with a wool cloth. Pass the balloon over a student's head and make his hair stand on end. Or blow up two balloons to the same size and suspend them from the ceiling so that they are about an inch apart. Rub each balloon vigorously with a wool cloth and observe. Your students will notice that the balloons become negatively charged and repel each other.

- **Electrical Safety**—Have a brainstorming session with your class to come up with some safety rules to follow concerning electricity and the use of electrical appliances. Have your students make safety posters to display around the school.

- **Simple Circuit**—Use a six-volt battery, two lengths of insulated copper bell wire (No. 20), a one-cell flashlight bulb, and a small porcelain socket to make a simple circuit. Remove the insulation from the ends of the wires so that the wire extends about one inch. Attach one wire to one terminal of the battery and then to one terminal of the socket. Do the same for the other wire. Your students will be thrilled when the bulb lights up.

- **Conductor Or Insulator**—Test objects such as a penny, nail, toothpick, rubber band, paper clip, or cardboard strip to see if they are conductors or insulators. Use the same materials from the simple circuit experiment above. Detach one wire from the bulb and begin testing the different materials. Touch the penny to the free wire while holding the penny to the bulb terminal. Does the bulb light? (Yes, it does. Copper is a good conductor of electricity.) Repeat the step using a toothpick. Does the bulb light? (No, wood is an insulator.) Try the other objects.

- **Appliances At Work**—Electrical appliances provide us with heat, light, and power. Have your students make lists of appliances that they have in their homes. Compare the lists to see how dependent we are on electricity.

Electricity At Work
stove
refrigerator
microwave
air conditioner
water heater
blender
blow dryer
lamps
fan
6-VOLT BATTERY

Name ____ Electricity contract

Power Station #10

Write a paragraph about what life would be like if electricity had not been discovered.

Find out how energy from the sun can be turned into electricity.

Write what you think it means when someone says that you have a "magnetic personality."

Find out how the wind can be turned into electricity.

Make a list of ten materials that are conductors of electricity.

Write 11 sentences telling how you can conserve electricity. The first word in each sentence must begin with a letter in the word ELECTRICITY.

Write and design a bumper sticker encouraging people to conserve energy.

Make up an energy song which would be sung by Flash and the Fuseboxes.

Write a play with these characters:
Captain Energex, the heroine
Zapnoid, the energy thief from a distant galaxy
Princess Twinkle, the fair maiden
Electronica, the evil king
Wattless, the captain's bumbling assistant

Write ten words that describe how you would feel if you suddenly became magnetic.

Put an X on each box as you complete the activity.

Electricity Rating
9–10 activities = You're supercharged!
6–8 activities = "Watt" a winner!
4–5 activities = You're turned on!

Bonus Box: Design a folder for storing your contract work.

Name ____________________

Amazing!

You are sure to be attracted to this game! Get a partner and read the directions below to play.

How To Play: One player holds the gameboard with both hands while the other player places a magnet under the maze and a small paper clip above the maze at the **Start** position. This player tries to move the paper clip through the maze as quickly as possible. If the paper clip falls off the board, he must go back to **Start.** For the expert player, try to move the clip through the maze as quickly as possible without touching any of the lines.

How To Win: The player who moves the paper clip through the maze in the shortest amount of time is the winner.

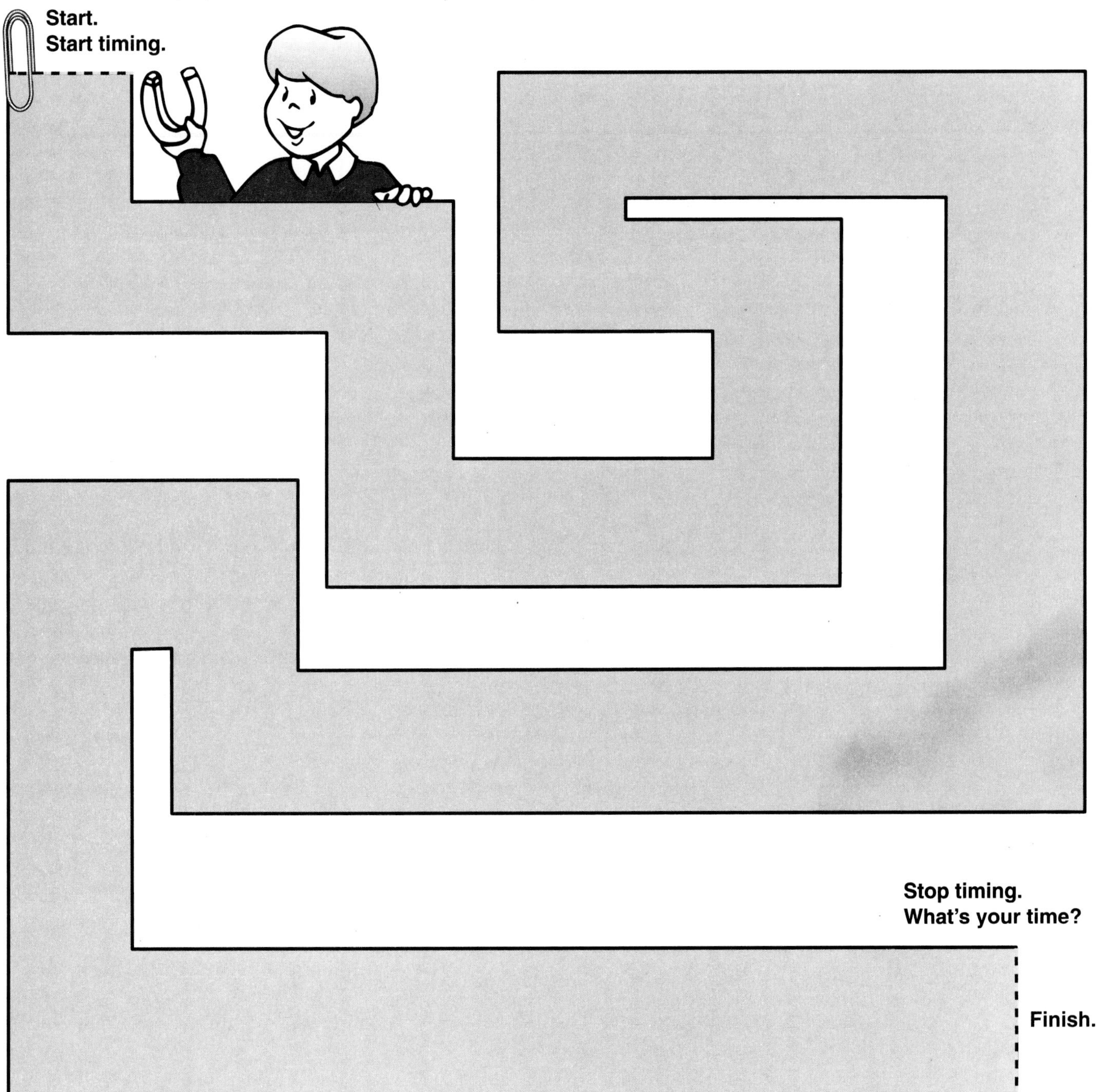

Start.
Start timing.
Stop timing.
What's your time?
Finish.

Bonus Box: Keep track of each student's time. Graph the results. Determine the class champ.

Note To Teacher: Reproduce copies of this maze, mount on poster board, and laminate. Players need a magnet, a paper clip, and a watch or clock with a second hand to play the game.

Name ____ Electricity experiment

In A Flash!

Can a strip of aluminum foil and a battery light up a bulb? Here's an easy experiment to see if aluminum foil conducts electricity. Pair up with a friend and follow the steps below.

Hypothesis: What do you think will happen in this experiment? ____________________

____

Materials: two size C batteries (Two size D batteries will also work.)
small bulb (flashlight size)
masking tape
aluminum foil

Procedure:

1. Stick a piece of narrow masking tape to the center of a 2" x 12" strip of aluminum foil. Cut off excess foil. Fold strip in half, tape side in. Flatten strip.
2. Place the *negative* (flat) end of the battery on one end of the foil strip and hold the bulb to the other notched, or *positive,* end of the battery.
3. Try touching the free end of the foil to the side of the battery. Does it work? Try different spots. What happens? Write your observations on line A below.

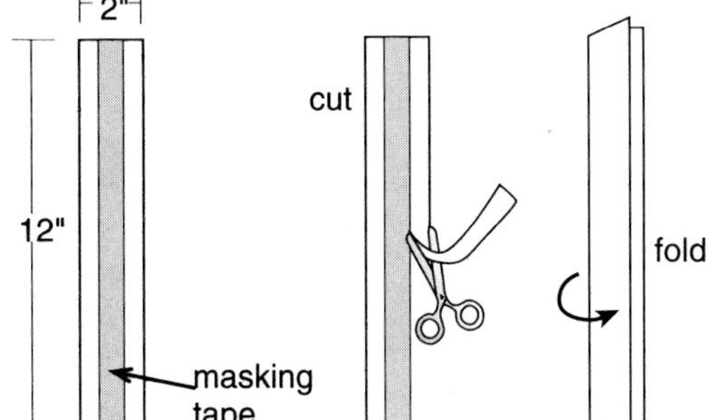

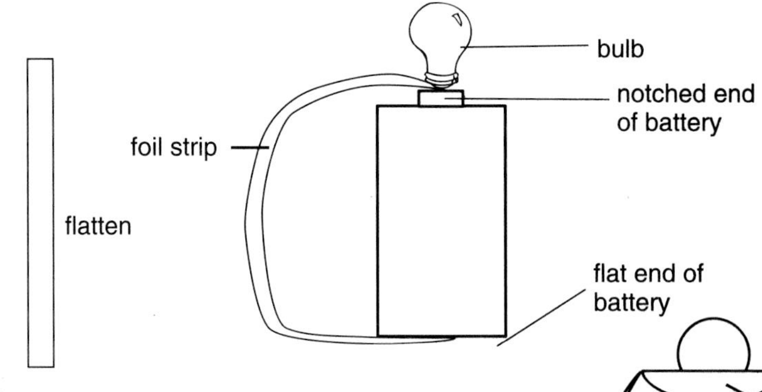

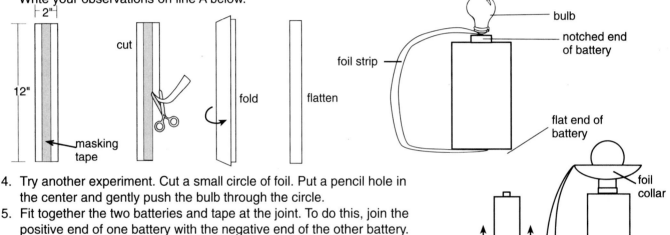

4. Try another experiment. Cut a small circle of foil. Put a pencil hole in the center and gently push the bulb through the circle.
5. Fit together the two batteries and tape at the joint. To do this, join the positive end of one battery with the negative end of the other battery.
6. Place the negative (flat) end of the bottom battery on one end of the foil strip. Put the foil collar and bulb on the positive end of the top battery.
7. Touch the free end of the foil strip to the foil collar. What happens? Write your observations on line B below.
8. Congratulations! You have just made a simple flashlight!

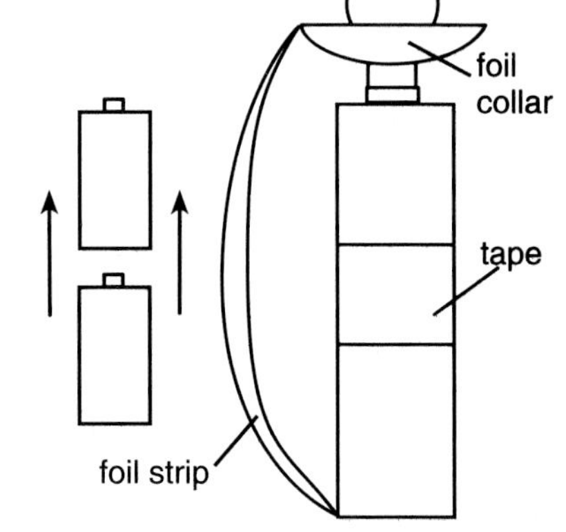

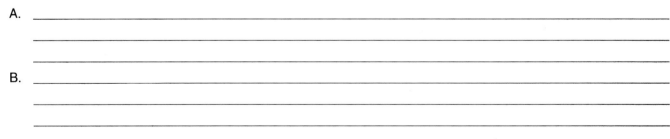

Observations: What changes did you observe?

A. ____

____

____

B. ____

____

____

Conclusions: What did you learn from these experiments?

____

____

____

____

Bonus Box: Try using foil that is longer, wider, wavier, or in two pieces. What happens?

Name ______________________________

Potato Power

Sometimes a battery is so old that it is hard to know which terminal is positive and which one is negative. Try this simple experiment to identify the positive and negative poles of a battery.

Hypothesis: What do you think will happen in this experiment? ______________________________

____

Materials: six-volt battery
potato, cut in half lengthwise
two pieces of 12-inch-long insulated copper wire

Procedure:
1. Cut a half-inch of the insulation away from both ends of both wires so that the copper wires extend.
2. Using a six-volt battery, connect one wire to one terminal and the second wire to the other.
3. Insert the other ends of the wires into the potato in two separate spots. Make sure the wires do **not** touch.

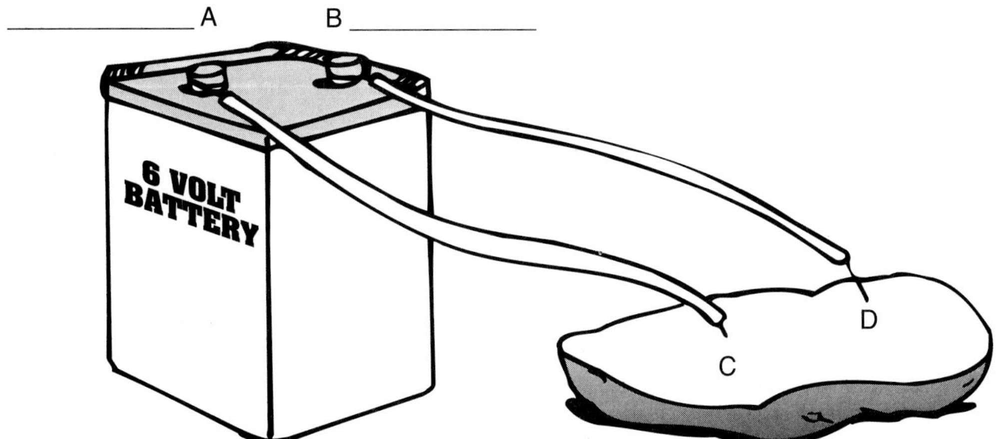

Observations:

A. What do you notice on the potato at wire end C? Sketch the reaction on the potato above.

____

____

____

B. What do you notice on the potato at wire end D? Sketch the reaction on the potato above.

____

____

____

C. The discoloration indicates that a wire is connected to the negative (–) terminal. The wire connected to the bubbles (or to no reaction) is connected to the positive (+) terminal. Identify the positive and negative terminals on the sketch above beside letters A and B..

Conclusions: What did you learn from this experiment?

____

____

____

Bonus Box: Try this same experiment with a lemon or orange instead of a potato.

They provide most of the earth's oxygen, give us much of our food, and control the earth's climate. Encourage your kids to respect and preserve...

THE OCEANS: A PRECIOUS ENVIRONMENT

by Bill O'Connor

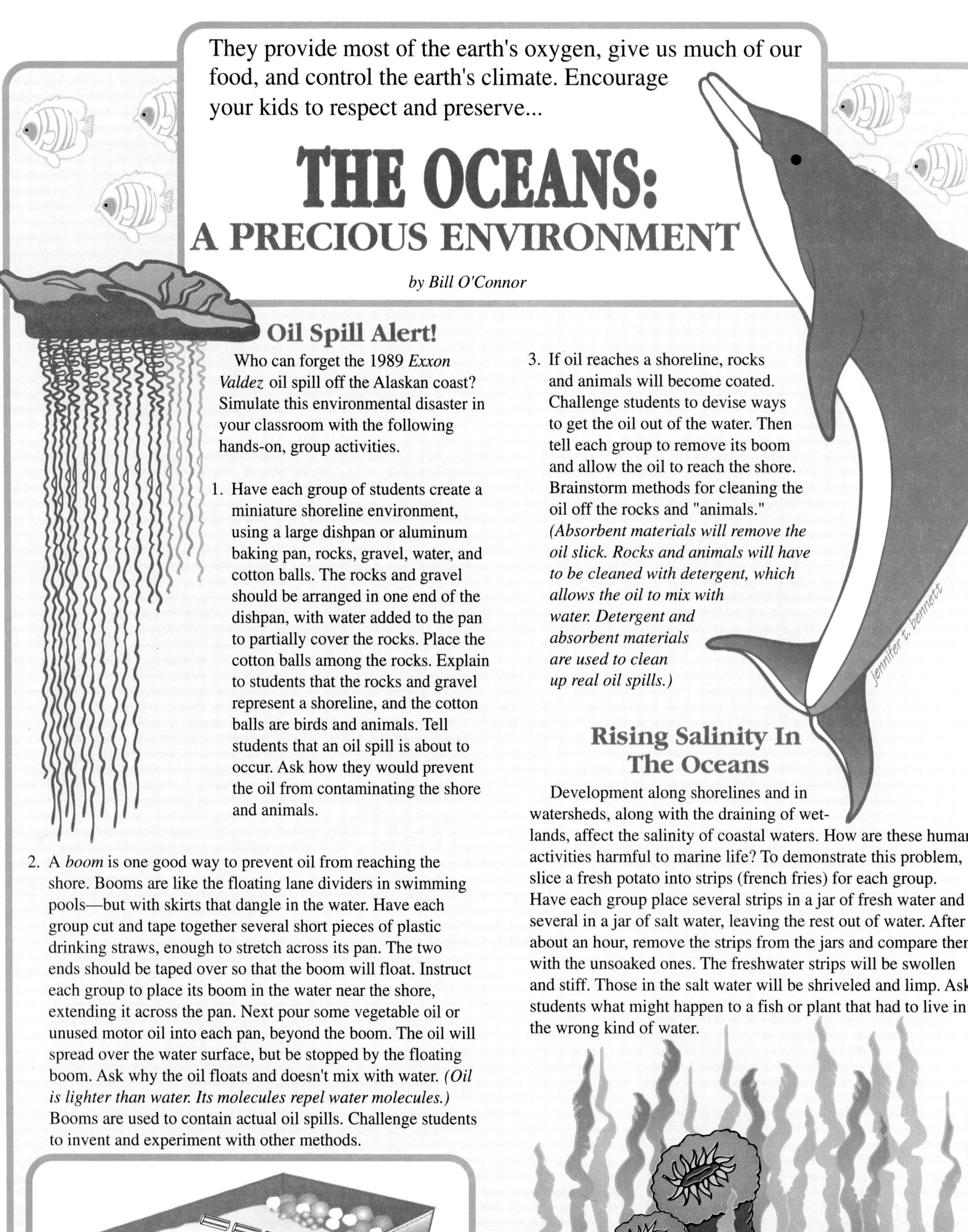

Oil Spill Alert!

Who can forget the 1989 *Exxon Valdez* oil spill off the Alaskan coast? Simulate this environmental disaster in your classroom with the following hands-on, group activities.

1. Have each group of students create a miniature shoreline environment, using a large dishpan or aluminum baking pan, rocks, gravel, water, and cotton balls. The rocks and gravel should be arranged in one end of the dishpan, with water added to the pan to partially cover the rocks. Place the cotton balls among the rocks. Explain to students that the rocks and gravel represent a shoreline, and the cotton balls are birds and animals. Tell students that an oil spill is about to occur. Ask how they would prevent the oil from contaminating the shore and animals.

2. A *boom* is one good way to prevent oil from reaching the shore. Booms are like the floating lane dividers in swimming pools—but with skirts that dangle in the water. Have each group cut and tape together several short pieces of plastic drinking straws, enough to stretch across its pan. The two ends should be taped over so that the boom will float. Instruct each group to place its boom in the water near the shore, extending it across the pan. Next pour some vegetable oil or unused motor oil into each pan, beyond the boom. The oil will spread over the water surface, but be stopped by the floating boom. Ask why the oil floats and doesn't mix with water. *(Oil is lighter than water. Its molecules repel water molecules.)* Booms are used to contain actual oil spills. Challenge students to invent and experiment with other methods.

3. If oil reaches a shoreline, rocks and animals will become coated. Challenge students to devise ways to get the oil out of the water. Then tell each group to remove its boom and allow the oil to reach the shore. Brainstorm methods for cleaning the oil off the rocks and "animals." *(Absorbent materials will remove the oil slick. Rocks and animals will have to be cleaned with detergent, which allows the oil to mix with water. Detergent and absorbent materials are used to clean up real oil spills.)*

Rising Salinity In The Oceans

Development along shorelines and in watersheds, along with the draining of wetlands, affect the salinity of coastal waters. How are these human activities harmful to marine life? To demonstrate this problem, slice a fresh potato into strips (french fries) for each group. Have each group place several strips in a jar of fresh water and several in a jar of salt water, leaving the rest out of water. After about an hour, remove the strips from the jars and compare them with the unsoaked ones. The freshwater strips will be swollen and stiff. Those in the salt water will be shriveled and limp. Ask students what might happen to a fish or plant that had to live in the wrong kind of water.

Waters Of The World

Directions: Number a sheet of paper 1–24. How many bodies of water can you identify?

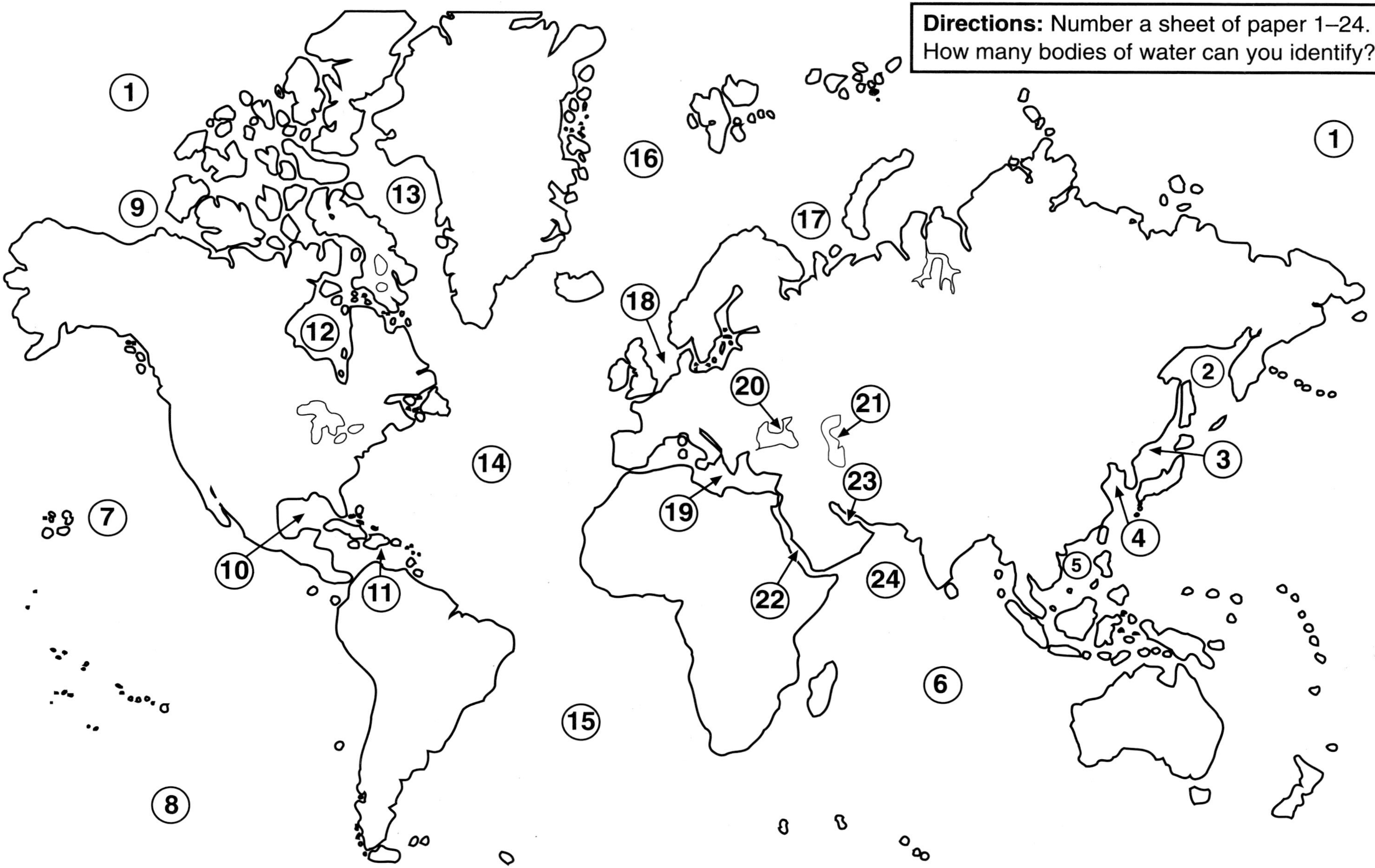

How Does Your Garden Grow?

Thematic Fun With Flowers

Throw a bloomin' bit of fun into your study of plants with the following thematic miniunit on flowers.

by Pat Goode—Gr. 4, Timbercreek Elementary, Flower Mound, TX

Activity 1: Funny Flowers

Tiger lily, pitcher plant, skunk cabbage—their names suggest things other than beautiful flowers! Introduce your class to literal translation through the colorful names of flowers. Begin by announcing that the class will publish an illustrated book of funny flower names. First share the following verse with students:

Open the pages of our book;
Take part in our flowery game.
Think of how a blossom would look
If it looked just like its name!

Have each student choose a flower from the list shown. On one side of a piece of paper, the child writes "How would a [name of chosen flower] look if it looked just like its name?" On the other side of the paper, the student answers the question by drawing a picture of how the flower might look if it looked just like its name. When all of the pages are completed, bind them together to make a class "Funny Flowers" book. (Have one child copy the verse above on a piece of paper for the book's preface or title page.) Share your book with other classes by donating it to your school's library. Display the book beside a plastic bucket of fresh or artificial flowers.

Flowers:

Bachelor's-Button	Pitcher Plant	Flame Azalea	Bridal Wreath
Goldenrod	Rattlesnake Master	Woolly Daisy	Fiddleneck
Canterbury Bell	Snapdragon	Bleeding Heart	Indian Paintbrush
Canary Creeper	Purple Owl's Clover	Teddy Bear Cholla	Tall Bearded Iris
Black-Eyed Susan	Soapweed	Foxglove	Firecracker Flower
Bluebell	Indian Pipe	Skunk Cabbage	Beardtongue
Sunflower	Tiger Lily	Fairy-Slipper	Dogtooth Violet
Dogwood	Bluebonnet	Lady's-Slipper	French Marigold

Activity 2: Flower Legends

Follow up the "Funny Flowers" activity with an opportunity for some flowery creative writing. Share with students two beautiful picture books by Tomie dePaola: *The Legend Of The Bluebonnet* and *The Legend Of The Indian Paintbrush*. Compare the two books and discuss the main characteristics found in both. Then have each child write an original legend to explain how his chosen flower received its name. Add these stories to the "Funny Flowers" class book. Or mount them on construction paper to display on a flower-covered bulletin board. (For a lovely bluebonnet art project, see the next page.)

Activity 3: The Most Important Thing...

Take your flowery investigations a step further by making blossom brochures. Provide library resources for students to research their flowers. After the research has been completed, share Margaret Wise Brown's classic *The Important Book*. Point out the pattern utilized by Brown in this popular picture book; then have each child fold a piece of duplicating paper in thirds. After numbering the pages 1 to 6, the student describes important facts about his flower on each page, copying the pattern used in *The Important Book*. Instruct students to end page 6 of their brochures as shown in the illustration.

The MOST important thing about bluebonnets is that they make me feel JOYOUS as they blanket the countryside in SPRING!
1
Finally the bluebonnet makes a new blossom
BUT...
6

Name____

Spring Bluebonnets

After reading Tomie dePaola's wonderful story *The Legend Of The Bluebonnet,* create your own bluebonnet bouquets.

Materials for one bluebonnet:
wooden shish kebab skewer
two plastic six-pack rings
scissors
blue and white spray paint

Directions:

1. Cut the two six-pack rings into 12 oval-shaped rings.
2. Fold an oval ring upward, making sure that the ends are on top of each other.
3. Holding the folded ends together, carefully push them onto the pointed end of the wooden skewer. Push the ring about three-fourths of the way down the skewer.
4. Repeat steps 2 and 3, alternately turning the rings to hide the skewer and create the look of blossoms.
5. Use about 12 rings to make one flower. Fold the last ring over the point of the skewer to form the end of the blossom.
6. Spray the bottom three-fourths of the rings with blue paint. Add white paint to the top of the flower. The paints will splatter and mix, enhancing the appearance of the final product.

Ann McMahon, Pasadena, TX

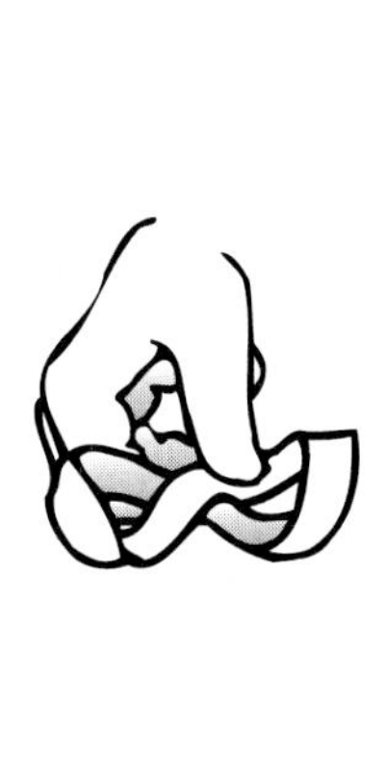

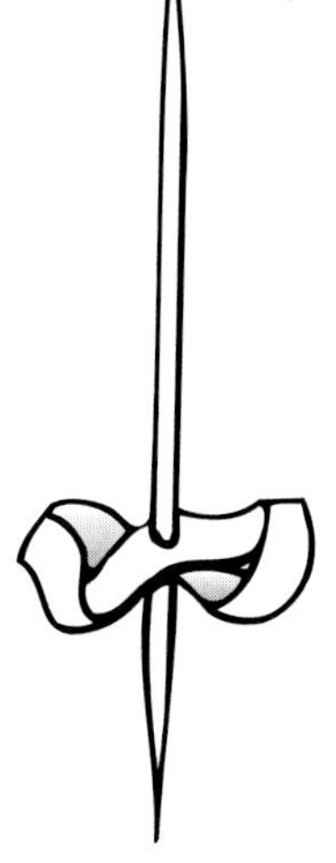

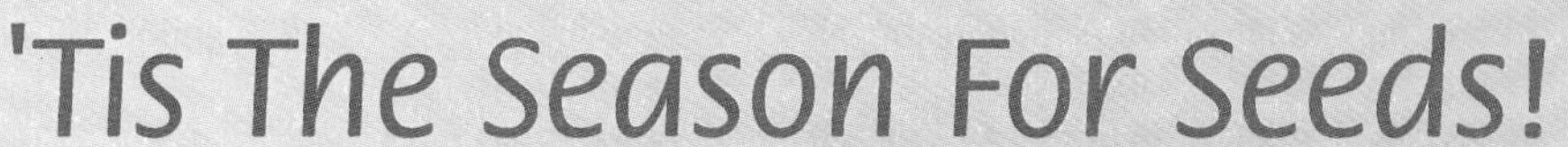

'Tis The Season For Seeds!

Trees and lots of smaller plants produce seeds in late summer. In early fall, take a close-up look at the fascinating world of seeds with the following activities and reproducible experiment.

by Bill O'Connor

Collecting Seeds

Begin a study of seeds by taking students for a walk through a grassy, weedy area. Instruct students to collect any seed heads they see and place them in plastic bags. Have volunteers drag an old blanket along the ground or wear pairs of old, long socks over their shoes to gather "hitchhiker" seeds. Try to collect milkweed, dandelion, and other airborne seeds. Examine and gather berries, fruits, and pods. (Avoid poison ivy and check for ticks after your walk!)

Classifying Seeds

After your walk, start a seed collection in your classroom science center. Have students classify the gathered seeds according to how they might be transported: by air, water, or animals. Ask students to estimate the number of seeds in one seed head or pod; then have groups count them. Sunflower seed heads are ideal for this activity.

Blowin' In The Wind

Many seeds are especially suited for dispersal by the wind: some have winglike structures that keep them aloft, others have fluffy coverings. Have students examine seeds with magnifying glasses to observe these characteristics. Hold a seed-flying contest to observe how seeds spread. Release seeds such as dandelion or milkweed in the classroom, and have students measure the distances the seeds travel. Repeat several times and find averages. Have students make graphs of the results.

Future Big Oaks

Collect acorns around your schoolyard, or have students bring in a supply from home. Have students examine the acorns to see how many different types they can observe, which ones have provided food or homes for animals, and which ones have begun to sprout. Most acorns will eventually sprout if they are in good condition (and if kept in a freezer for a month).

Sprouting Seeds

Have students sprout seeds for several weeks: try commercial birdseed, dry beans, alfalfa seeds, or radish seeds. (Seeds should be soaked overnight first.) Or try seeds from citrus fruits, whole grains such as wheat and corn, avocado pits, grass seeds, or other seeds that students find. A sure method for sprouting seeds is to place paper towels on the bottom of a plastic container or around the inside of a plastic cup. Moisten the towels and place seeds in contact with the paper. Containers can be covered, but allow for some air circulation. Check to make sure the paper towels are moist at all times.

Controlling Variables

After they've become adept "sprout farmers," have students try the reproducible activity on page 147. Students can learn about controlling variables, while determining what variables influence seed sprouting, or *germination.* Have students work in groups, using soaked bean, radish, or grass seeds. Each group should devise an experiment in which two groups of seeds are treated identically, except for *one* variable. Imagine—all that hands-on science from a few tiny seeds!

Name ____ Science experiment

What Makes A Seed Sprout?

Scientists are careful about variables when they do experiments. A *variable* is anything that might affect the outcome of an experiment. In order for an experiment to be "fair," only one variable should be changed at a time.

For example, if you want to see if **water** affects sprouting seeds, you wouldn't put some seeds in light and some in the dark. That would ruin the experiment! In an experiment, make sure all conditions are the same, except for one.

Directions:

1. List group members' names in the box.
2. In the "Seed Group 1" column, briefly tell how you will use each variable. List another variable in the "other" blank if you wish.
3. In the "Seed Group 2" column, write "same" for all variables except one. Tell how the one variable will be different from the same variable in "Seed Group 1."
4. Compare the two groups of seeds for ten days and write your observations below.

Group Members
____
____
____
____

Variables	Seed Group 1 (Describe how you will use each variable.)	Seed Group 2 (Write "same" for all except **one**.)
water		
light		
air		
temperature		
other ________		

Observations	Seed Group 1	Seed Group 2
Day 1		
Day 2		
Day 3		
Day 4		
Day 5		
Day 6		
Day 7		
Day 8		
Day 9		
Day 10		

Note To Teacher: See "Controlling Variables" on page 146.

MORE THAN SKIN AND BONES

Studying The Skeletal And Muscular Systems

Take a look under the skin at the skeleton and its partner in movement, the muscular system, with the following activities and reproducibles.

by Charlene Forsten

You Are What You Eat

The most important mineral in your bones is *calcium phosphate,* a chemical made of calcium, phosphorus, and oxygen. This mineral makes your bones hard and strong. What would happen if your bones lost this mineral? Try this demonstration. Remove all the meat from a small chicken bone and place the bone in a jar of strong vinegar. Leave it for one to two weeks. The acid in the vinegar will dissolve the minerals in the bone. After a period of time, the bone should become soft and even bendable. Discuss with students the implications of not getting enough calcium and phosphorus in our diets.

As a follow-up, have students research to identify foods that are rich in calcium and phosphorus. List the foods on a class chart; then ask students to bring cookbooks from home. Have students find recipes that are calcium- or phosphorus-rich. Duplicate the recipes, add student-designed covers, and bind into "Bone Builders" cookbooks to take home.

What's So Funny About A Bone?

What *is* a "funny bone"? Have you ever been called a "bonehead" or "hardheaded"? Have you ever been "chilled to the bone," pulled a "wishbone," or been "bone-dry" (an interesting phrase since our bones are 25% water)? Has anyone ever wanted to "pick a bone with you"? No bones about it, our language has many phrases associated with our skeletal system. With students, brainstorm a list of these phrases and discuss their meanings. Post the list on a bulletin board or door. Challenge students to look and listen for other phrases to add to the list.

Muscles Make Movement

From the slightest twitch to the gross movements used in tumbling, muscles allow all movement. Ask students to sit at their desks and make several small, voluntary movements. Discuss the muscles involved in their movements. Brainstorm a list of activities in which movement is pronounced.

Now get moving on a fun class project. Cover a bulletin board with butcher paper. Add the title "Muscles Make Movement." Have students cut out magazine and newspaper pictures that show movement, from the smallest facial gesture to a body leaping through the air. Instruct children to glue their pictures to the bulletin board collage-fashion. When the mural is finished, place reference books on the muscular system next to the display. Encourage students to search for diagrams showing the muscles used in the mural's pictures.

Muscle Math

Did you know that almost 50% of your body weight is made up of muscles? Or that you use over 200 muscles each time you take a single step? Or that there are 656 muscles in the body? Build math muscles using these facts and the following activities:

- Ask three students to come to the front of the room. Tell their classmates to listen carefully to the number of steps you ask each student to take. How many muscles were used by the students?
- Using cumulative records, find the total weight of your students. Write it on the board and ask, "How much muscle do we have in this room?" Discuss different methods for computing 50% of the total figure. After obtaining the answer, have students make a poster for your classroom door to let everyone know how much muscle power is packed inside (for example, "Enter At Your Own Risk! 700 Pounds Of Pure Muscle At Work!").
- Pose math challenges for students to tackle during free time. For example, "How many muscles are used during one play of a football game if each team has 11 players on the field?" (Answer: 656 x 22 = 14,432 muscles). Have students write their own problems using the information above.

Investing In Your Future

Osteoporosis—you've probably heard about it on television commercials, but do you know what it is? It's literally a loss of bone tissue, primarily affecting older women. Research has shown that young people who have diets high in calcium and exercise regularly are less likely to develop the disease when older. Invite the school nurse to discuss osteoporosis and other problems of the skeletal and muscular systems. After the discussion, have students make posters encouraging good nutrition and regular exercise. Spread the word about investing in your body's future by displaying the posters in the school cafeteria or library.

What Kind Of Joint Is This Anyway?

Even the best set of bones would be incapable of movement without the help of joints. Joints allow movement and prevent bones from moving in improper directions. Discuss with students the different types of joints: hinge, pivot, and ball-and-socket. Hinge joints, found in our fingers, knees, and elbows, allow movement in only one direction. The type of joint that allows us to turn our heads is called a pivot joint. Ball-and-socket joints, such as those found in the hips and shoulders, allow limited movement in all directions.

These same joints are used in many common objects. Have each student make three columns on his paper, labeling each with a type of joint. Instruct students to list examples of everyday objects containing the three types of joints. Examples could include a pencil sharpener (ball-and-socket), door hinge (hinge), and beaters of an electric mixer (pivot).

Read All About It!

Encourage students to read nonfiction with these excellent books about bones, muscles, and other body systems:

The Human Body by Giovanni Caselli
Your Wonderful Body by Donald J. Crump, ed.
The Body Victorious by Kjell Lindqvist and Stig Nordfeldt
Inspector Bodyguard Patrols The Land Of U by Vicki Cobb
Cuts, Breaks, Bruises, And Burns by Joanna Cole
The Human Body by Jonathan Miller
Blood And Guts: A Working Guide To Your Own Insides by Linda Allison
Movement by John Gaskin
What To Do When Your Mom Or Dad Says..."Stand Up Straight!" by Joy Berry
The Skeleton And Movement by Brian Ward

Name____ Completing a chart, setting goals

You Can't Be Fit If You Just Sit!

Think what life would be like if you could not move, and you'll get a picture of why it's so important to take care of your bones and muscles. These two vital systems depend on you for their care.

Your bones are made of two important minerals called calcium and phosphorus. To help grow and maintain strong bones, you must eat foods rich in these nutrients. Foods such as milk, cheese, yogurt, ice cream, whole wheat breads, almonds, eggs, cabbage, and scallops are rich in calcium and phosphorus.

Your muscular system depends on a balanced diet too. It also requires regular exercise. To stay physically fit, you should exercise at least three times a week. Exercising can build strength, endurance, and flexibility.

There are lots of easy-to-do exercises that will help build your body's strength, endurance, and flexibility. Sit-ups and push-ups are great ways to build strength. Endurance means being able to do something for a long period of time. Jogging, swimming, and bicycling can build endurance. Stretching exercises will build flexibility. Be sure to check with your physical education teacher or doctor before beginning a new exercise plan.

Directions: Keep the following chart for one week. At the end of the week, evaluate your chart carefully. How well are you treating your bones and muscles? On the back of this sheet, write a good health goal you want to set for yourself. List three steps you will take to reach your goal.

	SUN.	MON.	TUES.	WED.	THURS.	FRI.	SAT.
Foods eaten that contain calcium and phosphorus							
Exercises for strength							
Exercises for endurance							
Exercises for flexibility							

Bonus Box: Copy your goal on an index card. Decorate the card; then take it home. Tape it on your bathroom mirror or another place as a reminder to work on your goal.

Name ____________________

Boning Up On The Skeletal System

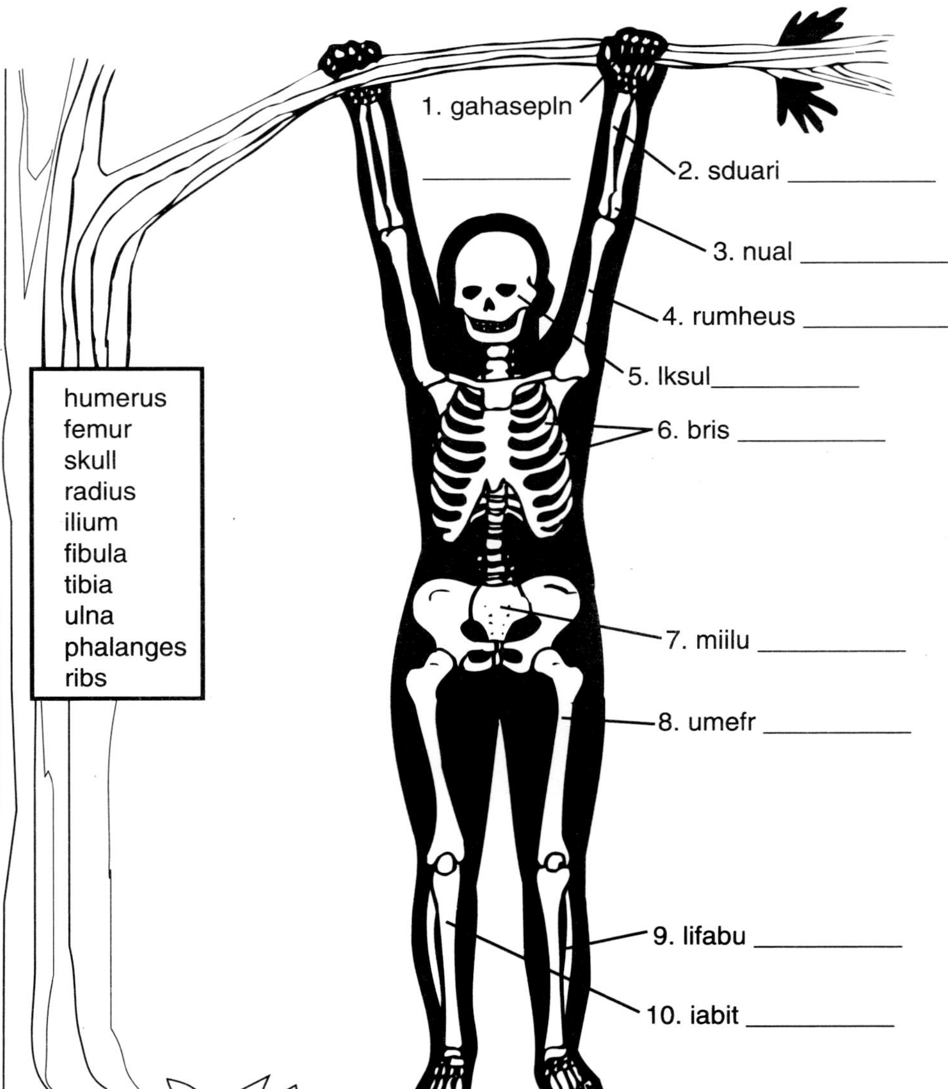

Read the paragraphs about bones and complete the coloring activity. Use the word box to unscramble and spell the names of the bones.

Your bones belong to four main categories. There are *long bones,* such as those in your arms and legs. They have a slight curve and allow you to support yourself. You use your long bones to run, jump, lift, and throw.

Short bones, which are about as wide as they are long, look almost square. Short bones are found in your wrists, ankles, and knees.

The bones in your backbone are called vertebrae. These bones, along with those in your middle ear, are called *irregular bones* because of their irregular shapes.

The last group of bones are called *flat bones.* They are actually slightly curved. Your ribs, breastbone, shoulder blades, and most of the bones of the skull are all types of flat bones.

Use the information above to complete this coloring activity:

1. Color the long bones red.
2. Color the short bones yellow.
3. Color the irregular bones green.
4. Color the flat bones blue.

Bonus Box: Use a dictionary to find out where the following bones are located: *maxilla, mandible, tarsals, patella, carpals, sternum, scapula.*

Name ______________________________ Creative thinking

"Undercover" Assignment

Meet Roscoe. He's a very smart dog. But, even though he's very intelligent, there are certain things he'll never be able to do. Part of the reason for this has to do with Roscoe's skeleton. For example, a human has fingers that can thread a needle, something a dog with paws could never do.

Because of the way their skeletons are built, animals can also do certain kinds of things. Some animals have long necks to reach high places. Others have large, strong jaws for tearing and chewing meat. What kinds of bones would allow an animal to peel fruit, swim in the water, walk or run on all four legs, fly, hang by its hands or tail, or jump long distances?

Examine the animal skeletons below. Think about what these animals can do because of their special skeletons.

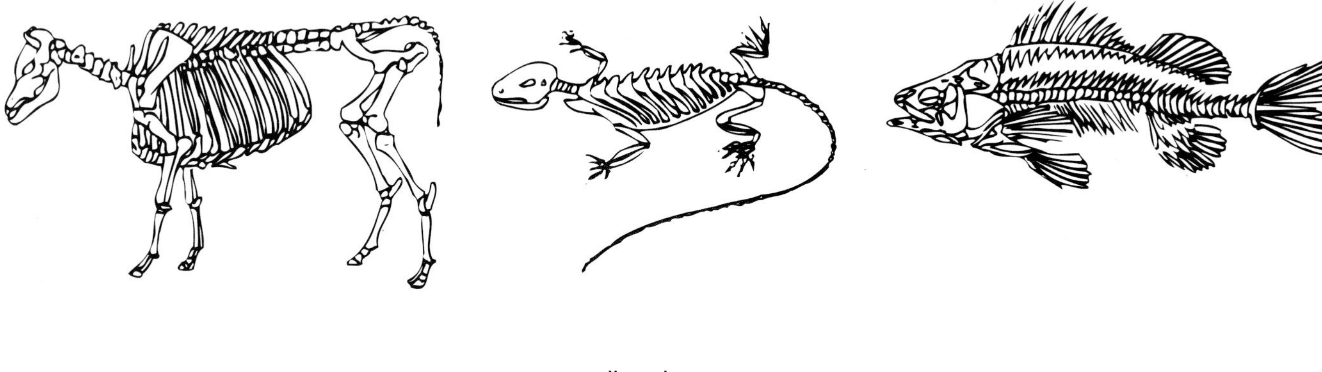

cow lizard perch

Directions: Pretend that you have discovered an animal never seen before.

1. Think carefully about your animal. What does it look like? What is its habitat? What kinds of movements can it make? In the box below, write five things your animal can do (such as fly, jump, climb, etc.).
2. On a scrap piece of paper, sketch a picture of your animal's skeleton. Keep in mind the five actions you listed and your animal's habitat.
3. When you are satisfied with your sketch, draw the skeleton in the space below.
4. Write your animal's name in the blank.

1. ____________
2. ____________
3. ____________
4. ____________
5. ____________

Name of animal: ______________________________

Bonus Box: On another sheet of paper, write a story about your imaginary animal. Describe what it looks like, its habitat, and any habits or features that make it unique.

Name ____________________

Work Those Muscles! Build Those Bones!

Color each section of the jump rope as you complete an activity.

I will complete ________ activities by ____________________.
(number) (date)

Signed: ______________________________

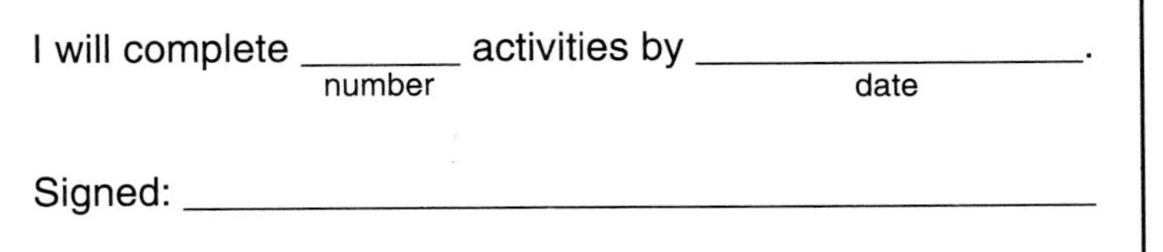

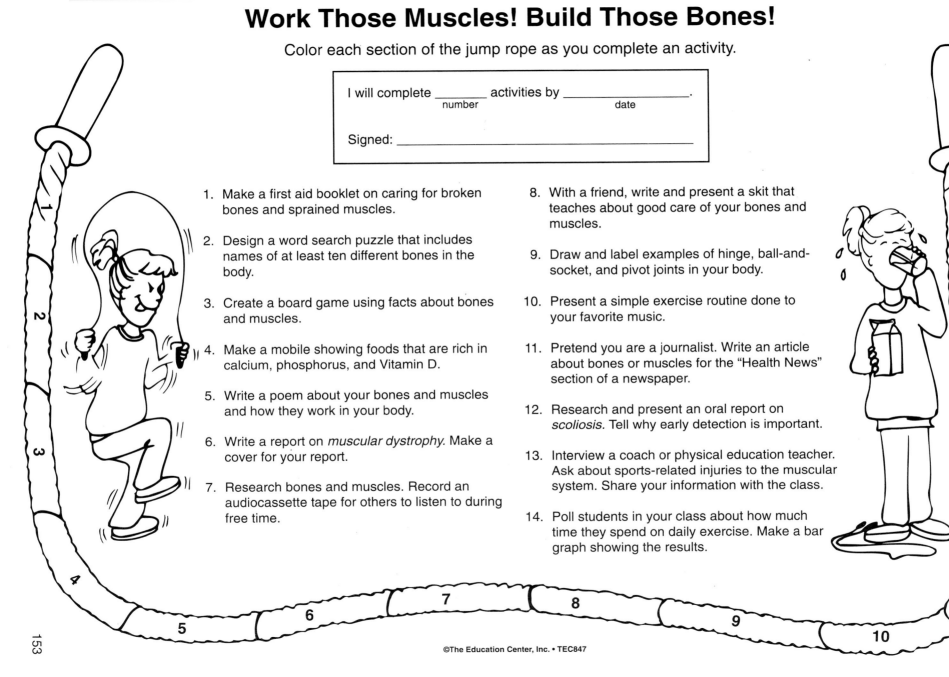

1. Make a first aid booklet on caring for broken bones and sprained muscles.
2. Design a word search puzzle that includes names of at least ten different bones in the body.
3. Create a board game using facts about bones and muscles.
4. Make a mobile showing foods that are rich in calcium, phosphorus, and Vitamin D.
5. Write a poem about your bones and muscles and how they work in your body.
6. Write a report on *muscular dystrophy.* Make a cover for your report.
7. Research bones and muscles. Record an audiocassette tape for others to listen to during free time.
8. With a friend, write and present a skit that teaches about good care of your bones and muscles.
9. Draw and label examples of hinge, ball-and-socket, and pivot joints in your body.
10. Present a simple exercise routine done to your favorite music.
11. Pretend you are a journalist. Write an article about bones or muscles for the "Health News" section of a newspaper.
12. Research and present an oral report on *scoliosis.* Tell why early detection is important.
13. Interview a coach or physical education teacher. Ask about sports-related injuries to the muscular system. Share your information with the class.
14. Poll students in your class about how much time they spend on daily exercise. Make a bar graph showing the results.

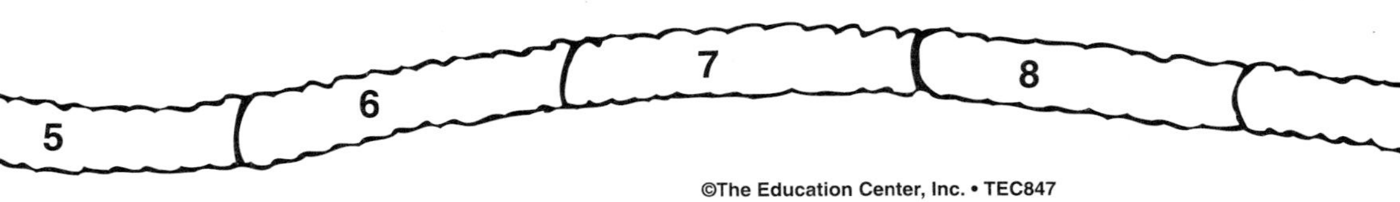

1 2 3 4 5 6 7 8 9 10 11 12 13 14

The Wonder Of Whales

Plunge into a fascinating study of those mysterious creatures of the deep called whales. Use these activities with the reproducibles on pages 156–161 for a whale of a unit!

by Amy Benson

Whale Experts

Generate lots of student research with this easy-to-make bulletin board. Use the pattern on page 159 to make a large tagboard whale. Laminate the whale and mount it on a bulletin board. Duplicate a copy of the contract on page 159 for each student. Challenge students to complete the contract using encyclopedias and resource books. When a student completes the contract satisfactorily, write her name on the whale with a wipe-off marker. Invite students to decorate the rest of the bulletin board with drawings or newly discovered facts about whales.

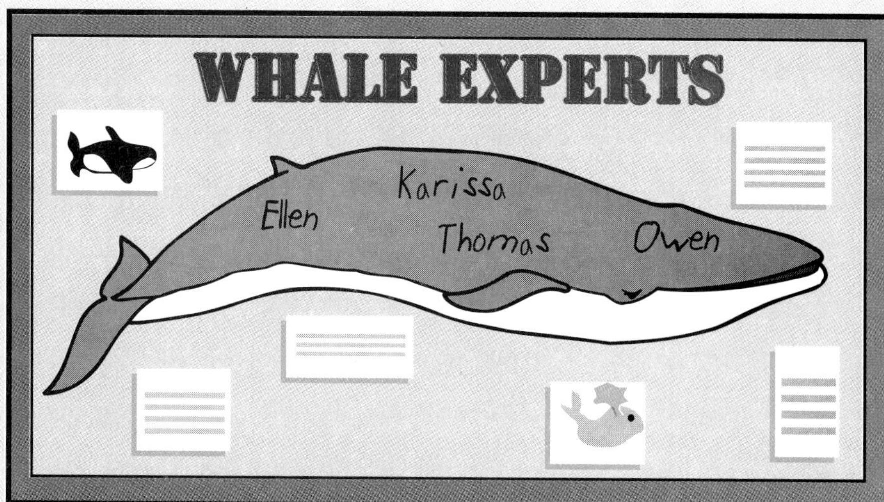

Whale Watch Timeline

Use the timeline below to acquaint your students with the history of whaling. Have students define unfamiliar words or choose a date to illustrate with original drawings. Post finished pictures with the timeline on a "Whale Watch" bulletin board.

Prehistoric Times—Man eats whales stranded on beaches.
890 A.D.—Norwegian whalers are the first to hunt and kill whales.
900s—Basques of France and Spain hunt whales near the shore from small boats.
1200s—Basques equip large sailing ships for whaling voyages.
1500s—Basques hunt farther out in the ocean as whales become scarcer.
1600s—Other European nations begin whaling. American colonists begin hunting whales off the Atlantic coast.
1700s—Sperm whaling develops into a major industry in America.
1820—American whaling industry prospers, employing 70,000 men.
1850—Many whalers leave for the California gold rush. Whaling declines.
1861–1865—Many whaling ships are sunk during the Civil War.
1900—Petroleum products replace sperm whale oil as fuel for lamps. Whaling continues to decline.
1900–1940—Modern methods make whaling easier. More whales are killed than ever before.
1946—The International Whaling Commission (IWC) is formed to protect whales from overhunting.
1962—66,000 whales are killed in one year.
1970—The IWC limits the number of whales that could be killed each year.
1979—The IWC limits the use of whale factory ships.
1985–1986—The IWC holds a moratorium on commercial whaling.

A Whale Of A Tale

Incorporate writing and literature into your study of whales. Read several tall tales to your students. Have them identify the common elements found in each story: an imaginary character with great strength or unusual powers, exaggeration, and humor. Then encourage each student to write a tall tale with a whale as the main character. Your students will have a "whale of a time" inventing their whale heroes, creating their adventures, and illustrating their tales.

Whale Talk

Scientists have discovered that whales are very social animals. They live and travel in groups called *pods.* Whales even communicate with one another by making a variety of sounds called *phonations.*

Set up an outdoor simulation to illustrate the importance of the whale's keen sense of hearing in communication and group life. Divide your class into several "pods." Have each pod develop its own unique noise to use in communicating with one another. Then separate and blindfold one member from each group to be his pod's "lost whale." Have the other students make their noises until the lost whales locate their pods. How long does it take? Have students speculate about the kinds of information whales might communicate to one another through phonations. For a fascinating follow-up, check your local public library for *Common Ground.* This album by saxophonist Paul Winter includes the recorded songs of humpback whales.

Papier-Mâché Whale

Teamwork is the name of the game when your class pulls together to create a giant papier-mâché whale. Shape chicken wire to form the frame of a large sperm whale. Have small groups of students completely cover the frame with papier-mâché. After allowing it to dry, paint the whale with blue-gray or black paint, and add facial features.

Phyllis Scarcell Marcus
Olean, NY

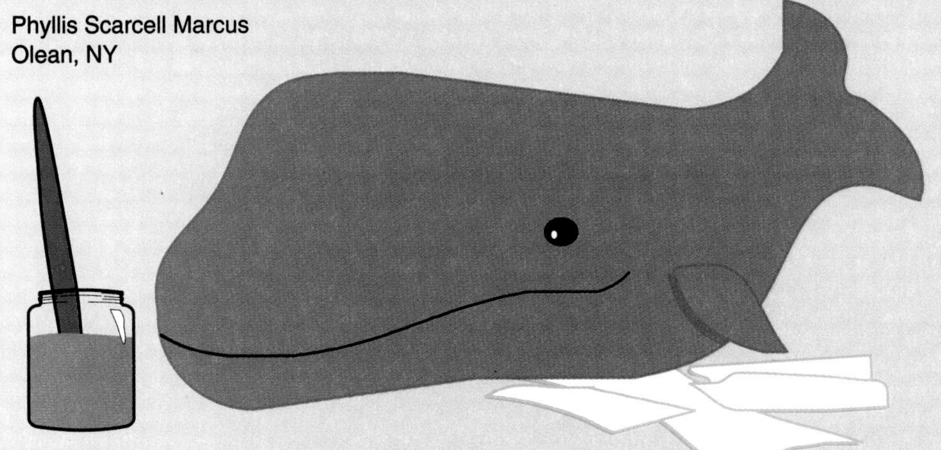

The Wonderful Whale Museum

Invite your students to investigate whales up close and personally. Using the list on page 157, have each student choose a whale to study. Let your researchers present their data in the form of written or videotaped reports (see the outline on page 158), booklets, or posters. When projects are completed, turn your classroom into a whale museum. Have each student write a short summary of his project to be printed in a museum directory. Decide as a class how to organize the exhibits. Write invitations to other classes, faculty members, and parents. Then open the doors to your whale museum and watch the curious crowds pour in!

Great Lengths

Your students will be fascinated by the huge size of many whales. Turn their interest into a lesson on measurement. On the next sunny day, head to the playground with a tape measure and the chart on page 157. Have students measure 100 feet, the length of a blue whale. For fun, see how many students it takes lying head-to-toe to equal that length! Then have students estimate the number of classmates needed to equal the lengths of other whales on the chart.

Name ____________________

Whale Watchers, Inc.

Five of the whale facts below are false. Rewrite the five false facts on your paper to make them true statements.

1. Whales are mammals.
2. Whales are some of the most intelligent animals.
3. Whales can breathe underwater.
4. A baby whale is called a *calf.*
5. Whales lay eggs.
6. Dolphins and porpoises are toothed whales.
7. Whales have no sense of smell.
8. Whales use lungs to breathe.
9. All whales have teeth.
10. A whale's skin is very rough.
11. People have hunted whales since prehistoric times.
12. The blue whale is the largest living animal.
13. Whales are members of the fish family.
14. Whales are warm-blooded.

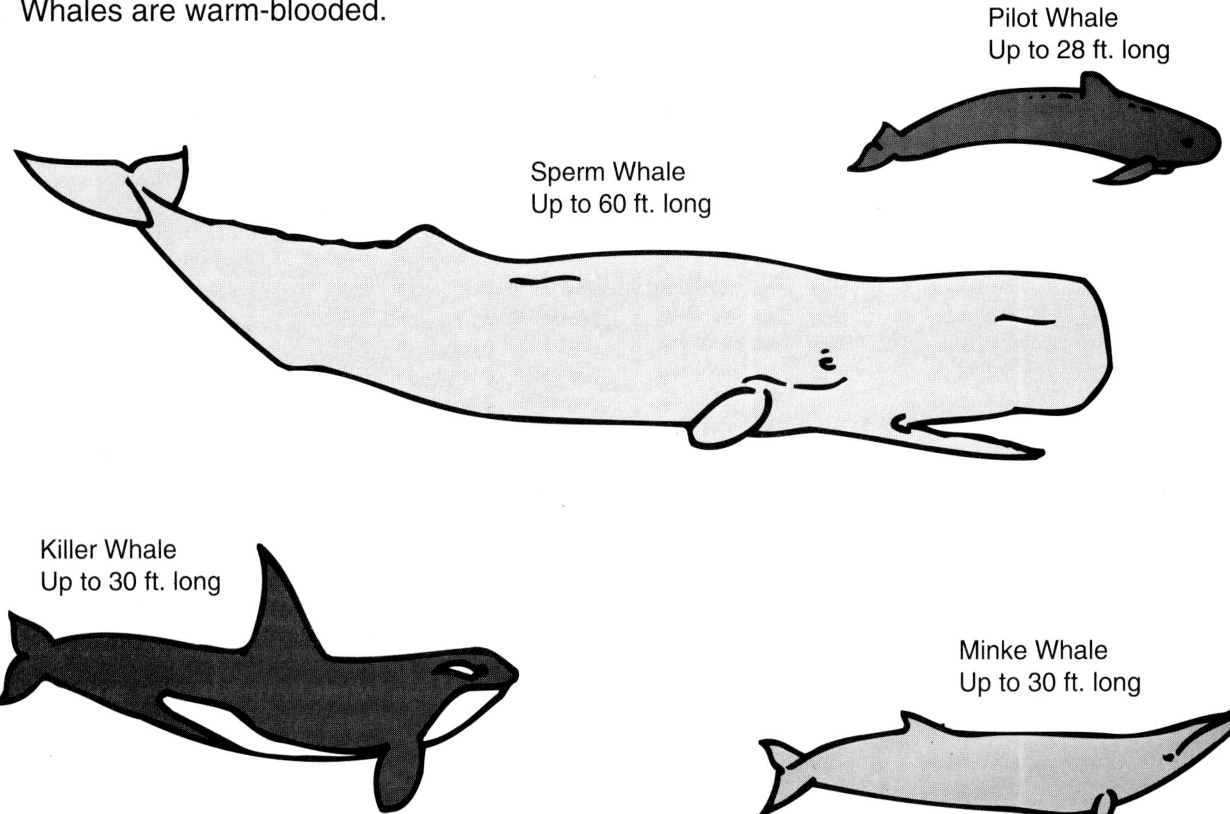

Name ____________________

Whales In The Wild

There are two major groups of whales.
Toothed whales have teeth.
Baleen whales do not have teeth.

KINDS OF WHALES

	Length	Color	Food	Location
TOOTHED				
sperm whale	up to 60 feet	blue-gray or black	cuttlefish, squid	lives in all oceans
narwhal	up to 15 feet	gray and white with dark spots	fish and squid	found mostly in Arctic Ocean
beluga	up to 15 feet	white when fully grown	fish and squid	found mostly in Arctic Ocean
killer whale	up to 30 feet	black with white areas	fish, seabirds, turtles	lives in all oceans
common dolphin	up to 8 feet	black and white with brown-gray stripes	fish and squid	lives in all oceans
common porpoise	up to 6 feet	black backs and white undersides	fish and squid	lives in all oceans
BALEEN				
blue whale	up to 100 feet	dull blue	krill	lives in all oceans
bowhead whale	up to 60 feet	black with white chin	plankton	Arctic Ocean
fin whale	up to 80 feet	black on top, white underneath	krill and small fish	lives in all oceans
humpback whale	up to 50 feet	black on top, white underneath	krill and small fish	lives in all oceans
gray whale	up to 50 feet	mottled gray	small sea animals, fish, plankton	North Pacific Ocean
Bryde's whale	up to 45 feet	blue-gray with a white belly	fish and squid	tropical and sub-tropical seas

Note To Teacher: See activities for this chart on page 155.

Name ______________________________

Choose a whale to study. Fill in the outline while you take notes or after you have collected all of your information.

____
(type of whale)

I. Body Structure

A. Size

1. ______________________________
2. ______________________________
3. ______________________________

B. Shape

1. ______________________________
2. ______________________________
3. ______________________________

C. Senses

1. ______________________________
2. ______________________________
3. ______________________________

D. Other Interesting Facts

1. ______________________________
2. ______________________________
3. ______________________________

II. The Life Of A Whale

A. Habitat

1. ______________________________
2. ______________________________
3. ______________________________

B. Food And Eating Habits

1. ______________________________
2. ______________________________
3. ______________________________

C. Whale Babies

1. ______________________________
2. ______________________________
3. ______________________________

D. Other Interesting Facts

1. ______________________________
2. ______________________________
3. ______________________________

Note To Teacher: Have students use their finished outlines to write reports about whales. Use this page with "The Wonderful Whale Museum" on page 155.

Name ______________________________ Contract

Be A Whale Expert

Complete this contract and become an official Whale Expert!

A. Write your answers on your paper. Use an encyclopedia to help you.

1. What are the two major groups of whales?
2. Which two senses (taste, hearing, sight, touch, smell) are well-developed in whales?
3. What are male and female whales called?
4. What are a whale's nostrils called? How many nostrils does a toothed whale have? How many nostrils does a baleen whale have?
5. Where are a whale's flukes located? How does a whale use its flukes?
6. What part of a whale's body keeps the whale warm?
7. List two foods of toothed whales.
8. List two foods of baleen whales.
9. Is a sperm whale a toothed or baleen whale?
10. List two ways whales are different from fish.

B. Each of these underlined words is in the wrong sentence. Switch the words and rewrite each sentence correctly on your paper. Use a dictionary to help you.

1. <u>A cetacean</u> is a layer of fat beneath a whale's skin.
2. Expensive perfumes contain <u>flukes</u>, a whale product.
3. Whales belong to a group of mammals called <u>ambergris</u>.
4. Whales swim by swinging their huge <u>krill</u> from side to side.
5. <u>Blubber</u> is a favorite food of blue whales.

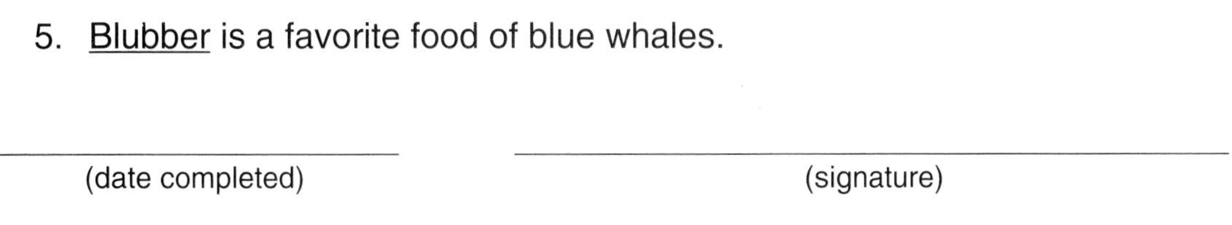

______________________ (date completed) ______________________________ (signature)

Note To Teacher: See the accompanying bulletin board idea on page 154.

Name ______________________________

Summer To Winter

What do many birds and whales have in common? They migrate thousands of miles each year! Most baleen (but not toothed) whales migrate every year. In the spring, the whales swim to the cold waters of the Arctic and Antarctic. There they spend the summer feeding on the thickest and best plankton. The whales eat to store large supplies of blubber.

As winter approaches, the polar waters begin to freeze. The whales make their journey back to the warmer waters near the equator. Because there is not much food in these waters, the whales live off their blubber. Mother whales even make some of their blubber into milk for their babies. Many whale babies are born in the winter months.

Two baleen whales do not make this yearly trip. Bryde's whales never leave the warm waters near the equator. Bowhead whales always stay in the cold Arctic.

Answer these questions about the article:

1. What do birds and whales have in common? ______________________________

____

2. Where do whales migrate to in the spring? ______________________________

____

3. Why do whales leave the Arctic and Antarctic waters in the winter? ______________________________

____

4. Where do whales live in the winter months? ______________________________

____

5. What do whales eat in the summer? ______________________________
6. How do mother whales feed their babies in the winter? ______________________________

____

7. What two types of baleen whales do not migrate? ______________________________

____

8. Which baleen whale lives in warm waters all year? ______________________________
9. Which baleen whale lives in cold waters all year? ______________________________
10. What would be another good title for this article? ______________________________

____

Bonus Box: Underline ten common nouns in the article. Write them in alphabetical order on the back of this sheet.

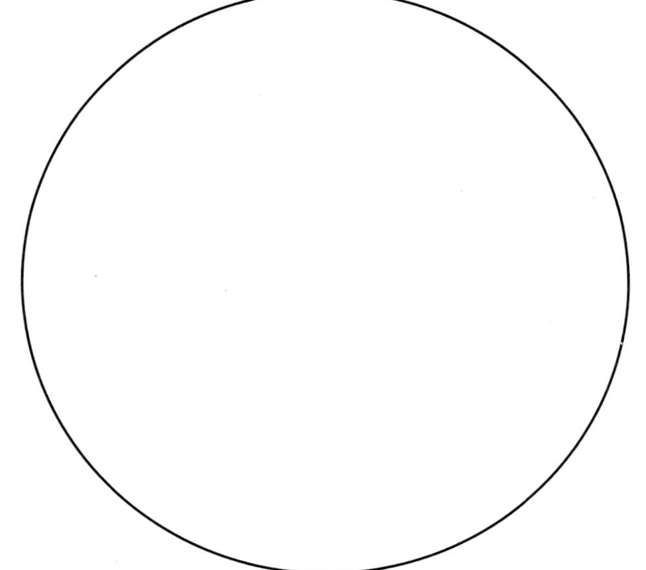

Dolphin Debate

Many people do not know that dolphins are members of the whale family. Some dolphins, like the killer whale, are even called whales. Dolphins are toothed whales that live in nearly all the oceans.

People have always been fascinated by dolphins. Long ago, artists decorated coins, pottery, and walls with pictures of dolphins. For many years, sailors believed that the dolphin was a sign of good luck. Today trained dolphins can be found in amusement parks, zoos, and aquariums. These smart, playful animals perform stunts and tricks for people around the world.

Each year thousands of dolphins are killed by hunters. The people and animals of some countries, including Japan and China, eat dolphin meat. The oil from the dolphin's body is also sold. Millions of dolphins drown in fishing nets that were meant to catch other fishes.

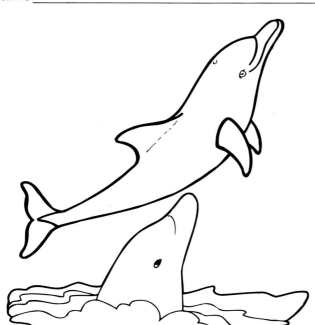

1. Read the article. Then, answer **one** of the following questions in a paragraph on the back of this sheet:

   a. Should dolphins be taken from their ocean homes to be trained for entertainment? Why or why not?
   b. Should nations be punished for killing dolphins, even if they provide food for their people? Why or why not?
   c. Should fishermen be punished for accidentally drowning dolphins in their nets? Why or why not?
   d. How can people of different nations work together to protect dolphins?

2. In the circle, design a badge to illustrate your paragraph. Be sure to include an interesting slogan. Color the badge.

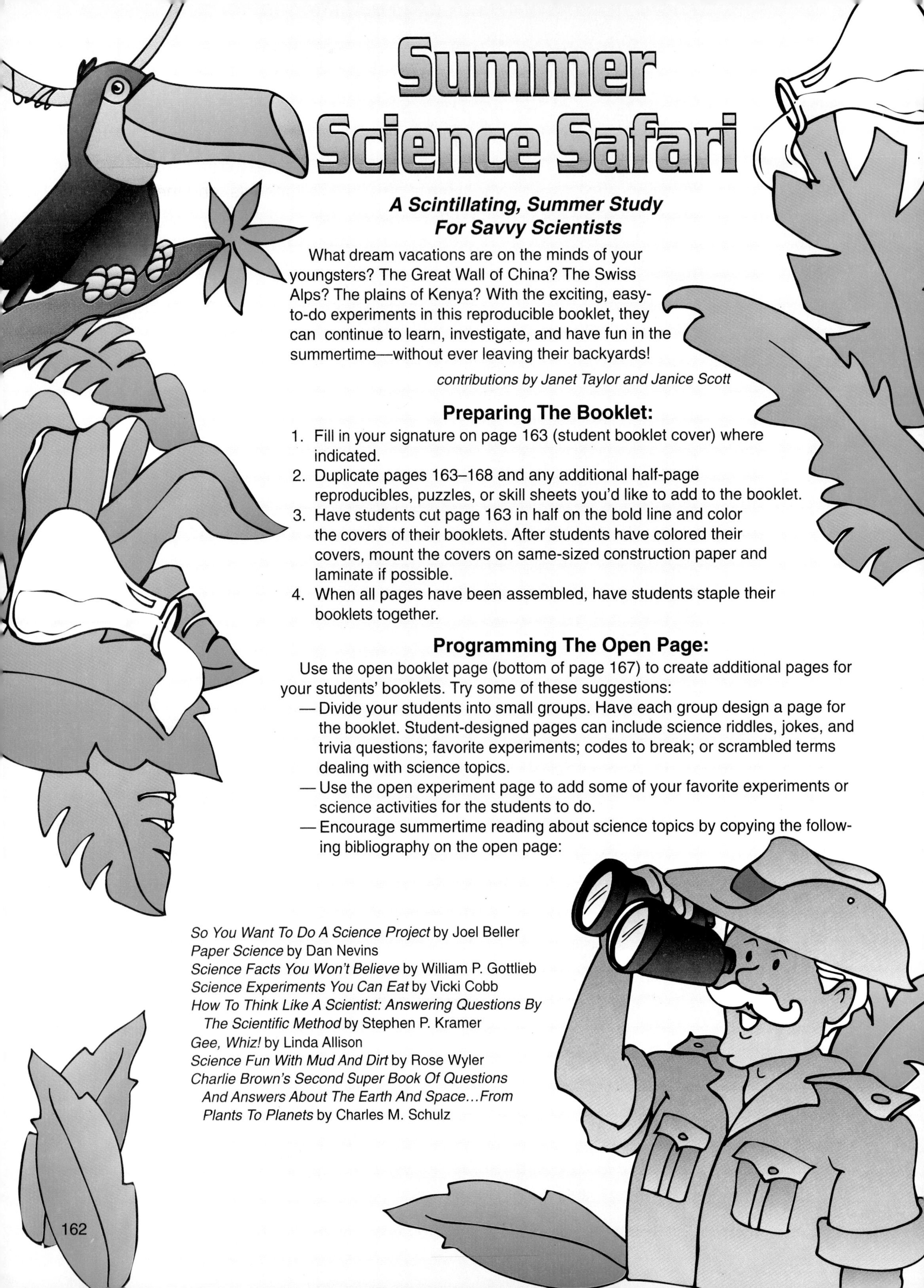

Summer Science Safari

A Scintillating, Summer Study For Savvy Scientists

What dream vacations are on the minds of your youngsters? The Great Wall of China? The Swiss Alps? The plains of Kenya? With the exciting, easy-to-do experiments in this reproducible booklet, they can continue to learn, investigate, and have fun in the summertime—without ever leaving their backyards!

contributions by Janet Taylor and Janice Scott

Preparing The Booklet:

1. Fill in your signature on page 163 (student booklet cover) where indicated.
2. Duplicate pages 163–168 and any additional half-page reproducibles, puzzles, or skill sheets you'd like to add to the booklet.
3. Have students cut page 163 in half on the bold line and color the covers of their booklets. After students have colored their covers, mount the covers on same-sized construction paper and laminate if possible.
4. When all pages have been assembled, have students staple their booklets together.

Programming The Open Page:

Use the open booklet page (bottom of page 167) to create additional pages for your students' booklets. Try some of these suggestions:

— Divide your students into small groups. Have each group design a page for the booklet. Student-designed pages can include science riddles, jokes, and trivia questions; favorite experiments; codes to break; or scrambled terms dealing with science topics.

— Use the open experiment page to add some of your favorite experiments or science activities for the students to do.

— Encourage summertime reading about science topics by copying the following bibliography on the open page:

So You Want To Do A Science Project by Joel Beller
Paper Science by Dan Nevins
Science Facts You Won't Believe by William P. Gottlieb
Science Experiments You Can Eat by Vicki Cobb
How To Think Like A Scientist: Answering Questions By The Scientific Method by Stephen P. Kramer
Gee, Whiz! by Linda Allison
Science Fun With Mud And Dirt by Rose Wyler
Charlie Brown's Second Super Book Of Questions And Answers About The Earth And Space...From Plants To Planets by Charles M. Schulz

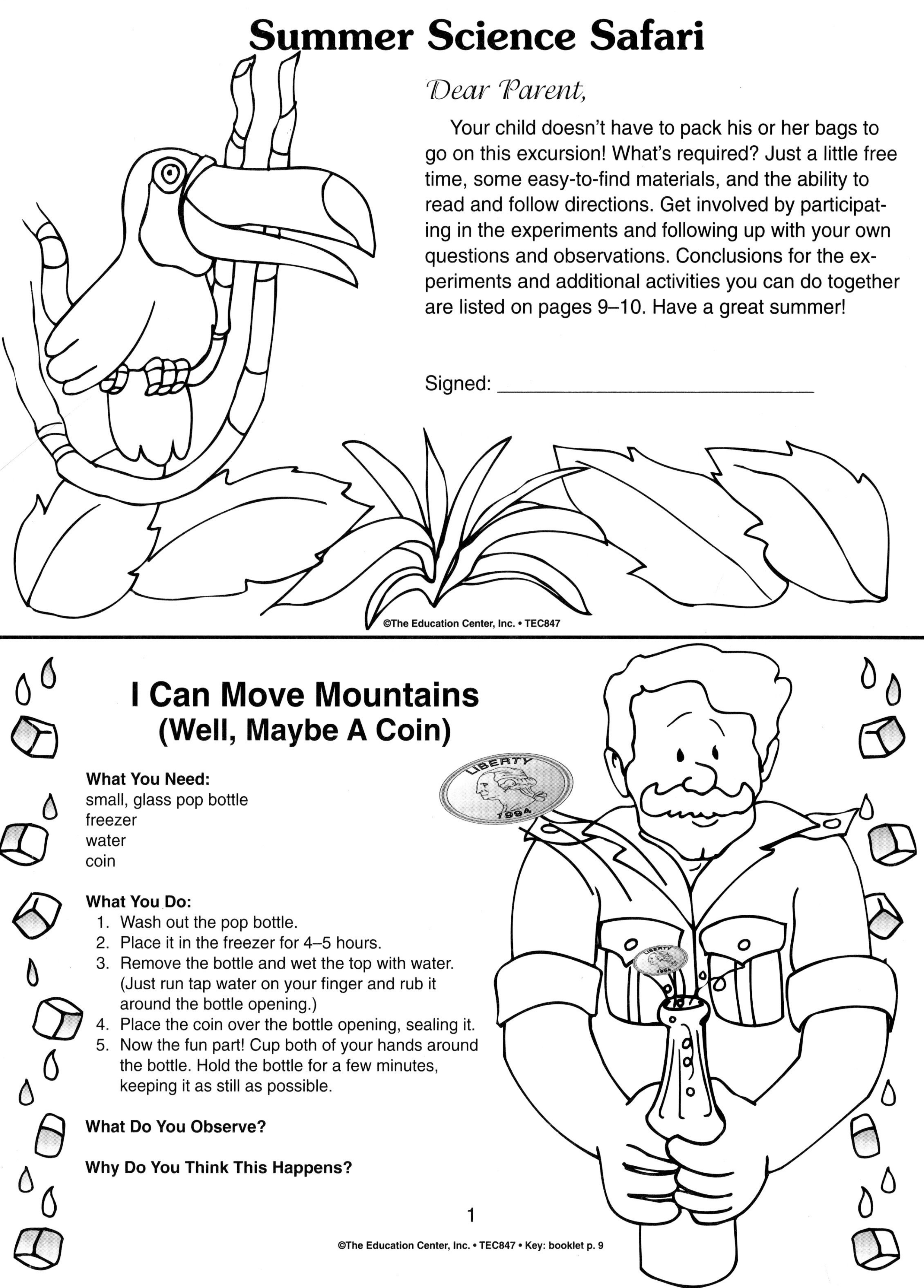

Summer Science Safari

Dear Parent,

Your child doesn't have to pack his or her bags to go on this excursion! What's required? Just a little free time, some easy-to-find materials, and the ability to read and follow directions. Get involved by participating in the experiments and following up with your own questions and observations. Conclusions for the experiments and additional activities you can do together are listed on pages 9–10. Have a great summer!

Signed: ______________________________

I Can Move Mountains (Well, Maybe A Coin)

What You Need:
small, glass pop bottle
freezer
water
coin

What You Do:

1. Wash out the pop bottle.
2. Place it in the freezer for 4–5 hours.
3. Remove the bottle and wet the top with water. (Just run tap water on your finger and rub it around the bottle opening.)
4. Place the coin over the bottle opening, sealing it.
5. Now the fun part! Cup both of your hands around the bottle. Hold the bottle for a few minutes, keeping it as still as possible.

What Do You Observe?

Why Do You Think This Happens?

Which Is Heavier—Salt Water Or Fresh Water?

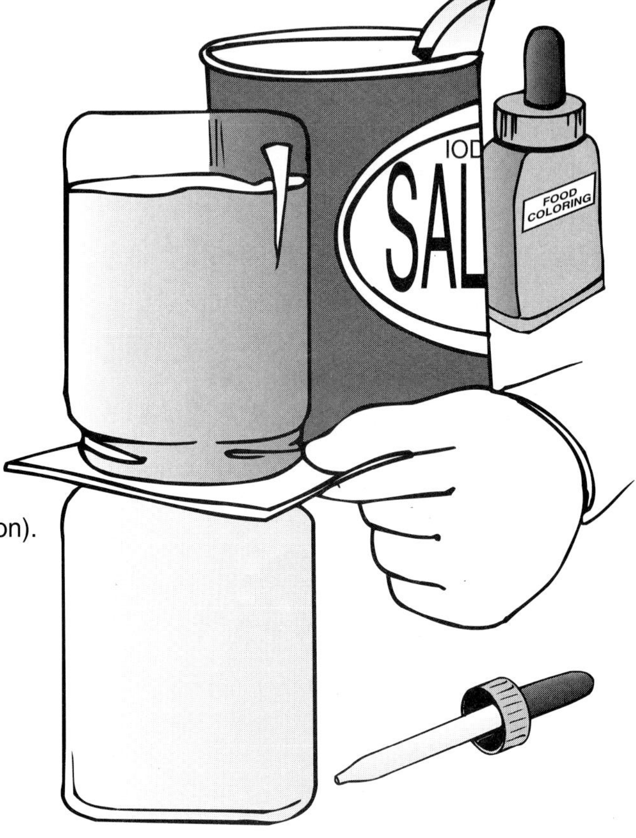

What You Need:
2 identical glass containers (pint-sized canning jars work nicely)
water
salt
blue food coloring
a stiff card (large enough to cover the opening of the jar)
measuring spoons

What You Do:
1. Fill both jars with regular tap water.
2. To one jar, add 10 teaspoons of salt and 1 teaspoon of blue food coloring. Dissolve thoroughly.
3. Place the card over the salt water jar's mouth.
4. While firmly holding the card over the jar of salt water, invert it and place it on top of the jar of regular tap water (see illustration).
5. Remove the card very slowly and carefully. (You might want to do this over the kitchen sink!)

What Do You Observe?

Why Do You Think This Happens?

Apples Are Airheads!

What You Need:
potato
carrot
apple
3 large bowls
water

What You Do:
1. Fill the bowls with water.
2. Pick up the food items, one at a time, and compare their weights.
3. Place one in each bowl.

What Do You Observe?

Why Do You Think This Happens?

Blue Water Magic

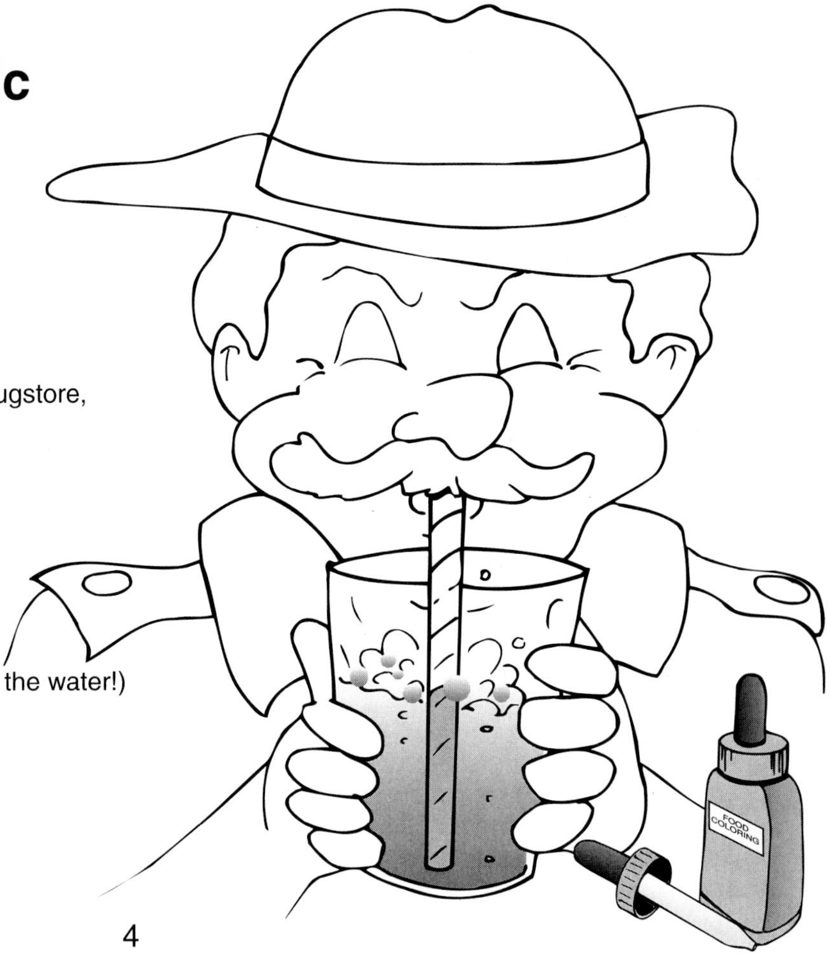

What You Need:
a clear plastic cup or glass
a soda straw
water
bromothymol blue (can be purchased from a drugstore, pet store, or swimming pool supplies store)
medicine dropper

What You Do:
1. Pour some water into the cup or glass.
2. Add a few drops of bromothymol blue to the water so that it becomes bright blue.
3. Put the soda straw into the water.
4. Blow into the straw. (Be careful **not** to drink the water!)

What Do You Observe?

Why Do You Think This Happens?

All Dried Up

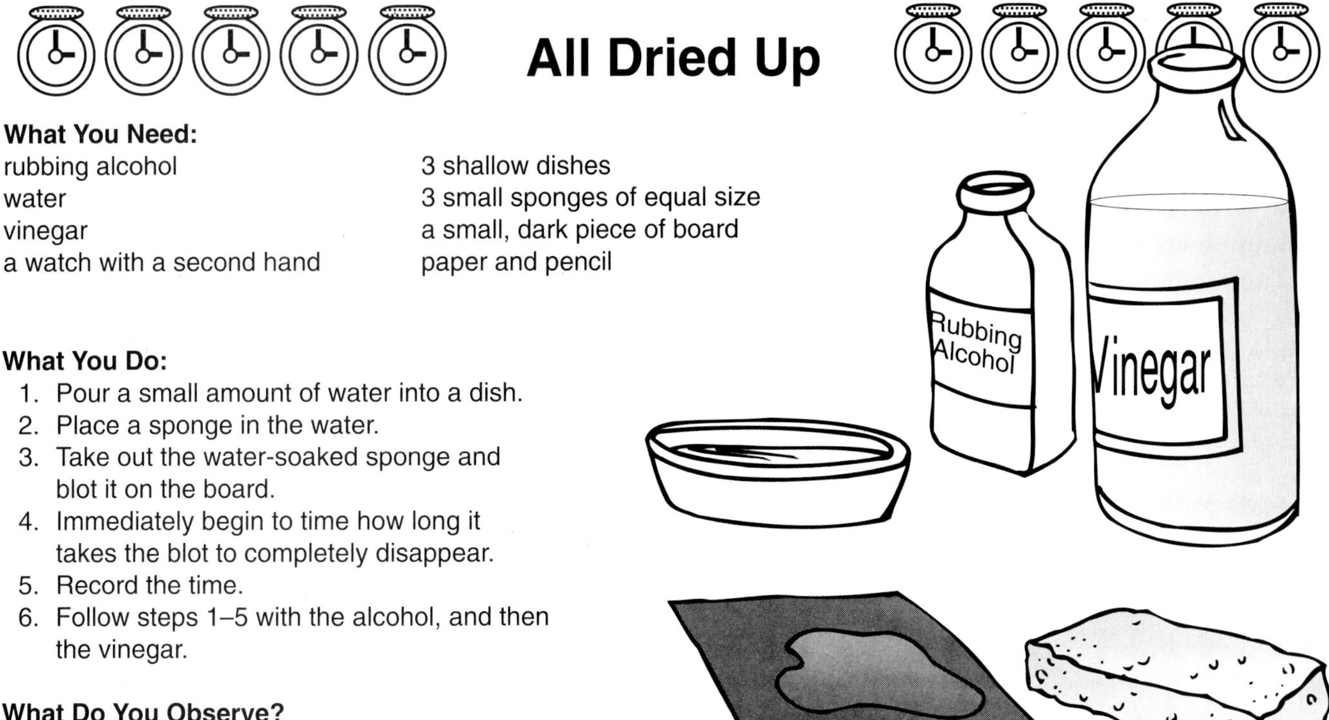

What You Need:
rubbing alcohol
water
vinegar
a watch with a second hand
3 shallow dishes
3 small sponges of equal size
a small, dark piece of board
paper and pencil

What You Do:
1. Pour a small amount of water into a dish.
2. Place a sponge in the water.
3. Take out the water-soaked sponge and blot it on the board.
4. Immediately begin to time how long it takes the blot to completely disappear.
5. Record the time.
6. Follow steps 1–5 with the alcohol, and then the vinegar.

What Do You Observe?

Why Do You Think This Happens?

Waterproof Matches

What You Need:
clear nail polish
wooden matches
some clay or Play-Doh

What You Do:
1. Paint the striking ends of several matches with clear nail polish, covering completely.
2. Place the other ends of the matches into the clay or Play-Doh so that the painted ends are sticking up.
3. Let the matches dry thoroughly.
4. Add a second coat of polish.
5. Let dry overnight.
6. The next day, take a match from the clay and run water over the striking end. **Give it to a parent to strike.**

What Do You Observe?

Why Do You Think This Happens?

Solar Salt-Zapper

What You Need:
pie pan
glass dish (smaller than the pie pan)
clear, mixing bowl (one that will fit in the pie pan
when inverted)
salt water (mix 1 teaspoon of salt into a half-pint of water)
sunshine

What You Do:
1. Place the glass dish in the pie pan.
2. Pour the salt water into the dish.
3. Cover the dish with the mixing bowl.
4. Place in an area that gets plenty of direct sunlight.
5. Check each day for several days.

What Do You Observe?

Why Do You Think This Happens?

Summer Science Bingo

How many of the following can you find, observe, read about, watch, or experience during summer vacation? First try to get bingo (five in a row); then continue and see if you can cross out all the items on the card.

a rhinoceros beetle	an ant colony	an earthworm	a dragonfly	a mammal's habitat
animal tracks (besides your pet's!)	a caterpillar	an example of evaporation	an example of erosion	a television special about a science topic
a biography of a famous scientist	some tadpoles	FREE SPACE	a praying mantis	a mint leaf
a cause of pollution	bread mold	a hummingbird	a recycling station	a full moon
a bird's nest	an animal skeleton	the North Star	an animal that camouflages itself for protection	a food chain consisting of at least four animals

Open

Science Experiment Conclusions And Additional Activities

1. The coin on top of the bottle traps cold air inside. When the air begins to warm, it expands and forces the coin up. Some air escapes and the coin falls back down. This continues until the air inside the bottle reaches the same temperature as the air outside it.

   Additional activity: After the experiment, let the pop bottle sit for a while. Then place the coin on the opening. Get another family member to cup his or her hands around the bottle, along with yours. What happens? Can you determine why?

2. The blue salt water sank to the bottom of the lower jar. The salt water sank because it is heavier than the tap water. The lighter tap water moved up over the saltier water.

   Additional activity: Get Mom or Dad to boil some water for you. Cover the water and let it cool. Now drink some of the water. Why does it taste different from regular tap water?

3. Foods, especially fruits and vegetables, vary greatly in the amount of air they contain. Carrot and potato matter is dense and very heavy. So they sink in the water. The apple is not as dense and has many air spaces, which allows it to float.

   Additional activity: Test the *buoyancy* (the tendency to float or rise when submerged in a liquid) of other fruits and vegetables. Can a person float easily? Do some research to find out why.

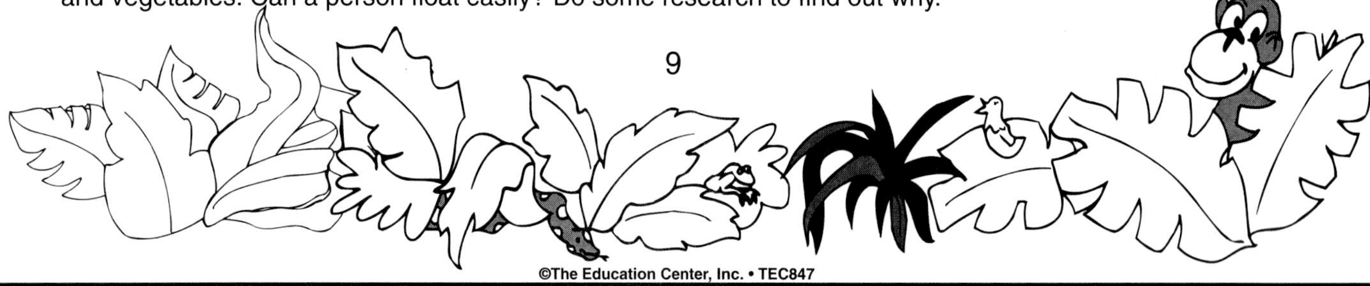

Science Experiment Conclusions And Additional Activities

4. You exhale carbon dioxide when you blow through the straw. The carbon dioxide combines with the chemical (bromothymol blue) in the water and causes the color to change.

5. The alcohol evaporates first, followed by the vinegar, and then the water. Alcohol and vinegar are composed of molecules that combine more readily with air at room temperature. Therefore they evaporate more quickly.

   Additional activity: If you did the experiment inside, try it again outside on a sunny day. Also try other types of liquids such as salt water, soda pop, lemon juice, and milk.

6. The nail polish that you put on the match tips seals them, creating a barrier to any type of moisture. When your mom or dad strikes the match, the seal is broken. This allows the chemicals to ignite as they normally would. (Prepare some matches for *your* next camping trip!)

7. The salt water evaporates and collects on the inside of the mixing bowl. Eventually the water will drop down the sides of the bowl and into the pie pan. This water is fresh. The salt will be left in the glass dish.

   Additional activity: Can you think of another way to remove salt from salt water? Try freezing a small amount of salt water. What happens?

Answer Key

Page 6

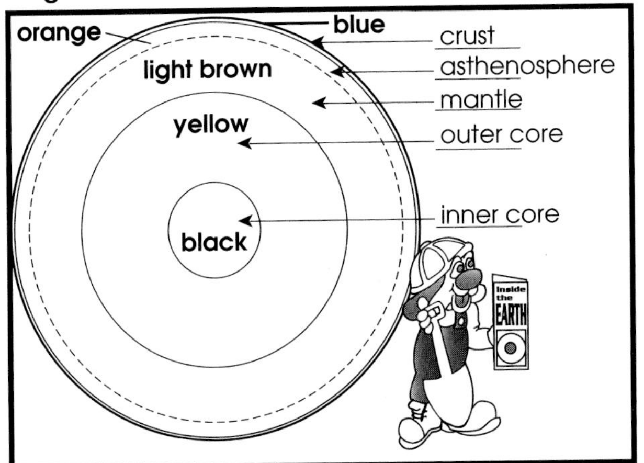

Page 7

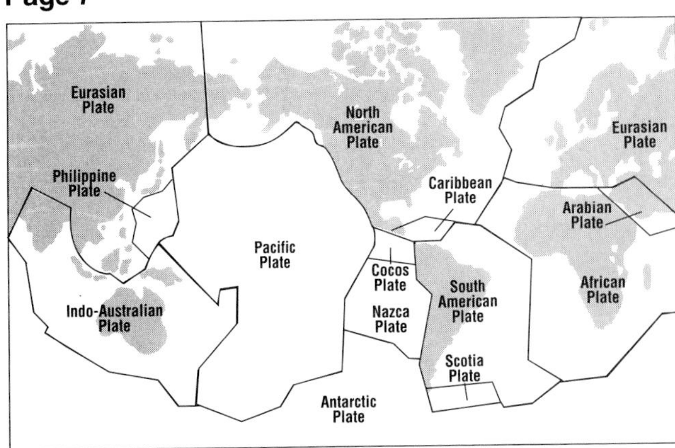

Page 8

Recording Station	March 8 (red circles)	October 2 (blue circles)	November 22 (green circles)
Santa Ana	12 mi.	4.5 mi.	11 mi.
Mudville	9 mi.	11.5 mi.	5.5 mi.
San Juan	5 mi.	12.5 mi.	9.5 mi.
City nearest to epicenter	Brookfield	El Niño	Barco

Page 9

1 S				2 M	A	G	M	3 A		4 C	O	5 R	E				
A		6 C		A				R		H		E					
N		R		N				E		A		7 A	N	G	E	8 R	
9 F	A	U	L	T			10 M	A	D	R	I	D				A	
R		S		L						L			11 D	12 R	I	F	T
13 A	S	T	H	E	N	O	S	14 P	H	E	R	E		I		T	
N								L		S				C			
C		15 T						16 A	F	T	E	R	S	H	O	17 C	K
I		18 S	C	A	L	E		T		O				T		O	
S		U					19 T	E	E	N				E		N	
C		N		20 K	I	T	E	S						R		T	
O		A					C									I	
		21 M	22 A	23 G	24 N	I	T	U	D	E			25 R	A	I	N	
26 S	E	I	S	M	O		O					27 P				E	
			I			28 A	N	C	H	O	R	A	G	E		N	
			A				I					I				T	
				29 E	P	I	C	E	N	T	E	R					

Page 13

3 dry, scaly skin
1,2 warm-blooded
4 most live on land and in water
5 breathe mainly through gills
4 breathe with lungs, skin, or gills
1,2,3 breathe with lungs only
5 eyes usually on sides of head
1 have hair or fur at some time in their lives
2 hollow or partly hollow bones
1 most give birth to live young
3,4,5 cold-blooded
1 young feed on mother's milk
4 moist, scaleless skin
2 wings and feathers
5 most use fins to swim
1 large, well-developed brains
2 lay hard-shelled eggs
3 dinosaurs were members of this group
3 most lay leathery eggs
4 eggs enclosed in jellylike substance

Write each of these animals under the correct vertebrate group: **tern, anaconda, tilapia, auk, newt, tuatara, goby, potto, caecilian, marmoset.** Use a dictionary or encyclopedias to help you.

Mammals
1. *potto*
2. *marmoset*

Birds
1. *tern*
2. *auk*

Reptiles
1. *anaconda*
2. *tuatara*

Amphibians
1. *newt*
2. *caecilian*

Fish
1. *tilapia*
2. *goby*

Page 15

Across: 1. bacteria 4. euglena 5. microbes 6. paramecium 8. fungi 9. protist 11. vaccine 15. protozoa 17. lichen
Down: 2. algae 3. kingdom 6. penicillin 7. microscopic 10. disease 12. amoeba 13. species 14. colony 16. mold
Bonus Box answer: He was a Dutch scientist who invented the light microscope.

Page 26

1. a. A
   b. 42 mm
   c. 42 mm
   Answers will vary.
2. a. Bert
   b. All of the boys are the same height.
   c. Each boy is approximately 36 mm tall.
   Answers will vary.
3. a. A
   b. 65 mm
   c. 65 mm
   Answers will vary.
4. a. No.
   b. Yes.
   c. Answers will vary.
   Answers will vary.

Answer Key continued ...

Page 34

1. Canada, Russia
2. Brazil
3. Possible answers: Central and South America—Mexico, Nicaragua, Guatemala, Panama, Honduras, El Salvador, Brazil, Colombia, Paraguay, Venezuela; Africa—Zaire, Republic of Congo, Gabon, Liberia; Asia—Thailand, Malaysia, Indonesia, Philippines
4. temperate deciduous
   Bonus Box answer: western South America—too mountainous; northern Africa—too little rainfall; Greenland—too cold; western United States—too mountainous and too little rainfall

Page 36

Grow A Tree!

1. Answers will vary.
2. The insects are food for birds, mice, and other small animals.
3. The water turns dark brown or black. This is caused by *tannin,* a chemical found in trees which is used to turn animal skins into leather.
4. Some species of oak won't germinate without an extended period of cold, or *dormancy.* This prevents them from sprouting in the fall, when they could not survive the winter.
5. The root grew first.

Page 35

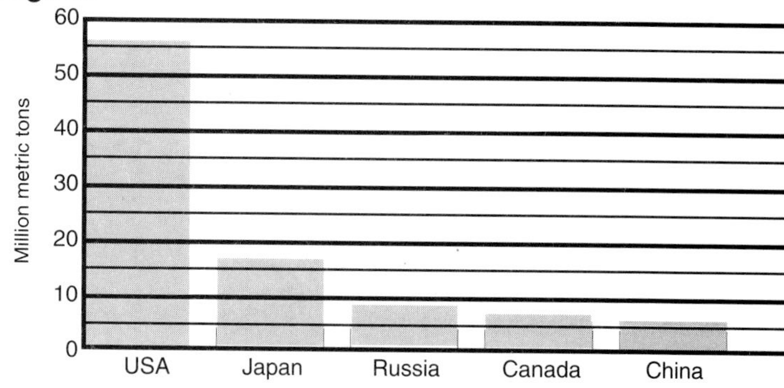

2. United States
3. Russia, Canada
4. Answers will vary. These countries are developed and industrial. They have the money and technology to manufacture paper. Access to forests provides resources. (Japan imports raw materials from southeast Asia.)
5. Answers will vary.
6. Answers will vary depending on resources used.
   Bonus Box answers: USA—3,600,000 sq. mi.; Japan—146,000 sq. mi.; Russia—8,650,000 sq. mi.; Canada—3,800,000 sq. mi.; China—3,700,000 sq. mi.

A Leaf's Hidden Colors

1. The green and other pigments in the leaf will be absorbed and travel up the paper. At a certain point, the pigment will collect into a narrow band. Then each individual pigment will form a separate band.
2. Answers will vary.
3. You may see several shades of green, red, brown, and perhaps yellow, depending on the species of plant.
4. You may see colors that weren't there because the green pigment (chlorophyll) may be changed into other forms. Some of the fall color pigments were present before, but were concealed by the chlorophyll.

Page 40

1. 150 times
2. 49 breaths
3. 180 times per minute
4. 180 breaths
5. 150 beats per minute

Page 42

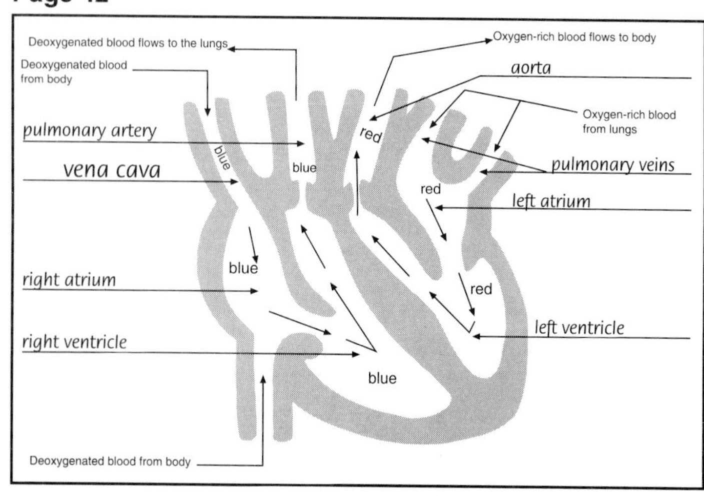

Page 43

1. Voluntary muscles are consciously controlled. Involuntary muscles are not consciously controlled.
2. walls of the heart, diaphragm
3. Involuntary control will cause you to faint and begin breathing again.
4. diaphragm
5. Your diaphragm goes into contractions and air rushes into your lungs. The epiglottis slaps shut, stopping the rush of air so quickly that the body is jolted.
6. Yes; by holding your breath
7. the flap covering your windpipe
8. sneezing, blinking

Page 44

1. bronchial tubes
2. skull
3. air pollution, cigarette smoking
4. pneumonia
5. pneumonia
6. oxygen, carbon dioxide
7. sinusitis
8. Cigarette smoking
9. lungs, heart
10. sinusitis

Page 49

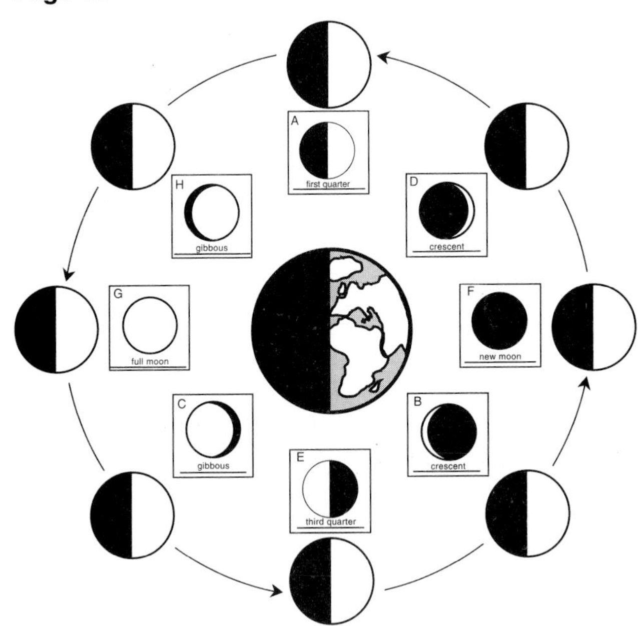

Page 57
Float Or Sink?

4. The egg sinks in Cup A and floats in Cup B.
5. Salt water is more dense and has more buoyancy than water without salt.
6. Ships ride higher in ocean water than in fresh water.

Is It Ice Yet?

4. Cup A is frozen solid. Cup B is not frozen. Cup C is frozen but not solid. There may also be salt crystals on the side of the cup.
5. The water containing salt did not freeze. The more salt there is in the water, the colder the temperature must be to freeze the pure water, leaving the salt behind.

Page 50

1. 240,000
2. 27
3. 10
4. 2,160
5. 6,800
6. 27
7. billions
8. 260° F
9. 25
10. about as high as

Page 50

method of travel	speed	time required to reach the moon hours	days
walking	2 mph	120,000	5,000
jogging	8 mph	30,000	1,250
bicycle	12 mph	20,000	833.3
automobile	55 mph	4,363.6	181.8
passenger jet	550 mph	436.4	18.2
Apollo spacecraft	3,300 mph (average)	72.7	3.0

Page 51

1. They were the lunar modules for the Apollo 11–17 moon expeditions.
2. A *selenographer* is a scientist who studies moon geography.
3. Jules Verne, a French novelist, wrote *From The Earth To The Moon.*
4. The line between the sunlit part of the moon's face and its dark part is called the *terminator.*
5. A seismic event on the moon is called a *moonquake.*
6. *Maria* are lowlands of rock on the moon covered by a thin layer of rocky soil.
7. The word *lunatic* comes from *luna,* a Latin word meaning "moon."
8. Edwin E. Aldrin, Jr., was the second human being on the moon.
9. The point where the moon orbits closest to the earth is called the moon's *perigee;* the moon's farthest point from the earth is the *apogee.*
10. If the moon had an atmosphere, it would leak away into space because of the moon's weak gravity.
11. No nation owns the moon. It cannot be claimed by any country.
12. Richard M. Nixon was president of the United States in 1969 when man first visited the moon.
13. The gravitational pull of the earth keeps the moon in its orbit.
14. The words *month* and *Monday* come from Old English words related to *moon.*

Bonus Box answer: Galileo discovered that the moon was not smooth and that it did not shine by its own light. He observed that the moon's surface was marked by valleys and mountains.

Page 64

"Pop Music"

1. The pitch and tone in each bottle are different because of the size of the chamber within the bottle.
2. The tone and pitch can also be affected by the shape of the chamber and by the material from which the container is made.
3. Enlarging the air space in a bottle creates a longer vibrating column of air. A long column results in a note of low pitch.
4. A larger container would make a lower pitch than the pop bottle. A larger container would lengthen a vibrating column of air.

A Rubber-Band Band

1. Short rubber bands will have a higher pitch than long ones.
2. Tight rubber bands will have a higher pitch than loose ones.
3. Narrow rubber bands will have a higher pitch than wide ones.
4. Light materials will have a higher pitch than heavy materials.

Page 73

The plants watered with vinegar should turn yellow, shrivel up, and die. (More advanced students may wish to experiment with weaker dilutions of vinegar and water, more precisely simulating typical acid rain.)

Page 74

Students should observe a fine powder on the bottom of the cups containing vinegar and limestone or marble after seven days. They may notice bubbles of gas on all of the rocks. Air can sometimes be trapped in porous rocks. Most of the air bubbles will disappear in a day or two. Bubbles may be observed on the limestone and marble even after seven days. These are carbon dioxide bubbles.

Page 65

sound	frequency	speed of sound (meters per second)	wavelength (meters)	speed of sound (feet per second)	wavelength (feet)
lowest sounds humans can hear	20 Hz	344	**17.2**	1,125	**56.25**
low G played on a bass violin	98 Hz	344	**3.51**	1,125	**11.48**
middle C played on a piano	262 Hz	344	**1.31**	1,125	**4.29**
A played on a clarinet	440 Hz	344	**0.78**	1,125	**2.56**
F played on a flute	698 Hz	344	**0.49**	1,125	**1.61**
high C sung by a soprano	1,048 Hz	344	**0.33**	1,125	**1.07**
highest sounds humans can hear	20,000 Hz	344	**0.02**	1,125	**0.06**

Bonus Box answer: 67,500 feet per minute; 4,050,000 feet per hour

Page 71

Acid	Neutral	Bases
vinegar water	*pure water*	*ammonia water*
lemon juice	*rain water*	*milk of magnesia*
boric acid solution	*salt water*	*baking soda solution*
soda water	*milk*	
cream of tartar solution	*sugar water*	

Page 72

1. vinegar
2. baking soda
3. soda lye
4. ammonia
5. blood
6. acid rain
7. seawater
8. pure water
9. sulfuric acid
10. milk of magnesia
11. lemon juice
12. tomato juice

Bonus Box answer:

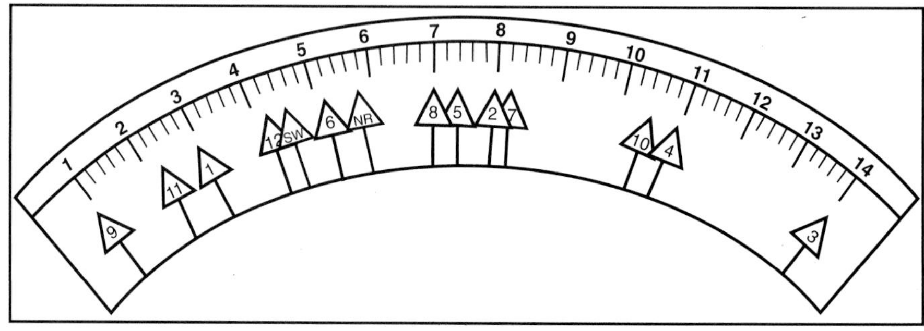

Answer Key continued ...

Page 80

Porifera: live at the bottom of oceans and other waters; do not have heads, arms, or internal organs; adult sponges do not move about; many look like plants; grow in colonies
Examples: Sycon, glass sponges, sulfur sponge, bath sponges

Coelenterata: soft bodies have jellylike material between two layers of cells; digestive cavity has one opening; most live in the sea; body may be shaped like a cylinder, a bell, or an umbrella
Examples: jellyfish, sea anemones, corals

Echinodermata: spiny-skinned sea animals; body parts are arranged around the center of the animal; body is usually divided into five sections; most have *tube feet,* which are used for moving, feeding, breathing, and sensing
Examples: starfish, sea urchins, sea cucumbers, sand dollars

Mollusca: soft-bodied, without bones; most have a hard armorlike shell; all have a skinlike organ called a *mantle,* which produces the substance that makes the shell; live in all types of environments; must keep their bodies moist to stay alive
Examples: clams, octopuses, oysters, slugs, snails, squids

Platyhelminthes: simplest kinds of worms; soft, thin, flattened bodies; bodies have three layers of cells; most live as parasites in other animals
Examples: flukes, tapeworms, planarians

Brachiopoda: have two-piece shells; attach themselves to rocks
Example: lamp shells

Annelida: long body divided into many segments; ringed appearance; covered with bristles
Examples: sandworms, earthworms, leeches

Arthropoda:

Crustacea: have no bones; an exoskeleton covers its body; two pairs of antennae; most live in salt water; some live in fresh water; a few kinds live on land
Examples: crabs, crayfish, lobsters, shrimp, barnacles, water fleas, wood lice

Arachnida: have no wings; two main body parts; land animals; four pairs of legs; no antennae (feelers)
Examples: spiders, daddy longlegs, ticks, scorpions, mites

Insecta: most have wings and a pair of antennae; skeleton is on outside of body; all have three pairs of legs; body is divided into three main parts; every insect starts life as an egg
Examples: bees, ants, wasps, butterflies, termites, houseflies, mosquitoes, fleas

Page 81

Answers are listed in order from left to right.

Osteichthyes (bony fish)
- cold-blooded
- scales
- spawning: eggs and sperm are released into the water; eggs are fertilized by sperm
- gills
- bony skeletons, live almost anywhere there is water, almost all have fins
- bass, catfish, cod, herring, minnows, perch, trout, tuna

Amphibia (amphibians)
- cold-blooded
- scaleless, moist skin
- fertilization (joining of egg and sperm) takes place outside the female's body in some and inside the female's body in others
- most breathe with lungs, some have gills, some have lungs and gills
- live part of their lives in water and part on land, live in moist habitats, most eat insects
- frogs, toads, salamanders

Reptilia (reptiles)
- cold-blooded
- dry, scaly skin
- fertilization: the sperm unite with eggs within the female's body
- lungs
- vary greatly in size, long life spans, most have good vision
- lizards, snakes, turtles, crocodiles, terrapins, tortoises

Aves (birds)
- warm-blooded
- all birds have feathers
- fertilization: male sperm unites with a female egg to produce a fertilized egg within the female's body
- lungs
- all birds have wings, do not have teeth, have a hard bill (or beak)
- flamingo, duck, hawk, turkey, pigeon, bluebird, cuckoo, toucan

Mammalia (mammals)
- warm-blooded
- hair
- fertilization: sperm unites with an egg inside the female's body; egg develops into a new individual
- lungs
- mammals nurse their babies, live almost everywhere, protect their young, and have well-developed brains
- cats, dogs, cattle, goats, hogs, anteaters, apes, people

Bonus Box answer: The four main groups of reptiles are: (1) lizards and snakes, (2) turtles, (3) crocodilians, and (4) the tuatara.

Page 82

	1. **lagomorphs**		4. **carnivores**		7. **bats**		10. **even-toed ungulates**
	2. **rodents**		5. **primates**		8. **sea cows**		
	3. **cetaceans**		6. **edentates**		9. **odd-toed ungulates**		

Page 89

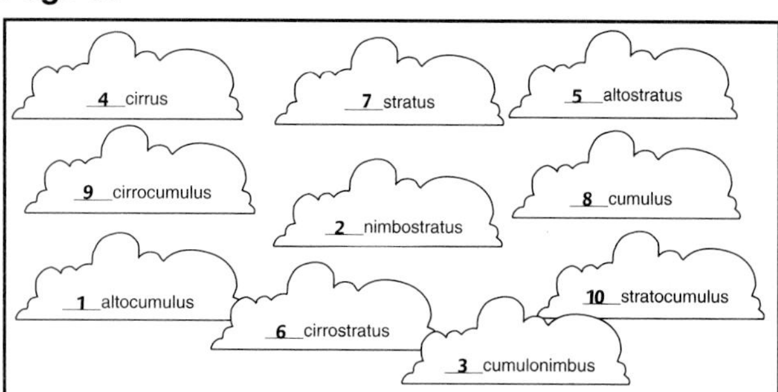

Page 93

Tornado: winds over 300 miles per hour; usually occurs in midwestern U.S.; can cause death and destruction; usually lasts less than an hour; rotating funnel cloud; several hundred yards in diameter; sometimes called *twister* or *cyclone*

Hurricane: several hundred miles in diameter; winds swirl around *eye;* develops over warm ocean water; sometimes called *cyclone* or *typhoon;* winds over 70 miles per hour; can cause death and destruction; produces huge waves, or *storm surge;* grows weaker as it moves over land

Page 90

1. F 2. T 3. T 4. T 5. F 6. F
7. T 8. F 9. T 10. F 11. F

Page 94

1 c	o	2 l	d						3 r										
l		i						4 s	a	t	e	l	5 l	i	6 t	e			
o		g							i				u		e				
u		7 h	u	r	r	i	c	a	n	e			8 c	u	m	u	l	u	s
d		t											k		p				
		9 n	i	m	b	u	s								e				
		i							10 b					11 f	r	o	n	t	
		n							a		12 a		13 h		a				
14 f	o	g				15 F	a	h	r	e	n	h	e	i	t				
									o		e		a		u				
16 i	17 c	e			18 t	h	e	r	m	o	m	e	t	19 e	r				
	i				h				e		o		20 s	l	e	e	t		
21 p	r	e	22 s	s	u	r	e		t		m			m					
	r		t		n				e		e								
	u		r		d				r		t				23 s	n	o	24 w	
	s		a		e					25 d	e	26 w						a	
			27 t	o	r	n	a	d	o			28 r	a	i	n			t	
			u									r						e	
			29 s	t	o	r	m					30 m	o	i	s	t	u	r	e

Page 92

1. Alaska
2. California
3. Hawaii
4. 1930s
5. January
6. Michigan
7. Hawaii; 86 degrees
8. AK=180°; CA=179°; DE=127°; FL=111°; ID=178°; MI=163°; MT=187°; NE=165°
9. Montana
10. Hawaii

Bonus Box answer: Yes—Alaska is the northernmost state. No—California recorded the highest temperature, but Hawaii is the southernmost state.

Page 106

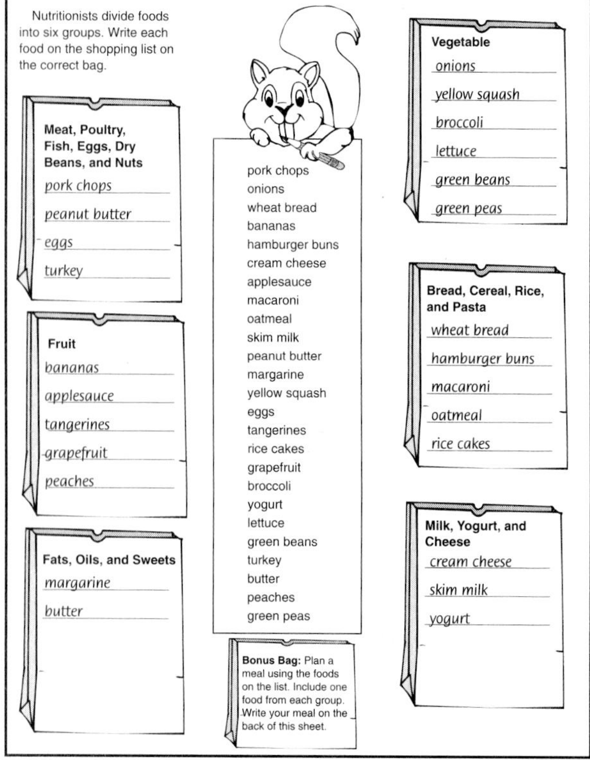

Page 107

1. carbohydrate, iron, protein, fat
2. salmon and sardines (fish), milk, cheese
3. iron
4. vegetable oils, margarine, mayonnaise
5. iron, carbohydrate, fat, calcium, protein
6. Answers will vary.
7. Answers will vary.
8. Answers will vary.
9. (any foods which are carbohydrates)
10. Answers will vary.
11. foods with calcium
12. calcium

Page 108

Across:

1. carbohydrate
3. vegetarian
5. fat
7. vitamin
8. iron
10. mineral
12. legumes
14. fiber
15. sodium
18. water
19. sugar

Down:

1. cholesterol
2. diabetes
4. grains
6. nutrient
9. diets
11. calcium
13. nutrition
16. dairy
17. fruit

Page 109

2. apple, doughnut, peanuts, popcorn
3. ice cream and peanuts; 5 minutes longer
4. about 300 calories
5. any of the snacks
6. 25 minutes
7. 360 calories; 1 hour and 9 minutes
8. 175 calories
9. 68 minutes
10. Answers will vary.

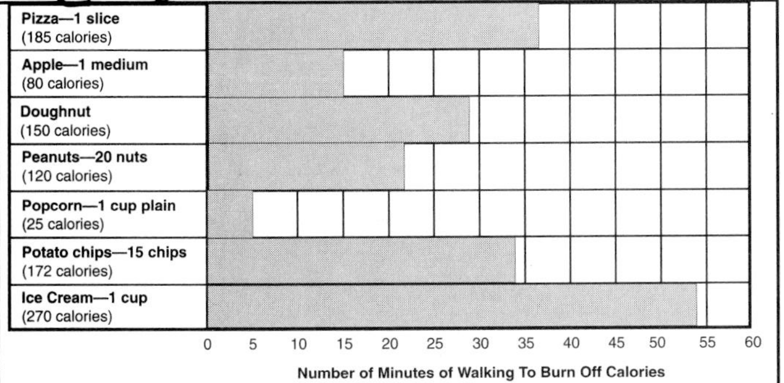

Page 115

1. fuel, oxidizer
2. to lift the wings, to provide oxygen to burn the fuel
3. A liquid-fuel rocket can be controlled, stopped, or restarted.
4. Solid-fuel rockets are more powerful and safer, and can be fueled ahead of time.
5. the hot, expanding gases created when the fuel and oxidizer react
6. Liquid fuel may explode.

Page 116

1. Venus, Saturn, and Uranus (Saturn and Uranus are larger, but less dense, than Earth.)
2. Pluto is a very small planet.
3. (Answers may vary.) They would find it very difficult to stand, walk, or move. Their bones or organs could be injured. Blood circulation would be impaired.

Page 117

The growth of roots and stems is controlled by different plant hormones. These hormones concentrate on the upward or downward side of the root or stem in response to gravity. Therefore, one side grows faster than the other. Leaves and stems grow away from the center of gravity of the earth; the course of growth for all roots, regardless of the position of the plant, is generally downward. The "earth" seeds' roots will grow downward. The "space" seeds' roots will probably show more erratic growth.

Page 123

True	False
①	3
⑤	2
7	①
④	6
2	⓪
⑧	3
①	5
⑨	6
8	③
6	②
8	①
⑦	3
④	5
⑥	0
2	⑧

Page 131

1. sedimentary
2. igneous
3. sedimentary
4. igneous
5. metamorphic
6. sedimentary
7. metamorphic
8. metamorphic
9. sedimentary
10. igneous

Page 132
Try The Acid Test

2. A chemical reaction is created when the vinegar touches the limestone. Tiny bubbles of the gas calcium carbonate are released.

Examine A Crystal
Salt crystals look like 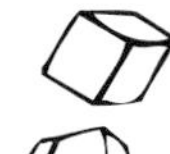 (isometric or cubic system).

Sugar crystals look like  (monoclinic system).

Page 133
Create A Conglomeration!

6. Rocks bind together by the pressure exerted by newer layers of sediment upon the old layers of sediment.

Try The Scratch Test

Penny Experiment

2. pencil, fingernail
3. file, sandpaper
4. between fingernail and file
5. 3.0/Answers may vary.

Glass Slide Experiment

2. pencil, fingernail, penny
3. file, sandpaper
4. between penny and file
5. 6.0/Answers may vary.

Page 134
Master The Mineral Maze

1. iron
2. copper
3. uranium
4. graphite
5. borax
6. aluminum
7. mica
8. salt
9. kaolin
10. diamond
11. gold

Bonus Box answer: silver

Page 140
Observations:
A) When the foil touches the side of the battery, it lights the bulb.
B) When the foil touches the foil collar, it lights the bulb.
Conclusion: (Answers may vary.)
Electrical energy can be created from a battery when the proper conductor (such as aluminum foil) is used. (Batteries must also be properly aligned.) The electrical current created can light a bulb.

Page 141
Observations:
A) A greenish discoloration occurs at C, indicating a connection to a negative (-) terminal.
B) A bubbly or no reaction occurs at D, indicating a connection to a positive (+) terminal.
Conclusion: (Answers may vary.)
A battery has a positive and a negative terminal. Each causes a different reaction.

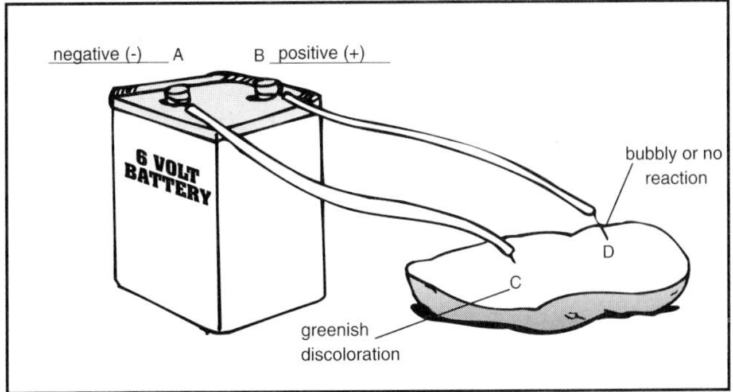

Page 143

1. Arctic Ocean
2. Sea Of Okhotsk
3. Sea Of Japan
4. Yellow Sea
5. South China Sea
6. Indian Ocean
7. North Pacific Ocean
8. South Pacific Ocean
9. Beaufort Sea
10. Gulf Of Mexico
11. Caribbean Sea
12. Hudson Bay
13. Baffin Bay
14. North Atlantic Ocean
15. South Atlantic Ocean
16. Greenland Sea
17. Barents Sea
18. North Sea
19. Mediterranean Sea
20. Black Sea
21. Caspian Sea
22. Red Sea
23. Persian Gulf
24. Arabian Sea

Page 151

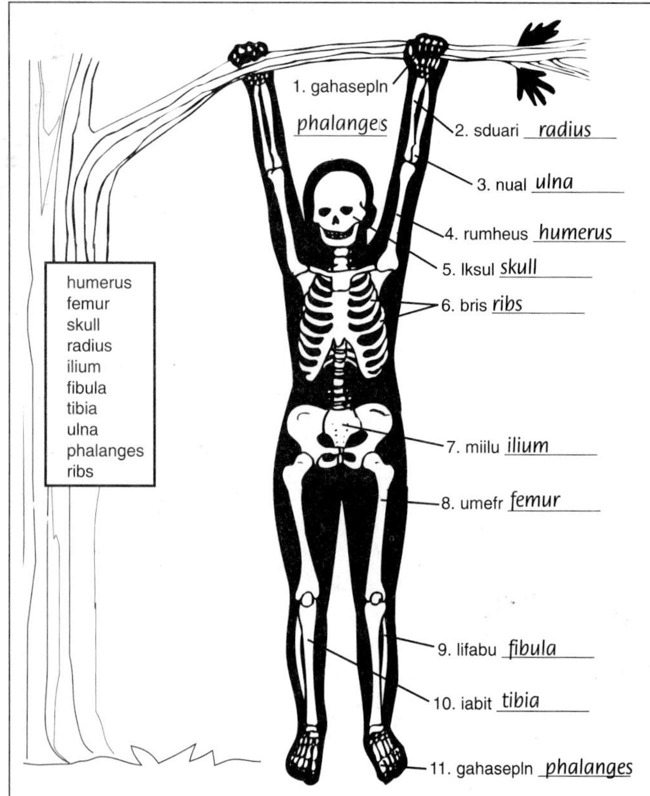

Page 156

(These are false facts that have been rewritten.)

3. Whales must come to the surface from time to time to breathe.
5. Whales give birth to live young.
9. Some whales have teeth. Baleen whales do not have teeth.
10. Whales have smooth skin.
13. Whales are mammals, not fish.

Page 159

A. 1. baleen whales, toothed whales
2. touch, hearing
3. male—bull; female—cow
4. blowholes; toothed whale—one blowhole; baleen whale—two blowholes
5. at the tail; to propel itself through the water
6. blubber
7. fish, cuttlefish, squid, small sea animals
8. plankton, krill, squid, small fish and sea animals
9. toothed
10. Fish: vertical tail fins, gills, lay eggs, cold-blooded, no hair
Whales: horizontal tail fins, lungs, live young, warm-blooded, some hair

B. 1. blubber
2. ambergris
3. cetacean
4. flukes
5. krill

Bonus Box answer:

maxilla—upper jaw
mandible—lower jaw
tarsals—ankle
patella—kneecap
carpals—wrist
sternum—breastbone
scapula—shoulder blade

Page 160

1. They both migrate each year.
2. cold waters of Arctic and Antarctic
3. The polar waters begin to freeze.
4. warmer waters near the equator
5. thickest and best plankton
6. make some of their blubber into milk
7. Bryde's whales, bowhead whales
8. Bryde's whale
9. bowhead whale
10. Answers will vary.